CHICAGO PUBLIC LIBRARY
BUSINESS / SCIENCE / TECHNOLOGY
400 S. STATE ST. 60605

R00219 32212

D1066294

INTERMEDIATE QUANTUM MECHANICS

LECTURE NOTES AND SUPPLEMENTS IN PHYSICS

John David Jackson and David Pines, *Editors*

Mathematics for Quantum Mechanics	*John David Jackson (Illinois)*
Elementary Excitations in Solids	*David Pines (Illinois)*
Fundamental Particles	*K. Nishijima (Illinois)*
Matrix Methods in Optical Instrument Design	*Willem Brouwer (Diffraction Limited)*
Relativistic Kinematics	*R. Hagedorn (CERN)*
Intermediate Quantum Mechanics	*H. A. Bethe (Cornell)*

INTERMEDIATE QUANTUM MECHANICS

HANS A. BETHE

Cornell University

Notes by

R. W. Jackiw

W. A. BENJAMIN, INC.

New York Amsterdam 1964

INTERMEDIATE QUANTUM MECHANICS

Copyright © 1964 by W. A. Benjamin, Inc.
All rights reserved

Library of Congress Catalog Card Number 64-13919
Manufactured in the United States of America

The final manuscript was put into production on September 16, 1963; this volume was published on March 13, 1964

The publisher is pleased to acknowledge the assistance of Zeb Delaire, who composed the volume; of Cecilia Duray-Bito, who produced the artwork, and of William Prokos, who designed the cover and dust jacket

REF
530.1
B465i
Cop2
Tech

W. A. BENJAMIN, INC.
2465 Broadway, New York, New York 10025

THE CHICAGO PUBLIC LIBRARY
JUL - 8 1964 M

CHICAGO PUBLIC LIBRARY
BUSINESS / SCIENCE / TECHNOLOGY
400 S. STATE ST. 60605

EDITORS' FOREWORD

Everyone concerned with the teaching of physics at the advanced undergraduate or graduate level is aware of the continuing need for a modernization and reorganization of the basic course material. Despite the existence today of many good textbooks in these areas, there is always an appreciable time-lag in the incorporation of new viewpoints and techniques which result from the most recent developments in physics research. Typically these changes in concepts and material take place first in the personal lecture notes of some of those who teach graduate courses. Eventually, printed notes may appear, and some fraction of such notes evolve into textbooks or monographs. But much of this fresh material remains available only to a very limited audience, to the detriment of all. Our series aims at filling this gap in the literature of physics by presenting occasional volumes with a contemporary approach to the classical topics of physics at the advanced undergraduate and graduate level. Clarity and soundness of treatment will, we hope, mark these volumes, as well as the freshness of the approach.

Another area in which the series hopes to make a contribution is by presenting useful supplementing material of well-defined scope. This may take the form of a survey of relevant mathematical principles, or a collection of reprints of basic papers in a field. Here the aim is to provide the instructor with added flexibility through the use of supplements at relatively low cost.

The scope of both the lecture notes and supplements is somewhat different from the "Frontiers in Physics" series. In spite of wide variations from institution to institution as to what comprises the basic graduate course program, there is a widely accepted group of "bread and butter" courses that deal with the classic topics in physics. These include: Mathematical methods of physics, electromagnetic theory, advanced dynamics, quantum mechanics, statistical mechanics, and frequently nuclear physics and/or solid-state physics. It is chiefly these areas that will be covered by the present series. The listing is perhaps best described as including all advanced undergraduate and graduate courses which are at a level below seminar courses dealing entirely with current research topics.

The publishing format for the series is in keeping with its intentions. Photo-offset printing is used throughout, and the books are paperbound in order to speed publication and reduce costs. It is hoped that books will thereby be within the financial reach of graduate students in this country and abroad.

Finally, because the series represents something of an experiment on the part of the editors and the publisher, suggestions from interested readers as to format, contributors, and contributions will be most welcome.

J. David Jackson
David Pines

PREFACE

This book is intended to serve as a text for a second course in quantum mechanics, for graduate students in both theoretical and experimental physics. It is assumed that the student has a knowledge of the principles of quantum mechanics, equivalent to the first eight chapters of Schiff's *Quantum Mechanics,* or the entire book of Merzbacher. I believe that the general exposition of the theory as given in these books should be followed by a discussion of the applications to problems in which the basic physics is essentially known and well understood, notably the structure of atoms and the theory of atomic collisions, so that the solidity of the theory becomes apparent. After this, the student will be better prepared to study nuclear physics, where the forces are unknown, or solid-state physics, where the physical approximations are often tentative. I have stressed the connection with experimental information and with the physical picture rather than the formal development of the theory. Some recent books have stressed all too much the formal side.

Good books are available for study at this level, e.g., Condon and Shortley, *Theory of Spectra;* Slater, *Quantum Mechanics of Atomic Structure;* Mott and Massey, *Atomic Collisions;* Heitler, *Quantum Theory of Radiation.* However these books are mainly intended for the expert, or at least the student who wishes to specialize in one particular field of quantum mechanics. The first volume of Slater's book, in my opinion, is not sufficient to give a good education to a graduate student in physics, while the second volume contains too much. The present book is intended to give to the graduate student in physics enough knowledge in at least one of the fields, namely, atomic structure, so that he can then intelligently follow discussions on various coupling schemes in atoms, nuclei, and fundamental particles. It will give him a working knowledge of Clebsch-

Gordan coefficients. It also gives a detailed treatment of optical transition probabilities, including quantitative calculation.

Unfortunately the book does not do a complete job because it contains hardly any collision theory. This is due to the fact that it grew out of a regular, four-hour course for one semester. A selection of topics had to be made. Most instructors will want to spend considerably more time on collision theory than the book does. However Schiff's book covers the theory of collision appreciably more in detail than that of atomic structure.

The second and third parts of the book deal with the relativistic wave equations and an introduction to field theory. It may be regarded as a terminal course for experimental physicists in these areas. Subjects covered parallel Schiff. The treatment of field theory stays closer to the classic article by Fermi in *Reviews of Modern Physics,* 1932, and tries to avoid the complications, either in algebra or in concept, which are not absolutely necessary.

H. A. Bethe

Ithaca, New York
January 1964

CONTENTS

Part I

THEORY OF ATOMIC STRUCTURE

THERE are at least three important reasons for undertaking a careful study of the structure of atoms. First of all, on the basis of the quantum theory every known feature of the electronic structure of atoms can be explained. Knowledge of this structure is important for chemistry, solid-state physics, spectroscopic determination of nuclear properties (hyperfine structure, etc.), and many other applications. The quantitative validity of these explanations is limited only by computational difficulties. Second, the excellent agreement between theoretical and experimental results in the tremendously wide range of atomic phenomena provides a crucial test for the validity of quantum mechanics. Finally the theory of atomic structure is a convenient "theoretical laboratory" in which one can become acquainted with many physical ideas and mathematical tools which are relevant to other branches of physics. Some aspects of the theory of nuclear structure, for example, parallel quite closely atomic theory.

Chapter 1

SCHRÖDINGER EQUATION AND APPROXIMATE METHODS OF SOLUTION

The starting point for a nonrelativistic quantum mechanical description of the electronic configuration of an atom with nuclear charge Ze is the *Schrödinger equation*:

$$i\hbar \frac{\partial}{\partial t} \Psi = H\Psi \tag{1-1}$$

Assuming a time-independent Hamiltonian, the usual separation occurs:

$$\Psi = \psi e^{-iEt/\hbar} \tag{1-2}$$

$$H\psi = E\psi \tag{1-3}$$

where E is the total energy of the electrons. If we neglect all the spin interactions of the electrons and all nuclear effects (e.g., finite size and mass) (1-3) has the form

$$\left(-\frac{\hbar^2}{2m} \sum_j \nabla_j^2 - E - Ze^2 \sum_j \frac{1}{r_j} + \sum_{i>j} \frac{e^2}{r_{ij}} \right) \psi = 0 \tag{1-4}$$

where m is the electronic mass, e the electronic charge, r_j the absolute value of the position vector of the jth electron, and $r_{ij} = |\mathbf{r}_i - \mathbf{r}_j|$. The summations in the first and third term extend over all the N electrons. The summation in the last term is over all pairs $(i \neq j)$, each pair being counted once; i.e.,

$$\sum_{i>j} = \sum_{i=1}^{i=N} \sum_{j=1}^{j=i-1}$$

The first term in (1-4) represents the kinetic energy of the electrons; the third term is the Coulomb interaction of the electrons with the nucleus; the last term is the interelectron Coulomb interaction.

For one electron (1-4) can be solved exactly. The solutions are described by three quantum numbers n, ℓ, m; the so-called principal, azimuthal, and magnetic quantum numbers, respectively (Bethe and Salpeter, pp. 4–33). For more than one electron no exact solutions of (1-4) have been found. For two electrons very accurate approximation methods exist; for multielectron systems only less exact methods are available.

PERTURBATION METHODS

In the approximate treatment we shall need to make use of perturbation theory. The principal results of the *bound state perturbation theory* are the following. Suppose in solving (1-3) we can write

$$H = H^0 + H^1$$

where the effect of H^1 is small, and $H^0 u_n = E_n u_n$. That is, we assume the unperturbed system is in a definite state u_n with energy E_n, and the effect of the perturbation H^1 is such that E is much closer to E_n than to $E_{n\pm1}$.

If E_n is nondegenerate, we can write

$$\begin{aligned} E &\approx E^0 + E^1 + E^2 \\ E^0 &= E_n \\ E^1 &= H^1_{nn} \\ E^2 &= \sum_m{}' \frac{|H^1_{nm}|^2}{E_n - E_m} \\ H^1_{nm} &= \int u_n^* H^1 u_m \, d\tau \end{aligned} \tag{1-5}$$

The prime on the sum indicates that the term $m = n$ is omitted. If the unperturbed state is degenerate, we must find the proper linear combination of the degenerate unperturbed eigenfunctions such that the perturbing Hamiltonian is diagonal (Schiff, pp. 151-161).

The *time-dependent perturbation theory* proceeds by replacing the equation

$$i\hbar \frac{\partial \Psi}{\partial t} = H\Psi \tag{1-1}$$

by

$$i\hbar \frac{\partial a_k}{\partial t} = \lambda \sum_n H^1_{kn} e^{i\omega_{kn} t} a_n \tag{1-6a}$$

where

$$H = H^0 + \lambda H^1$$

$$H^0 u_n = E_n u_n$$

$$\Psi = \sum_n a_n u_n e^{-iE_n t/\hbar} \tag{1-6b}$$

$$\omega_{kn} = \frac{E_k - E_n}{\hbar}$$

The set of equations (1-6a) for all k is entirely equivalent to (1-1). They can be solved by successive approximation, i.e., by substituting

$$a_n = \sum_{i=0}^{\infty} \lambda^i a_n^{(i)} \tag{1-7}$$

in (1-6a) and equating equal powers of λ. If it is assumed that initially the system is in the state m we put

$$\begin{aligned} a_k^{(0)} &= \delta_{km} \\ a_k^{(1)} &= (i\hbar)^{-1} \int_{-\infty}^{t} H^1_{km}(t') e^{i\omega_{km} t'} \, dt' \end{aligned} \tag{1-8}$$

If H^1 is independent of time, except for being "turned on" and "off" at times 0 and t, respectively,

$$a_k^{(1)} = \frac{-H^1_{km}}{\hbar} \frac{e^{i\omega_{km} t} - 1}{\omega_{km}} \tag{1-9a}$$

$$|a_k^{(1)}(t)|^2 = 4 |H^1_{km}|^2 \frac{\sin^2 \frac{1}{2}\omega_{km} t}{\hbar^2 \omega_{km}^2} \tag{1-9b}$$

Equation (1-9b) is the first-order probability of transition from state m to state $k \neq m$. The *transition probability per unit time* will then be

$$w = \frac{2\pi}{\hbar} \left|H^1_{km}\right|^2 \frac{1}{\hbar} \left(\frac{2 \sin^2 \frac{1}{2}\omega_{km} t}{\pi \omega^2_{km} t} \right) \tag{1-10a}$$

The term in parentheses may be recognized as a representation of the Dirac delta function in the limit $t \to \infty$. (We assume the perturbing Hamiltonian has been "turned on" for a long time—as we must if both the states k and m are assumed to be defined with no uncertainty.) We may then rewrite the above as

$$w = \frac{2\pi}{\hbar} \left|H^1_{km}\right|^2 \frac{1}{\hbar}\, \delta(\omega_{km}) \tag{1-10b}$$

$$w = \frac{2\pi}{\hbar} \left|H^1_{km}\right|^2 \delta(E_n - E_m) \tag{1-10c}$$

This explicitly exhibits the fact that energy is conserved in first-order transitions. If the transition is to a continuum (or quasi-continuum) of states about state k, we describe the density of final states by $\rho(E_k)$ and replace the delta function by the density function, thus obtaining the well-known *Fermi golden rule*:

$$w = \frac{2\pi}{\hbar} \left|H^1_{km}\right|^2 \rho(E_k) \tag{1-11}$$

VARIATION METHODS

The variation principle consists in selecting a function Ψ, varying the quantity $\langle \psi | H | \psi \rangle$ in some arbitrary fashion subject to the condition $\langle \psi | \psi \rangle = 1$ and thus obtaining a stationary value for $\langle \psi | H | \psi \rangle$. This has a wide variety of applications which can be classified according to the trial function and variations used. One extreme is the arbitrary trial function and variation which leads to Schrödinger's equation.

$$\delta \int \psi^* H \psi \; d\tau = 0 \qquad \int \psi^* \psi \; d\tau = 1 \tag{1-12}$$

The subsidiary normalization condition is introduced by a Lagrange multiplier E, i.e.,

$$\delta \left[\int \psi^* H \psi \; d\tau - E \int \psi^* \psi \; d\tau \right] = 0$$

$$\delta \int \psi^* (H - E) \psi \; d\tau = 0 \tag{1-13}$$

$$0 = \int \delta\psi^* (H - E)\psi \; d\tau + \int [(H - E)\psi^*]\, \delta\psi \; d\tau$$

The hermiticity of H − E was used in the last equation (1-13). Considering the variation of ψ^* and ψ to be independently arbitrary

$$\begin{aligned} (H - E)\psi &= 0 \\ (H - E)\psi^* &= 0 \end{aligned} \tag{1-14}$$

For the other extreme, the trial function is chosen to depend on several parameters and the variation is accomplished by varying these parameters. This is the Ritz method. Whenever a special form of trial function or a particular method of variation is used, the stationary value of $\langle H \rangle$ is no longer the exact eigenvalue of H. The following set of equations show that a variational estimate for $\langle H \rangle$ is always an upper bound for the lowest-energy eigenvalue.

$$\begin{aligned} \psi &= \sum_n a_n u_n \\ \langle \psi | \psi \rangle &= 1 = \sum_n |a_n|^2 \\ Hu_n &= E_n u_n \\ H\psi &= \sum_n a_n u_n \\ \langle \psi | H | \psi \rangle &= \sum_n |a_n|^2 E_n \geq E_0 \sum_n |a_n|^2 = E_0 \end{aligned} \tag{1-15a}$$

E_0 is the lowest-energy state. Hence

$$\langle H \rangle \geq E_0 \tag{1-15b}$$

One can also obtain upper bounds for one of the higher levels if the trial function is orthogonal to the eigenfunctions of all the lower states.

We shall make use of the Ritz method as well as of more general variational procedures.

Chapter 2

CONSTANTS OF MOTION

The diagonalization of the Hamiltonian is facilitated by a knowledge of the constants of motion. This is so, because if P is such a constant, the operators P and H commute. If P is diagonal

$$0 = [P, H]_{mn} = P_{mm} H_{mn} - H_{mn} P_{nn}$$

$$= H_{mn}(P_{mm} - P_{nn}) \qquad (2\text{-}1)$$

In a representation that diagonalizes P, H has nonzero matrix elements only between states with the same eigenvalue of P. That is, H breaks up into nonvanishing submatrices only between states of equal P. Since it is frequently possible to find a diagonal representation for P from the symmetries of the problem, the secular problem of diagonalizing H is vastly simplified.

Parity will be such a constant if H is invariant under inversion, which is certainly the case for spherically symmetric potentials, and can be true for other more general potentials also. The total angular momentum **J** will always be a constant of the motion for isolated systems, since **J** is the generator of infinitesimal rotations and we assume that space is isotropic.

From considerations of infinitesimal rotations we obtain the commutation relations for **J**:

$$\left[J_i, J_j\right] = i\hbar J_k \qquad (2\text{-}2a)$$

which can be symbolically summarized by

$$\mathbf{J} \times \mathbf{J} = i\hbar \mathbf{J} \qquad (2\text{-}2b)$$

From this it follows that

$$[J_x, J^2] = 0 \tag{2-3}$$

and similarly for the y and z components of **J**. In a representation in which J^2 and J_z are diagonal, if we label the rows and columns by a pair of symbols j and m we find that the eigenvalues of J_z for a fixed j are $m\hbar$, where m ranges in unit steps from $-j$ to j. The eigenvalues of J^2 for any m are $j(j+1)\hbar^2$, where 2j is a positive integer or zero.

The elements of J_x and J_y can be obtained from the matrix J_+ defined by

$$J_+ = J_x + iJ_y \tag{2-4}$$

The only nonzero element of J_+ is

$$\langle j, m+1 | J_+ | j, m \rangle = \hbar\sqrt{(j-m)(j+m+1)} \tag{2-5}$$

so that J_+ has the property that for any state $|j,m\rangle$

$$J_+ | j,m \rangle = \hbar\sqrt{(j-m)(j+m+1)}\, | j, m+1 \rangle \tag{2-6}$$

The adjoint $J_+^\dagger \equiv J_-$ has the property

$$J_- | j,m \rangle = \hbar\sqrt{(j+m)(j-m+1)}\, | j, m-1 \rangle \tag{2-7}$$

J_+ and J_- are called the *raising* and *lowering operators*, respectively.

The representations of J_x, J_y, and J_z corresponding to integral j can arise from the orbital angular momentum **L** defined by

$$\mathbf{L} = \sum_i \mathbf{r}_i \times \mathbf{p}_i \tag{2-8}$$

where $\mathbf{p}_i$ is the linear momentum of the ith particle. **L** satisfies the commutation relations (2-2) and the eigenfunctions are the spherical harmonics. For a given quantum system, e.g., an atom, **L** need not be conserved, since it generates rotations only in the position variables under which the isolated system need not be invariant. If L^2 happens to be a constant, this is a consequence of a specific physical feature of the Hamiltonian and not of general geometrical properties of the space. Specifically, for a radially symmetric Hamiltonian with no spin-orbit coupling L^2 is conserved (Schiff, pp. 74–76, 141–148).

SPIN

A particle may possess intrinsic angular momentum which cannot be expressed in terms of the classical position and momentum coordinates. The components of this angular momentum can be half-integers, since J_z no longer has the representation $(\hbar/i)(\partial/\partial\varphi)$. Spin has no analogue in classical mechanics. In particular, early models of the "spinning electron" are wholly meaningless. In dealing with spin we shall replace **J** by **S**, j by s, and m by m_s. Every fundamental particle has a definite spin s, i.e.,

$$S^2 = s(s+1)\hbar^2 I$$

$$S_z = m_s \hbar I \qquad -s \le m_s \le s$$

2s is zero or a positive integer, and I is the unit operator in spin space.

Since s is fixed for every particle, $\lim_{\hbar \to 0} \hbar\sqrt{s(s+1)} = 0$, which shows that there is no classical analogue to spin. It is an empirical question what the magnitude of the spin of a specific particle is. (Although the Dirac relativistic theory predicts spin $\frac{1}{2}$ for electrons, an equally consistent theory can be constructed which predicts zero for the spin.) Electrons, nucleons, and μ-mesons have spin $\frac{1}{2}$; π-mesons have spin 0; photons, as much as they can be considered particles, have spin 1. **S** clearly commutes with **r** and **p**, hence if the one-particle Hamiltonian has no spin terms, **S** will be a constant of the motion (see also Chapter 8).

The state function of a particle must depend on the 2s + 1 components of the spin. In general, if the Hamiltonian couples strongly space motion and spin motion, 2s + 1 space-spin functions of the form $\psi(\mathbf{r}, m_s)$ will be required to specify that particle. If the coupling can be ignored, the wave function separates:

$$\psi(\mathbf{r}, m_s) = \psi(\mathbf{r})\chi(m_s) \tag{2-9}$$

Since spin space consists only of 2s + 1 points, $\chi(m_s)$ is completely specified by 2s + 1 numbers. An obvious choice for these spin functions is the set of eigenvectors of the diagonalized S^2 and S_z matrices. For example, for the case $s = \frac{3}{2}$

$$\chi(\tfrac{3}{2}) = \begin{pmatrix}1\\0\\0\\0\end{pmatrix} \quad \chi(\tfrac{1}{2}) = \begin{pmatrix}0\\1\\0\\0\end{pmatrix} \quad \chi(-\tfrac{1}{2}) = \begin{pmatrix}0\\0\\1\\0\end{pmatrix} \quad \chi(-\tfrac{3}{2}) = \begin{pmatrix}0\\0\\0\\1\end{pmatrix}$$

The spin $\frac{1}{2}$ functions and spin matrices shall be our main concern since they describe a single electron. Writing $\mathbf{S} = \frac{1}{2}\hbar\boldsymbol{\sigma}$ we find from the general expression (2-5), (2-7) for J_+, J_-:

$$\sigma_x = \begin{pmatrix} 0 & 1 \\ 1 & 0 \end{pmatrix} \qquad \sigma_y = \begin{pmatrix} 0 & -i \\ i & 0 \end{pmatrix} \qquad \sigma_z = \begin{pmatrix} 1 & 0 \\ 0 & -1 \end{pmatrix}$$

$$\chi(\tfrac{1}{2}) \equiv \alpha = \begin{pmatrix} 1 \\ 0 \end{pmatrix} \qquad \chi(-\tfrac{1}{2}) \equiv \beta = \begin{pmatrix} 0 \\ 1 \end{pmatrix} \tag{2-10}$$

$\sigma_x, \sigma_y, \sigma_z$ are called the *Pauli spin matrices*. The following relations for the Pauli spin matrices can be verified:

$$\sigma_i \sigma_j = i\sigma_k \qquad \text{(ijk a cyclic permutation of xyz)} \tag{2-11}$$

$$\sigma_i \sigma_j + \sigma_j \sigma_i = 2\delta_{ij}$$

For two (or more) angular momenta we can form the operator $\mathbf{J} = \mathbf{J}_1 + \mathbf{J}_2$.

$$[J_x, J_y] = [J_{1x} + J_{2x}, J_{1y} + J_{2y}]$$

$$= i\hbar J_z + [J_{2x}, J_{1y}] + [J_{1x}, J_{2y}] \tag{2-12}$$

Hence if $\mathbf{J}_1$ and $\mathbf{J}_2$ commute in all components, $\mathbf{J}$ is again an angular momentum operator. Since the spin operators of two electrons commute, $\mathbf{S} = \mathbf{S}_1 + \mathbf{S}_2$ is a spin operator again. Four orthonormal spin functions for a pair of electrons can be chosen to be $\alpha_1\alpha_2$, $\beta_1\beta_2$, $\alpha_1\beta_2$, $\beta_1\alpha_2$. In such products of spin functions, $\mathbf{S}_1$ operates only on the first spin function, $\mathbf{S}_2$ only on the second. The four spin functions correspond to total m_S: 1, −1, 0, 0, respectively. Since $\mathbf{S}$ is an angular momentum it should be possible to find a representation in which S_z and S^2 are diagonal. It can be verified that $\alpha_1\alpha_2$, $\beta_1\beta_2$ are eigenvectors of S^2. To construct the remaining eigenvectors from $\alpha_1\beta_2$ and $\alpha_2\beta_1$ we observe that $\alpha_1\alpha_2$ is symmetric and corresponds to $s = 1$, $m_S = 1$. Therefore the lowering operator S_- will generate the wave function corresponding to $s = 1$, $m_S = 0$, and since $\alpha_1\alpha_2$ is symmetric, the resulting wave function will also be symmetric, explicitly,

$$S_-\alpha_1\alpha_2 = 2^{1/2}\hbar\,|s = 1, m_S = 0\rangle = \hbar[\beta_1\alpha_2 + \alpha_1\beta_2]$$

$$|s = 1, m_S = 0\rangle = 2^{-1/2}[\alpha_1\beta_2 + \beta_1\alpha_2] \tag{2-13}$$

The fourth eigenvector is obtained by observing that the only normalized linear combination of $\alpha_1\beta_2$ and $\beta_1\alpha_2$ which is orthogonal to (2-13) is the antisymmetric

$$|s = 0, m_S = 0\rangle = 2^{-1/2}[\alpha_1\beta_2 - \beta_1\alpha_2] \tag{2-14}$$

Table 2-1

	S^2	s	m_s
$(\alpha_1\alpha_2)$	$2\hbar^2$	1	1
$2^{-1/2}[(\alpha_1\beta_2) + (\beta_1\alpha_2)]$	$2\hbar^2$	1	0
$(\beta_1\beta_2)$	$2\hbar^2$	1	−1
$2^{-1/2}[(\alpha_1\beta_2) - (\beta_1\alpha_2)]$	0	0	0

Table 2-1 lists the four basis vectors for a diagonal representation of S^2 and S_z, together with the eigenvalues of S^2, the total spin s, and the total z component m_s. The first three states, corresponding to s = 1, are described by symmetric spin functions and are called a *triplet*. The last one, with s = 0, is antisymmetric and is called a *singlet*. (In adding two equal, nonzero, angular momenta $\mathbf{J} = \mathbf{J}_1 + \mathbf{J}_2$, the simultaneous eigenfunctions of J^2 and J_z will always be either symmetric or antisymmetric. However, for general addition of angular momenta this need not be so.)

Strictly speaking, such sums as $\mathbf{J} = \mathbf{J}_1 + \mathbf{J}_2$ and such products as $\alpha_1\alpha_2$ must be interpreted in the following fashion. $\mathbf{J}_1$ and $\mathbf{J}_2$, α_1 and α_2 are defined for two different vector spaces V_1 and V_2. $\mathbf{J}$ and the vectors it operates on are defined for the product space $V_1 \otimes V_2$. Therefore, $\mathbf{J}_1 + \mathbf{J}_2$ is to be taken as short for $\mathbf{J}_1 \otimes I + I \otimes \mathbf{J}_2$, and $\alpha_1\alpha_2$ as $\alpha_1 \otimes \alpha_2$. It then follows that $\mathbf{J}_1$ operates only on α_1, $\mathbf{J}_2$ only on α_2. The dot product between two such product vectors is, for example,

$$\alpha_1\alpha_2 \cdot \beta_1\beta_2 = (\alpha_1 \cdot \beta_1)(\alpha_2 \cdot \beta_2) \tag{2-15}$$

Chapter 3

IDENTICAL PARTICLES AND SYMMETRY

The Hamiltonian for a system of n particles that are identical, that is, particles that can be substituted for each other with no physical change, must be completely symmetric under any interchange of its arguments. Let $\Psi(1, 2, \ldots, i, \ldots, n)$ be any solution of the Schrödinger equation, depending on the coordinates (spatial and spin) of the n identical particles 1 to n, and let P be any permutation of the n numbers 1 to n. Then $P\Psi(1, \ldots, n) \equiv \Psi(P1, P2, \ldots, Pn)$ is a function which depends on the coordinates of particle Pi in the same manner as the original function Ψ depended on the coordinates of particle i. Then the operator P commutes with the Hamiltonian,

$$H(P\Psi) = P(H\Psi) \tag{3-1}$$

Thus if Ψ is a solution of the Schrödinger equation, then $P\Psi$ is also a solution (belonging to the same eigenvalue, if we are considering a stationary solution). There are n! different permutations of n objects, so in this manner we get n! wave functions. Some of these may be (and in general are) linear combinations of others, but *in general* we find several linearly independent solutions by our procedure. Thus most of the eigenvalues of a Hamiltonian which is symmetric in n particles will be degenerate. This phenomenon is called *exchange degeneracy* and will be discussed in more detail below.

There will be some nondegenerate eigenvalues of H. For such an eigenvalue, the function $P\Psi$ must be simply a multiple of Ψ, since Ψ is by assumption the only solution for the given eigenvalue. Moreover, since $P\Psi$ and Ψ have the same normalization,

$$P\Psi = e^{i\alpha}\,\Psi \tag{3-2}$$

where α is real. Consider now an especially simple permutation, viz., the simple interchange P_{ij} of particles i and j,

$$P_{ij}\Psi(1, \ldots, i, \ldots, j, \ldots, n) = \Psi(1, \ldots, j, \ldots, i, \ldots, n) \qquad (3\text{-}3)$$

Then if this interchange is applied twice we get back to the original; therefore, using (3-2), $e^{2i\alpha} = 1$, and

$$P_{ij}\Psi = \pm\Psi \qquad (3\text{-}4)$$

Now it is a fact of nature, established by many observations, that all actual wave functions in physics obey (3-4), either with the plus or the minus sign. In other words, from the great multitude of mathematical solutions of $H\Psi = E\Psi$, nature has selected only the nondegenerate ones. The character of the solution depends on the sign to be taken in (3-4); the plus sign leads to a wave function which is symmetric in all particles, the minus sign corresponds to an antisymmetric wave function. Which symmetry applies depends on the type of identical particles involved; experiment shows that Ψ is antisymmetric for electrons, protons, neutrons, μ-mesons, hyperons; symmetric for π-mesons, K-mesons, and photons. A system may of course contain several types of particles, e.g., protons, neutrons, and π-mesons. Then its wave function will change sign if we interchange the coordinates of any two protons, or of any two neutrons; it will remain unchanged if we interchange two π-mesons; finally if we interchange the coordinates of two particles of different type, e.g., one proton and one neutron, the resulting wave function will in general have no simple relation to the original one.

ARGUMENTS FOR SIMPLE SYMMETRY

As we have pointed out, the special symmetry of the wave function, e.g., the antisymmetry in the coordinates of all electrons in the system, does not follow from the symmetry of the Hamiltonian but is an additional requirement selecting the physically meaningful solutions from among the much larger number of mathematically possible solutions of the Schrödinger equation. We shall now give some arguments which make it reasonable that the physical solutions have such a simple symmetry.

Whatever the symmetry of the wave function may be initially, it will be preserved for all time. This follows immediately from the fact that P_{ij} commutes with the Hamiltonian H; hence P_{ij} is a time-independent operator and will be represented by a time-independent matrix. Or, in other words, $H\Psi$ has the same symmetry with respect to any permutation P as Ψ itself; thus $\partial\Psi/\partial t$ has the same symmetry, and by integrating the Schrödinger equation in small steps of time we see that Ψ will retain its initial symmetry. (This applies also to the degenerate solutions whose symmetry is in general complicated; see below.) Thus if "initially" the wave function of the universe was antisymmetric in all electrons, it will remain so for all time. (The above is not an argument for the simple symmetries. It merely shows that a consistent statement about symmetry can be made.)

First of all, we may simply postulate that all the physical properties which we may derive from the wave function should remain unchanged if we interchange two identical particles. This reasonable interpretation of the meaning of "identity" requires that $|P_{ij}\Psi|^2 = |\Psi|^2$, which is equivalent to (3-2) and hence leads to (3-4).

To develop the second argument, we must first investigate the other possible types of symmetry of the wave function, aside from complete symmetry and antisymmetry. For this purpose, it is simplest to consider an approximate Hamiltonian which will also be very useful to us throughout our study of atoms. This is,

$$H_0 = H_0'(1) + H_0'(2) + \cdots + H_0'(n) \tag{3-5}$$

i.e., a Hamiltonian which may be written as a sum of terms, each referring to an individual particle. Let ϕ_a, ϕ_b, etc., be normalized eigenfunctions of H_0', thus:

$$H_0'(1)\phi_a(1) = E_a\,\phi_a(1) \tag{3-6}$$

Then a possible eigenfunction of H_0 is

$$\Psi = \phi_a(1)\,\phi_b(2)\cdots\phi_k(n) \tag{3-7}$$

with the eigenvalue

$$E = E_a + E_b + \cdots + E_k \tag{3-8}$$

This is because $H_0'(1)$ commutes with all functions of coordinates other than those of particle 1. Along with (3-7), the function

$$P\Psi = \phi_a(P1)\,\phi_b(P2)\cdots\phi_k(Pn) \tag{3-9}$$

is an eigenfunction of H_0 with the same eigenvalue (3-8), where P is an arbitrary permutation of the n numbers $1, \ldots, n$. (We could have permuted the functions ϕ_a, etc., instead of their arguments, and would have obtained the same result.) There are $n!$ permutations P, hence (3-9) gives $n!$ linearly independent eigenfunctions if the one-particle functions $\phi_a, \ldots, \phi_k$ are all different. These one-particle functions are called *orbitals*.

All the $n!$ functions $P\Psi$ are degenerate, a phenomenon called *exchange degeneracy*. They are unsymmetric, and we can form more symmetric functions by linear combination. However, the totally symmetric and the antisymmetric function account only for two of these. The remaining $n!-2$ linear combinations must then have lesser symmetry. Only in the special, but important, case $n = 2$ do the symmetric and antisymmetric functions exhaust all linearly independent combinations.

To illustrate the other possible symmetries, it suffices to consider the case of three particles, with two orbitals being alike. Then we have the three functions

$$\begin{aligned} \Psi_1 &= \phi_b(1)\,\phi_a(2)\,\phi_a(3) \\ \Psi_2 &= \phi_a(1)\,\phi_b(2)\,\phi_a(3) \\ \Psi_3 &= \phi_a(1)\,\phi_a(2)\,\phi_b(3) \end{aligned} \tag{3-10}$$

The totally symmetric normalized function is

$$\Psi_S = 3^{-1/2}(\Psi_1 + \Psi_2 + \Psi_3) \tag{3-11a}$$

There is no totally antisymmetric function. Two other linear combinations, orthonormal to Ψ_S are

$$\begin{aligned} \Psi_4 &= 6^{-1/2}(2\Psi_1 - \Psi_2 - \Psi_3) \\ \Psi_5 &= 2^{-1/2}(\Psi_2 - \Psi_3) \end{aligned} \tag{3-11b}$$

Evidently, Ψ_4 is symmetric, Ψ_5 antisymmetric, in particles 2 and 3. If we apply the permutation P_{12} to Ψ_4 we find

$$P_{12}\Psi_4 = -\tfrac{1}{2}\Psi_4 + \frac{\sqrt{3}}{2}\Psi_5 \tag{3-12}$$

and similarly for $P_{13}\Psi_4$, etc. Thus the two functions Ψ_4 and Ψ_5 obviously belong together: The permutations P_{12} and P_{13} transform these into linear combinations of each other and are represented by 2×2 matrices in the "subspace" of Ψ_4, Ψ_5. The symmetric function Ψ_S stands by itself; it transforms into itself under any permutation P, so that all permutations are represented by 1×1 matrices, viz., unity, in the subspace of Ψ_S.

The problem of the matrix representation of the permutations can best be studied by group theory, and this has been done by Wigner and collaborators in the late 1920's. Now the matrix representation of the permutation group carries over to the case of a *general* Hamiltonian H which does not separate into one-particle Hamiltonians as H_0 does, but which of course is still symmetrical in all particles. Thus for a general symmetric Hamiltonian involving three particles, and for solutions corresponding to two equal and one different orbital, we get two types of eigenfunctions: One type is totally symmetric like Ψ_S, and these eigenfunctions are nondegenerate; the other type is always doubly degenerate and transforms under permutations like the functions Ψ_4, Ψ_5 in (3-11). With a general Hamiltonian, doubly degenerate eigenvalues are in general different from the nondegenerate ones corresponding to totally symmetric eigenfunctions; a coincidence between these eigenvalues could only occur by pure accident (in contrast to the simple Hamiltonian H_0). Thus part of the n!-fold exchange degeneracy is removed when we go from H_0 to H, but some degeneracy will remain. This result holds generally, for any number of particles, and whether or not some orbitals are equal. Thus mathematically, the Schrödinger equation for n identical particles has many solutions, of different symmetry, and most of its eigenvalues are degenerate.

Now we can give the second argument why the physical solutions should be either totally symmetric or antisymmetric. Assume the wave function of the universe has one of the complicated symmetries we discussed with respect to the electrons. This means it will be symmetric with respect to the interchange of certain electron pairs, antisymmetric with respect to others, and it will keep this symmetry for all time. Then we may consider two helium atoms, one containing two electrons with symmetric wave function, the other containing antisymmetric electrons. These two atoms will have different eigenvalues, hence different optical spectra. Thus we would find in nature two different types of helium atoms, and still more varieties of any heavier atom like carbon. But we know that all atoms of given nuclear charge are alike, both chemically and spectroscopically. Hence only one symmetry of the wave function of electrons in one atom can be allowed, and this means that the wave function of the universe must have one of the simple symmetries, either totally symmetric or antisymmetric.

To reach this conclusion we had to make use of an empirical fact. But this was a simple, qualitative, and long-established fact, namely, the identical behavior of all atoms of the same chemical element. Since atoms are composite systems containing electrons, their identical physical behavior is sufficient to establish that the symmetry of the wave function with respect to all electrons in the universe is simple. Which symmetry is to be chosen, i.e., symmetry or antisymmetry, can of course only be decided on the basis of more quantitative information. Similar arguments establish simple symmetry with respect to other fundamental particles, e.g., protons and neutrons.

SYMMETRY FOR COMPOSITES

We shall presently show that particles described by a symmetric wave function obey Bose statistics, those described by an antisymmetric wave function Fermi statistics. They are therefore commonly called *bosons* and *fermions*, respectively. Consider now tightly bound composite objects like nuclei. It then makes sense to ask for the symmetry of the wave function of a system containing many identical objects of the same type, e.g., many He^4 nuclei. This symmetry can be deduced by imagining that the interchange of two composites is carried out particle by particle. Each interchange of fermions changes the sign of the wave function. Hence the composite will be a fermion if and only if it contains an odd number of fermions, a boson if the number of fermions in the composite is even. The number of bosons contained in the composite does not matter. If the wave function contains coordinates of several types of particles, definite symmetry exists only for interchange within each type.

CONSTRUCTION OF SYMMETRIZED WAVE FUNCTIONS

We may construct the properly symmetrized (unnormalized) wave function for n identical particles from one unsymmetric solution. For this purpose, we obtain the n! solutions by permuting the indices and forming the sums

$$\sum_{P} \Psi[P(1, 2, \ldots, n)] \tag{3-13}$$

$$\sum_{P} \epsilon_P \Psi[P(1, 2, \ldots, n)] \tag{3-14}$$

where the summations are over all the permutations and $\epsilon_P = -1$ for odd permutations of $1, 2, \ldots, n$, $\epsilon_P = +1$ for even ones. An odd permutation is one which may be obtained by carrying out an odd number of simple interchanges of pairs of particles in succession. It is seen that equation (3-13) gives a symmetric wave function and (3-14) an antisymmetric one.

If the interaction of the n identical particles in the system is weak, then the Hamiltonian H_0 in (3-5) is a good approximation to the true Hamiltonian, and the product wave function (3-7) a good approximation to the eigenfunction. From this we can form a symmetric or antisymmetric wave function using (3-13) and (3-14), respectively. The normalized antisymmetric function may conveniently be written as a determinant of n rows and columns, the so-called *Slater determinant*:

$$(n!)^{-1/2}\begin{vmatrix} \phi_a(1)\,\phi_a(2) & \cdots & \phi_a(n) \\ \phi_b(1)\,\phi_b(2) & \cdots & \phi_b(n) \\ & \vdots & \\ \phi_k(1)\,\phi_k(2) & \cdots & \phi_k(n) \end{vmatrix} \qquad (3\text{-}15)$$

Interchange of two coordinates will interchange two columns, which changes the sign of the determinant demonstrating the required antisymmetry. In addition the interchange of two *states*, i.e., of two orbitals, interchanges two rows, which also changes the sign of the determinant. Therefore if two particles are in the same state, i.e., if two orbitals are the same, the determinant is zero. This follows also from the well-known theorem that a determinant with two equal rows must vanish. We have thereby proved the famous *Pauli exclusion principle*, which states that no two electrons in a given system can occupy the same quantum state (orbital). This principle was postulated by Pauli in 1924 to explain the periodic table of elements. In quantum mechanics, it follows automatically from the antisymmetry of the wave function. Or vice versa, knowing the periodic system, we must conclude that the electron eigenfunction must be antisymmetric rather than symmetric.

STATISTICAL MECHANICS

In a system of weakly interacting particles, we don't need to write down the wave function explicitly as we have done in (3-15), but it suffices to specify which orbitals are occupied by particles, and by how many. This is the method of *statistical mechanics*. We specify the "occupation numbers" $n_a, n_b, \ldots$ of orbitals a, b, ... If the wave function is antisymmetric, we can only have $n_a = 0$ or 1; this type of statistics was first postulated by Fermi and bears his name, hence the particles obeying these statistics are called *fermions*. For a symmetric wave function, any occupation number is possible; this is known as Bose statistics (*bosons*). There is one and only one symmetric eigenfunction for a given set of occupation numbers $n_a, n_b, \ldots$; hence the statistical weight for any such set is the same in Bose statistics (unity).

We have previously listed the particles which are empirically fermions, and it will be noted that all these particles have spin $\frac{1}{2}$. Similarly, all particles which are observed to be bosons have spin 0 (π- and K-mesons) or 1 (photons). Pauli (1940) proved that relativistic theories can be consistent only if half-integer-spin particles are fermions and integer-spin particles are bosons.

EXPERIMENTAL DETERMINATION OF SYMMETRY

The symmetry of the wave function has direct, observable physical consequences. Probably the most useful is the wave function of the spatial motion of the two nuclei in a homonuclear molecule, such as C_2^{12}. It can easily be shown (see, e.g., Bethe, 1936) that such a molecule will only have rotational states of even angular momentum j if the nuclei are bosons without spin, only odd j if they are fermions without spin (if such objects existed). Observation of the rotational band spectrum shows that C_2^{12} has indeed only even rotational states; therefore C^{12} is a boson. More important, this shows that all C^{12} nuclei are truly identical. The same can be done, e.g., for molecules like H_2^3, involving two radioactive nuclei H^3. Experiment shows that all nuclei H^3 are identical, because the rotational spectrum of H_2^3 is just such as would be expected for fermions of spin $\frac{1}{2}$. If the nuclei were not identical, the wave function would be unsymmetrical in their coordinates, and *all* rotational quantum numbers would be equally likely. Now H^3 decays radioactively into He^3 plus a β^--particle, with a half-life of 12 years. The two H^3 nuclei in a H_2^3 molecule will in general decay at different times. Yet direct experiment shows that they are identical: thus there is no "hidden variable" in the nucleus which indicates when they will decay. If there were such a variable, even if it had no influence on the energy and dynamics of the system, it would still influence the symmetry of the wave function. Wave mechanics really gives us a specific handle to determine identity of particles, not simply by the absence of observable differences between them.

In the last 10 years there have been attempts to replace the probabilistic predictions of quantum mechanics by strictly casual ones. It has been suggested (Bohm, de Broglie) that there exist hidden variables in terms of which these casual descriptions could be effected. These variables are "hidden" in the sense that they do not affect energy eigenvalues. The existence of identical particles and composites show that such hidden variables cannot have any observable consequences (as in the example of radioactivity) and are therefore empty. It assures us that the present description must be complete.

For electrons it is a particularly simple observation that no further quantum numbers are needed to describe possible states. If there were degrees of freedom which we have not specified, we would expect that we could find electrons in nature which are described by different values of these hidden variables. That is, the observed degeneracy of electronic states would have to be greater than that predicted by our present theory. The overwhelming success of the explanation of the periodic table in terms of the present theory indicates that this is not the case; i.e., no further degrees of freedom exist.

Another application of the symmetry of the rotational wave function of a homonuclear diatomic molecule was to determine the statistics of the nuclei involved. In particular, Rasetti (1930) found that the N^{14} nucleus is a boson. This helped to disprove the "nuclear electron" hypothesis, which claimed that the N^{14} nucleus was constituted of 14 protons and 7 electrons, which would have made it a fermion (Bethe, 1936).

Gross effects of the symmetry of the wave function are found in statistical mechanics. The Fermi statistics of the electrons in solids is fundamental to the understanding of the behavior of metals. The Bose statistics of He^4 atoms (4 nucleons, 2 electrons) is the reason for the peculiar behavior of liquid He^4 (modification II) at low temperatures, such as superfluidity. He^3 is a fermion and liquid He^3 behaves differently.

CLASSICAL LIMIT

We shall now examine the behavior of a system of identical particles in the limit of classical mechanics. The only method for distinguishing classical identical particles is by following their orbits, which are of course well defined. It is the lack of well-defined orbits for particles obeying quantum mechanics which gives rise to exchange effects. In particular if the wave functions of two particles overlap in space we can no longer distinguish the two orbits. In the classical limit the state functions become well-defined, nonoverlapping wave packets. Explicitly if the two particles are described by

$$\Psi(1,2) \pm \Psi(2,1) \tag{3-16}$$

the coordinate probability density is

$$|\Psi(1,2)|^2 + |\Psi(2,1)|^2 \pm 2\,\mathrm{Re}[\Psi(1,2)\Psi^*(2,1)] \tag{3-17}$$

If $\Psi(1,2)$ is zero unless coordinate 1 is in some region A and coordinate 2 is in some region B, and A and B do not overlap, the interference term will vanish. The coordinate probability density then becomes that of two particles which could be distinguished. Hence we do not find any exchange effects in classical descriptions.

It should be realized that even in nonclassical descriptions identical particles can be distinguished if their wave functions do not overlap; i.e., if they are in sufficiently different states. If the wave functions do overlap, there is an "exchange density" in (3-17) which leads to observable consequences. Thus, e.g., when two identical particles scatter each other, their wave functions will overlap at some time, and there are then interference terms arising from the symmetry of the wave function.

Chapter 4

TWO-ELECTRON ATOMS: PERTURBATION CALCULATION

We shall solve equation (1-4) for two electrons by perturbation theory. In the calculations of atomic structure it is convenient to use atomic units (Hartree). The unit of mass is the rest mass of the electron; of charge, the magnitude of the electronic charge; of length, the first Bohr radius of the hydrogen atom $\hbar^2/me^2$. In these units (1-4) for two electrons becomes

$$\left[\nabla_1^2 + \nabla_2^2 + 2\left(E + \frac{Z}{r_1} + \frac{Z}{r_2} - \frac{1}{r_{12}}\right)\right]\psi = 0 \tag{4-1}$$

The above equation does not separate. Since the Hamiltonian contains no spin term, $\psi(1,2) = U(1,2)\chi(1,2)$, where u is the space part and χ is the spin part of the wave function. ψ must be antisymmetric under interchange of the two electrons. The Hamiltonian is symmetric under interchange of the space coordinates. Thus we can take the spatial functions to be entirely symmetric or antisymmetric. The former case is called *para*; the latter, *ortho*.

$$\begin{aligned} U_p(1,2) &= U_p(2,1) \\ U_o(1,2) &= -U_o(2,1) \end{aligned} \tag{4-2}$$

The over-all antisymmetry of Ψ determines the symmetry properties of the spin function.

$$\begin{aligned} \chi_p(1,2) &= -\chi_p(2,1) \\ \chi_o(1,2) &= \chi_o(2,1) \end{aligned} \tag{4-3}$$

From Table 2-1 we see that the only antisymmetric two-electron spin function is the singlet

$$\chi_p(1,2) = 2^{-1/2}[(\alpha_1\beta_2) - (\beta_1\alpha_2)] \tag{4-4a}$$

There are three linearly independent, symmetric (ortho) spin functions, and it is convenient to choose them to be eigenfunctions of S^2 and S_z,

$$\chi_o^{+1}(1,2) = (\alpha_1\alpha_2)$$

$$\chi_o^{0}(1,2) = 2^{-1/2}[(\alpha_1\beta_2) + (\beta_1\alpha_2)] \tag{4-4b}$$

$$\chi_o^{-1}(1,2) = (\beta_1\beta_2)$$

Since there are three spin functions, the ortho states are also called *triplet states*.

For purposes of perturbation calculations, the complete Hamiltonian appearing in equation (4-1) can be written as $H^0 + \lambda H^1$, where

$$\begin{aligned} H^0 &= -\tfrac{1}{2}(\nabla_1^2 + \nabla_2^2) + V_1(r_1) + V_2(r_2) \\ \lambda H^1 &= -\frac{Z}{r_1} - V_1(r_1) - \frac{Z}{r_2} - V_2(r_2) + \frac{1}{r_{12}} \end{aligned} \tag{4-5}$$

Powers of λ will distinguish orders of the perturbation. The criteria for choosing V_1 and V_2 are that H^0 lead to a soluble equation and that the effect of H^1 be small. If u_1 and u_2 are any two normalized solutions $u_{n\ell m}$ of the single-particle equation

$$[\tfrac{1}{2}\nabla^2 + \mathcal{E}_{n\ell} - V(r)]u_{n\ell m} = 0 \tag{4-6}$$

then the zero-order wave equation

$$(H^0 - E^0)U^0 = 0 \tag{4-7}$$

is solved by the substitution

$$\begin{aligned} E^0 &= \mathcal{E}_{1n\ell} + \mathcal{E}_{2n\ell} \\ U^0 &= u_1(\mathbf{r}_1)u_2(\mathbf{r}_2) \end{aligned} \tag{4-8}$$

Since $V(r)$ is central, a solution of (4-6) can be written

$$u_{n\ell m}(\mathbf{r}) = R_{n\ell}(r) Y_{\ell m}(\Omega)$$

$$Y_{\ell m}(\Omega) = \sqrt{\frac{(\ell - |m|)!}{(\ell + |m|)!} \frac{2\ell + 1}{4\pi}} (-1)^{(m+|m|)/2}$$

$$\times P_\ell^{|m|}(\cos\theta) e^{im\varphi} \tag{4-9}$$

where $P_\ell^{|m|}$ is the associated Legendre function. If V(r) is chosen to be of the Coulomb form, we have

$$V(r) = -\frac{(Z - s)}{r} \qquad \mathcal{E}_n = -\frac{1}{2}\frac{(Z - s)^2}{n^2} \tag{4-10}$$

For helium (and other He-like ions) only those states are of practical importance in which at least one electron is in the ground state for the following reason. One finds that the energy for any He state where both electrons are excited is higher than the ground-state energy of a He^+ ion plus a free electron. Such doubly excited states would therefore quickly disintegrate into a He^+ ion and a free electron; they are states in the continuous spectrum, not discrete states Hence we shall only deal with the case when one electron is in the 1s state. The states of such atoms will then be described by only three quantum numbers; n, ℓ, m plus the designation ortho and para.

The symmetrized, normalized, zero-order wave functions are

$$U^0_{n\ell m} = 2^{-1/2}[u_1(\mathbf{r}_1) u_{n\ell m}(\mathbf{r}_2) \pm u_1(\mathbf{r}_2) u_{n\ell m}(\mathbf{r}_1)] \tag{4-11}$$

where the + sign holds in the para and the − sign holds in the ortho case. The subscript 1 designates the ground state. We see that for both electrons in the ground state, the zero-order ortho wave function vanishes identically, so that no solution is obtained. We conclude that the lowest-energy state must be para. Generally for ortho state $U^0 = 0$ whenever the two electrons coincide, $\mathbf{r}_1 = \mathbf{r}_2$. For para states this is not so. Therefore the probability that the two electrons are very close to each other is much smaller for ortho than for para states. This in turn means that the energy of para states should be larger than that of ortho states. Furthermore we expect optical combinations between ortho and para states (or vice versa) to be forbidden for the following reason. The operator for the electric dipole moment $(x_1 + x_2)$ and the spatial para wave function are unchanged under interchange of the two electrons, while the spatial ortho wave function changes sign. The transition matrix element involves an integral over the spatial coordinates of both electrons. This integral vanishes from symmetry considerations.

To summarize: The level scheme of helium and of ions with two

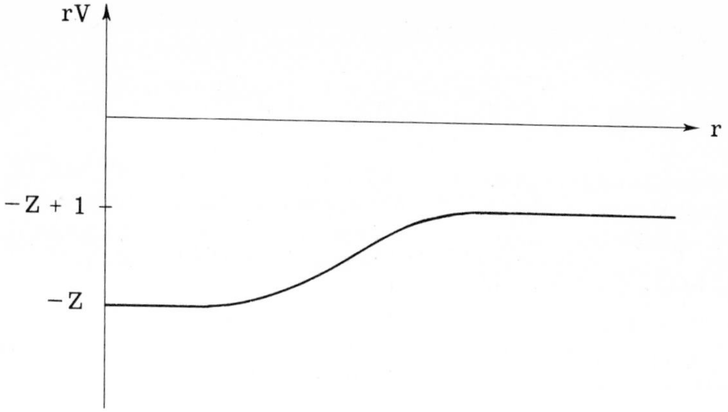

Figure 4-1

electrons consists of two systems of levels, one containing triplet levels (orthohelium) and the other singlet levels (parahelium) which do not combine optically with each other. The lowest-energy state is para. For all excited states, the energy eigenvalues of the para states are larger than those of the corresponding ortho states.

We shall now make a specific choice for V_1 and V_2 occurring in (4-5), which is due to Heisenberg (1927). A reasonable assumption for the effective single-particle potential would be the following. For small enough r, the electron 1 "sees" the entire nuclear charge Z. For sufficiently large r the nuclear charge is screened by electron 2 and electron 1 "sees" a charge Z − 1. Figure 4-1 exhibits the qualitative behavior of a potential describing this situation. With Heisenberg we now assume that electron 1 is in the ground state and electron 2 is in an excited state. We are thus led to the following choice of potentials:

$$V_1(r_1) = -\frac{Z}{r_1} \qquad V_2(r_2) = -\frac{Z-1}{r_2} \tag{4-12}$$

This treats the two electrons unsymmetrically and we must modify the first-order perturbation theory to handle this unsymmetry. We split the Hamiltonian H into a zero-order Hamiltonian and a small perturbation part in two ways.

$$H = H_a^0 + \lambda H_a^1 = H_b^0 + \lambda H_b^1 \tag{4-13}$$

All four Hamiltonians are Hermitian. The two zero-order Hamiltonians differ from each other only by a term of first order in λ:

$$H_a^0 - H_b^0 = \lambda\left(H_b^1 - H_a^1\right) \tag{4-14}$$

Let U_a^0 and U_b^0 be particular normalized eigenfunctions of H_a^0 and H_b^0, respectively.

$$\left(H_a^0 - E_a^0\right)U_a^0 = \left(H_b^0 - E_b^0\right)U_b^0 = 0 \tag{4-15}$$

We restrict ourselves to cases $E_a^0 = E_b^0 \equiv E^0$. Since H_a^0 and H_b^0 are identical to zero order in λ, their eigenfunctions are identical to zero order. Assuming a degenerate eigenvalue spectrum we choose U_a^0 and U_b^0 orthogonal to each other in zero order in λ. We put

$$\begin{aligned} &(H - E)U = 0, \qquad E = E^0 + \lambda E^1 \\ &U = U^0 + \lambda U^1 = 2^{-1/2}\left(U_a^0 + U_b^0\right) + \lambda U^1 \end{aligned} \tag{4-16}$$

From (4-13), (4-15), and (4-16) we obtain

$$\begin{aligned} \lambda 2^{+1/2}(H - E)U^1 &+ \lambda\left(H_a^1 U_a^0 + H_b^1 U_b^0\right) \\ &- \lambda E^1\left(U_a^0 + U_b^0\right) = 0 \end{aligned} \tag{4-17}$$

Multiplying (4-17) by $(U_a^0 + U_b^0)^*$ and integrating we obtain

$$\begin{aligned} \lambda 2^{1/2} &\int \left(U_a^0 + U_b^0\right)^* (H - E)U^1\, d\tau \\ &+ \lambda \int \left(U_a^0 + U_b^0\right)^* \left(H_a^1 U_a^0 + H_b^1 U_b^0\right) d\tau \\ &- \lambda E^1 \int \left(U_a^0 + U_b^0\right)^* \left(U_a^0 + U_b^0\right) d\tau = 0 \end{aligned} \tag{4-18}$$

Since $(H - E)$ is an Hermitian operator, the first integral can be written as

$$\lambda 2^{1/2} \int \left[(H - E)\left(U_a^0 + U_b^0\right)\right]^* U^1\, d\tau$$

Now

$$\begin{aligned} (H - E)\left(U_a^0 + U_b^0\right) &= (H - E)\, 2^{1/2} U - (H - E)\, 2^{1/2} \lambda U^1 \\ &= -2^{1/2} \lambda (H - E)U^1 \end{aligned}$$

Since we shall only keep terms of first order in λ, the first integral vanishes. The third integral is

$$\begin{aligned} -\lambda E^1 \Big[\int |U_a^0|^2\, d\tau &+ \int |U_b^0|^2\, d\tau \\ &+ \int U_b^{0*} U_a^0\, d\tau + \int U_a^{0*} U_b^0\, d\tau\Big] = 2\lambda E^1 \end{aligned}$$

since U_a^0, U_b^0 are orthonormal to zero order in λ. Thus (4-18) reduces to

$$E^1 = \tfrac{1}{2}\int \left(U_a^0 + U_b^0\right)^* \left(H_a^1 U_a^0 + H_b^1 U_b^0\right) d\tau \tag{4-19}$$

Returning now to our specific problem we write

$$\begin{aligned} H_a^0 &= -\tfrac{1}{2}(\nabla_1^2 + \nabla_2^2) - \frac{Z}{r_1} - \frac{Z-1}{r_2} \\ \lambda H_a^1 &= \frac{1}{r_{12}} - \frac{1}{r_2} \\ H_b^0 &= -\tfrac{1}{2}(\nabla_1^2 + \nabla_2^2) - \frac{Z-1}{r_1} - \frac{Z}{r_2} \\ \lambda H_b^1 &= \frac{1}{r_{12}} - \frac{1}{r_1} \\ E^0 &= -\tfrac{1}{2}Z^2 - \frac{1}{2n^2}(Z-1)^2 \end{aligned} \tag{4-20}$$

We set

$$\begin{aligned} U_a^0 &= u_1(\mathbf{r}_1)\, u_{n\ell m}(\mathbf{r}_2) \\ U_b^0 &= \pm u_1(\mathbf{r}_2)\, u_{n\ell m}(\mathbf{r}_1) \end{aligned} \tag{4-21}$$

where $u_1(\mathbf{r})$ is the normalized ground-state wave function of a hydrogen-like atom of charge Z; $u_{n\ell m}(\mathbf{r})$ is the normalized hydrogen-like wave function for an excited state with charge $Z - 1$. The plus sign refers to para states; the minus sign, to ortho states. We must now assume that u_1 and $u_{n\ell m}$ are orthogonal, so that U_a^0 and U_b^0 be orthogonal. (This is always true for $\ell \neq 0$. For $\ell = 0$ we consider the two functions orthogonal to zero order.) Following (4-11) and (4-16) the zero-order wave functions are

$$U_\pm^0 = 2^{1/2}[u_1(\mathbf{r}_1)\, u_{n\ell m}(\mathbf{r}_2) \pm u_{n\ell m}(\mathbf{r}_1)\, u_1(\mathbf{r}_2)] \tag{4-22}$$

and the first-order perturbation energy

$$E^1 = 2^{-1/2}\int U_\pm^{0*}\left[\left(\frac{1}{r_{12}} - \frac{1}{r_2}\right) u_1(\mathbf{r}_1)\, u_{n\ell m}(\mathbf{r}_2) \pm \left(\frac{1}{r_{12}} - \frac{1}{r_1}\right) u_1(\mathbf{r}_2)\, u_{n\ell m}(\mathbf{r}_1)\right] d\tau_1\, d\tau_2 \tag{4-23}$$

Using the orthogonality of u_1 and $u_{n\ell m}$, (4-23) reduces to

$$E^1 = J \pm K$$

$$J \equiv \int d\tau_1\, d\tau_2 \left(\frac{1}{r_{12}} - \frac{1}{r_2}\right) u_1^2(\mathbf{r}_1)\, |u_{n\ell m}(\mathbf{r}_2)|^2 \tag{4-24}$$

$$K \equiv \int d\tau_1\, d\tau_2\, u_1(\mathbf{r}_1) u_{n\ell m}^*(\mathbf{r}_1) \frac{1}{r_{12}} u_2(\mathbf{r}_2) u_{n\ell m}(\mathbf{r}_2)$$

J is called the *direct integral* and represents the Coulomb interaction between the charge distributions of the two electrons plus the interaction of the outer electron with one unit of positive charge concentrated at the nucleus. K is called the *exchange integral.* It measures the frequency with which the two electrons exchange their quantum states.

To make this clear, let us assume we know that at time $t = 0$ electron 1 is in the ground state and electron 2 is in an excited state. Then the wave function at $t = 0$ is

$$\Psi(0) = u_1(\mathbf{r}_1) u_{n\ell m}(\mathbf{r}_2) = 2^{-1/2}(U_+ + U_-)$$

At any later time

$$\begin{aligned} \Psi(t) &= 2^{-1/2}(\Psi_+(t) + \Psi_-(t)) \\ &= 2^{-1/2}\left(U_+ e^{-i(E'+K)t} + U_- e^{-i(E'-K)t}\right) \\ &= e^{-iE't}(u_1(\mathbf{r}_1) u_{n\ell m}(\mathbf{r}_2) \cos Kt \\ &\quad - i u_1(\mathbf{r}_2) u_{n\ell m}(\mathbf{r}_1) \sin Kt) \end{aligned} \tag{4-25}$$

$$E' \equiv E^0 + J$$

After the time interval $\pi/2K$ has elapsed, the two electrons have interchanged their roles: electron 1 is now excited, electron 2 is in the ground state. (This explanation assumed we could distinguish electron 1 from electron 2 at time $t = 0$, which of course violates the principle of indistinguishability. Hence the entire argument should not be taken too seriously.)

To evaluate J we write

$$\begin{aligned} J &= \int_0^\infty \int_0^\infty r_1^2\, dr_1\, r_2^2\, dr_2\, R_{10}^2(r_1) R_{n\ell}^2(r_2) J(r_1, r_2) \\ J(r_1,r_2) &\equiv \iint d\Omega_1\, d\Omega_2\, Y_{00}^2(\Omega_1)\, |Y_{\ell m}(\Omega_2)|^2 \left(\frac{1}{r_{12}} - \frac{1}{r_2}\right) \end{aligned} \tag{4-26}$$

$$\frac{1}{r_{12}} = \frac{1}{r_>} \sum_{\ell'=0}^{\infty} \left(\frac{r_<}{r_>}\right)^{\ell'} P_{\ell'}(\cos\Theta)$$

$$= \frac{1}{r_>} \sum_{\ell'=0}^{\infty} \left(\frac{r_<}{r_>}\right)^{\ell'} \frac{4\pi}{2\ell'+1} \sum_{m'=-\ell'}^{m'=\ell'} Y_{\ell' m'}(\Omega_1)\, Y^*_{\ell' m'}(\Omega_2) \qquad (4\text{-}27)$$

where

$$r_> = \max\,[r_1, r_2]$$

$$r_< = \min\,[r_1, r_2]$$

$$\cos\Theta = \mathbf{r}_1 \cdot \mathbf{r}_2 / r_1 r_2$$

One then obtains

$$J(r_1,r_2) = \begin{cases} 1/r_1 - 1/r_2 & r_1 > r_2 \\ 0 & r_1 < r_2 \end{cases} \qquad (4\text{-}28)$$

Recalling $R_{10}(r) = 2Z^{3/2}e^{-Zr}$, we obtain

$$J = \int_0^\infty r_2^2 R_{n\ell}^2(r_2)\, dr_2 \int_{r_2}^\infty 4Z^3 r_1^2\, e^{-2Zr_1} \left(\frac{1}{r_1} - \frac{1}{r_2}\right) dr_1$$

$$= -\int_0^\infty \left(Z + \frac{1}{r_2}\right) e^{-2Zr_2}\, r_2^2 R_{n\ell}^2(r_2)\, dr_2 \qquad (4\text{-}29)$$

Equation (4-29) can be evaluated for specific values of n and ℓ (Bethe and Salpeter, pp. 133–134). Specifically for large n one obtains

$$J \approx \frac{1}{n^3} F(Z,\ell) \qquad (4\text{-}30)$$

where $F(Z,\ell)$ falls off rapidly with ℓ.

To see this we make use of the WKB approximation, which is valid for large n. If we set $v = Rr$,

$$\frac{d^2 v}{dr^2} + \Phi v \equiv \frac{d^2 v}{dr^2} + \left(-\frac{Z^2}{n^2} + \frac{2Z}{r} - \frac{\ell(\ell+1)}{r^2}\right) v = 0 \qquad (4\text{-}31)$$

The coefficient Φ of v represents the kinetic energy of the electron and is positive for $r_1 < r < r_2$, where

$$r_{1,2} = \frac{n^2}{Z} \pm \frac{n}{Z}(n^2 - \ell(\ell + 1))^{1/2} \tag{4-32}$$

In this region, the eigenfunctions can be represented as

$$v = a\Phi^{-1/4} \cos\left[\int^r \Phi^{1/2}\, dr' - \frac{\pi}{4}\right] \tag{4-33}$$

To obtain the normalization factor a, we need only consider the region $r_1 < r < r_2$ in the normalization integral. Since $n \gg 1$, there are many oscillations of the cosine, so that we can replace $\cos^2$ by its average value $\frac{1}{2}$. Then

$$1 = \int_0^\infty v^2\, dr \approx \tfrac{1}{2}a^2 \int_{r_1}^{r_2} \frac{dr}{\Phi^{1/2}} \approx \tfrac{1}{2}a^2 \pi Z^{-2} n^3$$

by actual integration or by the observation that $\Phi^{-1/2} \sim n/Z$ and $r_2 - r_1 \sim n^2/Z$. Therefore,

$$a \sim n^{-3/2} \tag{4-34}$$

Now for small r (of order 1/Z) and large n, the term Z^2/n^2 is negligible compared with the other terms in (4-31). Then it is easily seen that both (4-33) and the exact solution of (4-31) will have the form

$$rR_{n\ell} \equiv v = af(r,Z,\ell) \tag{4-33a}$$

where f is independent of n and only a depends on n. Since only values of r_2 of order 1/Z contribute to (4-39), this integral becomes

$$J \approx F(Z,\ell)/n^3 \tag{4-30}$$

$F(Z,\ell)$ falls off rapidly for large ℓ, since according to (4-28) only the region $r_2 < r_1$ contributes to J. Electrons with small orbital quantum number are more likely to penetrate the 1s shell than those with large ℓ (the probability of finding an electron in the neighborhood of the nucleus is proportional to $r^{2\ell}$). Defining $\delta_C = F(Z,\ell)/(Z-1)^2$, we can sum up the unperturbed energy and the perturbation J of the outer electron in the field of nuclear charge Z − 1:

$$-\frac{(Z-1)^2}{2n^2} + J = -\frac{(Z-1)^2}{2n^2}\left[1 - \frac{2\delta_C}{n}\right] \approx -\frac{(Z-1)^2}{2n^2}\left[1 + \frac{\delta_C}{n}\right]^{-2}$$

$$= -\frac{(Z-1)^2}{2(n+\delta_C)^2} \tag{4-35}$$

which is Rydberg's form for an energy level, customary in spectroscopy.

To evaluate K we write

$$K = \int_0^\infty \int_0^\infty r_1^2\,dr_1\, r_2^2\,dr_2\, R_{10}(r_1) R_{n\ell}(r_1) \times R_{10}(r_2) R_{n\ell}(r_2) K(r_1,r_2) \tag{4-36}$$

$$K(r_1,r_2) \equiv \iint d\Omega_1\, d\Omega_2\, Y_{00}(\Omega_1) Y_{00}(\Omega_2) Y_{\ell m}^*(\Omega_1) Y_{\ell m}(\Omega_2) \frac{1}{r_{12}}$$

Expanding $1/r_{12}$ in spherical harmonics we see that only the term $\ell' = \ell$, $m' = m$ contributes; all others vanish by orthogonality of the spherical harmonics upon integration over $d\Omega_1$ (or $d\Omega_2$). Thus we obtain

$$K(r_1,r_2) = \frac{1}{2\ell + 1} \frac{r_<^\ell}{r_>^{\ell+1}} \tag{4-37}$$

and

$$K = \frac{2}{2\ell + 1} \int_0^\infty r_2^{\ell+2}\, dr_2\, R_{10}(r_2) R_{n\ell}(r_2) \times \int_{r_2}^\infty r_1^{-\ell+1}\, dr_1\, R_{10}(r_1) R_{n\ell}(r_1) \tag{4-38}$$

where the symmetry of the integrand in r_1 and r_2 has been used.

The same qualitative considerations apply to K as to J. Evidently we can write

$$K \approx \frac{G(Z,\ell)}{n^3} \tag{4-39}$$

where $G(Z,\ell)$ falls off quickly for large ℓ. Defining

$$\delta_A = \frac{G(Z,\ell)}{(Z-1)^2}$$

we can write

$$E + \tfrac{1}{2} Z^2 = -\frac{1}{2} \frac{(Z-1)^2}{(N + \delta_C \pm \delta_A)^2} \tag{4-40}$$

The positive sign belongs to parahelium, the negative to orthohelium. The term $\delta_C \pm \delta_A$ is called the *Rydberg correction*; our calculation shows that this attains a limit for large n.

In reality the correct He wave functions cannot be exactly of the simple form of a product of two independent single-particle wave functions. The presence of one electron at a particular position affects the wave function of the other. The Coulomb repulsion due to one electron polarizes the charge distribution of the other such as to increase their mutual separation. One calculates the effect of polarization on the Coulomb correction δ_C, and on the exchange term δ_A. The correction to δ_A is very small (Bethe and Salpeter, p. 140), but the correction δ_π to the Coulomb term is sizeable. It is found that

$$E + \tfrac{1}{2}Z^2 = -\frac{1}{2}\frac{(Z-1)^2}{(n + \delta_C + \delta_\pi \pm \delta_A)^2} \tag{4-41}$$

δ_π is constant for large n and decreases with increasing ℓ, but not as rapidly as δ_C (Bethe and Salpeter, pp. 137–139).

Table 4-1 shows the comparison between observed and calculated values of the Rydberg correction $\delta_C + \delta_\pi \pm \delta_A$ for helium. δ_p is the observed Rydberg correction for parahelium; δ_o, for orthohelium. The columns $\delta_C + \delta_\pi$ and $\frac{1}{2}(\delta_o + \delta_p)$ represent, respectively, the calculated and observed *average* Rydgerg correction and should agree likewise, the last two columns of the table should agree.

Table 4-1

Rydberg Corrections for He States
with Large Principal Quantum Number

	$-(\delta_C + \delta_\pi)$	$-\frac{1}{2}(\delta_o + \delta_p)$	δ_A	$\frac{1}{2}(\delta_p - \delta_o)$
S	0.216	0.218	0.376	0.078
P	0.0248	0.0279	0.0351	0.0398
D	0.00262	0.00252	0.00066	0.00035
F	8×10^{-5}	13×10^{-5}	$< 10^{-5}$	8×10^{-5}

The agreement is fair for P and D states. For the exchange part δ_A of the S states it is seen that the Heisenberg method fails. (The exact agreement for the Coulomb part is accidental.) If the lack of orthogonality of 1s and ns states is taken into account, the result for the exchange term even has the wrong sign. Better wave functions are therefore necessary. Such functions are provided by Fock's method, discussed in detail below. The calculated Rydberg corrections are then -0.289 and -0.160 for ortho- and parahelium, respectively. The experimental values are -0.298 and -0.140.

Chapter 5

TWO-ELECTRON ATOMS: VARIATION CALCULATION

HELIUM ATOM

By far the most successful method for obtaining an accurate value for the ground state of two-electron atoms is the Ritz variation method.

The simplest trial function for a variation calculation is the product of two hydrogenic wave functions,

$$\psi = e^{-\alpha(r_1+r_2)} \tag{5-1}$$

with α as the variation parameter. Then some algebra yields (Schiff, pp. 174–175)

$$\langle H \rangle = \alpha^2 - 2Z\alpha + \tfrac{5}{8}\alpha \tag{5-2}$$

The first term on the right-hand side represents the expectation value of the kinetic energy; the second, the expectation value of the nuclear potential energy. The third term is the expectation value of the interaction energy between the electrons. The relevant integral for this term was evaluated by expanding $1/r_{12}$ in the usual fashion in spherical harmonics.

Minimizing (5-4) as a function of α gives

$$\alpha = Z - \tfrac{5}{16} \tag{5-3}$$

Thus the hydrogenic wave functions give the best energy when Z is replaced by $Z - \frac{5}{16}$, indicating that each electron screens the nucleus from the other electron. We find for the ground-state energy

$$E = -(Z - \tfrac{5}{16})^2 \qquad \text{atomic units} \tag{5-4}$$

Had we performed the most naïve perturbation calculation by considering $1/r_{12}$ as the perturbation, we would have obtained (5-1) for the zero-order (unnormalized) wave function, and (5-2) for the ground-state energy correct to first order, both with $\alpha = Z$. This would give an energy of $-Z^2 + \frac{5}{8}Z$. Our variation calculation has decreased this value by $(\frac{5}{16})^2 = 0.098$.

The experimentally measured quantity is not the total energy E of a helium-like atom, but its ionization potential I. I equals $E_0 - E$, where E_0 is the ground-state energy of the singly ionized (hydrogen-like) atom $E_0 = -Z^2/2$.

$$I = \frac{Z^2}{2} - \frac{5Z}{8} + \frac{25}{256} \text{ au}$$

$$= Z^2 - \frac{5Z}{4} + \frac{25}{128} \text{ Ry} \tag{5-5}$$

[We recall that 1 Ry unit of energy is one-half an atomic unit (au) of energy.]

For $Z = 2$, the calculated ionization potential is 1.693 Ry; the observed is 1.807 Ry. The naïve perturbation calculation discussed above would give 1.500 Ry. Table 5-1 lists the calculated (variational) and the measured values for the ionization potential in terms of the Rydberg. It is interesting to note that the difference between this simple variation result and the experimental value is almost independent of Z.

Higher approximations in the variation treatment begin with the assumption that

$$\psi(\mathbf{r}_1, \mathbf{r}_2) = e^{-\alpha(r_1+r_2)} P(\mathbf{r}_1, \mathbf{r}_2) \tag{5-6}$$

The first approximation (5-1) corresponds to $P = 1$. Higher approximations result in expanding $P(\mathbf{r}_1, \mathbf{r}_2)$. One could try writing

$$P(\mathbf{r}_1, \mathbf{r}_2) = \sum_{\ell} f_{\ell}(r_1, r_2) P_{\ell}(\cos \theta_{12}) \tag{5-7}$$

This is not successful, for reasons which will become clear below.

Table 5-1

Ionization Potential for Helium-Like Atoms

	H^-	He	Li^+	Be^{++}
Theoretical	−0.055	1.695	5.445	11.195
Experimental	0.055	1.807	5.560	11.312
Difference	0.110	0.112	0.115	0.117

It was Hylleraas (1928, 1929) who suggested that the trial function ought to depend on r_{12}. He introduced symmetric coordinates

$$s = \alpha(r_1 + r_2) \qquad t = \alpha(r_1 - r_2) \qquad u = \alpha r_{12} \tag{5-8}$$

and

$$\psi = e^{-s/2} P(s,t,u) \tag{5-9}$$

The "effective charge" α is fixed by the condition that $\langle H \rangle$ be minimum. It is also now clear why (5-7) was an unsatisfactory expansion. The difficulty lay in the fact that the expansion of r_{12} in terms of $P_\ell(\cos\theta_{12})$ converged very slowly.

P is expanded in power series of s, t, and u.

$$P = \sum_{\ell,n,m=0}^{\infty} c_{n,2\ell,m}\, s^n t^{2\ell} u^m \tag{5-10}$$

Only even powers of t occur, since ψ must be symmetric in r_1, r_2. One proceeds with the variation formalism and obtains $\langle H \rangle$ as a quadratic function of $c_{n,2\ell,m}$ and of α. This then is minimized. The coefficient c and the "effective nuclear charge" α are obtained from

$$\frac{\partial \langle H \rangle}{\partial c_{n,2\ell,m}} = 0 \qquad \frac{\partial \langle H \rangle}{\partial \alpha} = 0 \tag{5-11}$$

More recently Kinoshita has used variational wave functions of a more general type than (5-10). Besides the terms occurring in (5-10), he also includes terms of the form

$$c_{h,i,j}\, s^{h+1} \left(\frac{u}{s}\right)^i \left(\frac{t}{u}\right)^{2j} \tag{5-12}$$

These terms have no singularities in the region of integration for h,i,j positive since $|t| \le u \le s$.

An eighty-parameter calculation, combined with a reasonable extrapolation, gives for the ionization potential

$$I = 198317.45 \pm 0.11 \text{ cm}^{-1} \tag{5-13}$$

Table 5-2 lists the parameters used in some calculations and their coefficients (normalized such that $c_{0,0,0}$ is unity).

A further refinement of these methods is due to Pekeris (1958). He uses 210 terms in his expansion and expands in powers of $r_1 + r_2 - r_{12}$, $r_{12} + r_1 - r_2$, and $r_{12} - r_1 + r_2$. This permits him to determine the

Table 5-2
Variational Wave Functions for the Helium Ground State

	Term:	c(u)	c(s)	$c(t^2)$	$c(u^2/S)$
Hylleraas	3 param.	0.081		0.010	
	6 param.	0.097	−0.028	0.010	
Kinoshita	10 param.	0.121	−0.052	0.0055	−0.024

coefficients in the power series by recursion formulas which simplifies the numerical work. His result for I is

$$I = 198317.374 \pm 0.022 \text{ cm}^{-1} \tag{5-14}$$

This result is somewhat smaller than Kinoshita's (5-13). But it should be remembered that (5-13) is not a direct variational result but is obtained by extrapolation; therefore it can well be too large. Equation (5-14) is within the estimated error of Kinoshita's result. In judging the accuracy of Pekeris' result (5-14) it should be pointed out that 0.012 cm^{-1} of the error is due to the inaccuracy of the Rydberg constant for helium, only 0.010 cm^{-1}, or 1 part in 20 million, is due to Pekeris' approximations.

The experimental result is

$$I = 198310.82 \pm 0.15 \text{ cm}^{-1} \tag{5-15}$$

It is seen to be lower than the variation calculation result (5-14), and far outside the two stated limits of error, which is at first sight not very satisfactory, since the variation method ought to give a lower bound for I (recall $I = -E + E_0$).

This discrepancy is in part due to the motion of the nucleus which we have been ignoring so far. To account for this we write the total kinetic-energy operator for the system in ordinary units.

$$-\frac{\hbar^2}{2}\left[\frac{1}{M}\nabla_R^2 + \frac{1}{m}\left(\nabla_{r_1}^2 + \nabla_{r_2}^2\right)\right] \tag{5-16}$$

where $\mathbf{R} = (X,Y,Z)$ is the position vector and M the mass of the nucleus. Introducing coordinates of the center of mass

$$\rho = (\rho_X, \rho_Y, \rho_Z) = \frac{1}{M + 2m}(M\mathbf{R} + m\mathbf{r}_1 + m\mathbf{r}_2) \tag{5-17a}$$

and relative coordinates

$$\mathbf{R}_i = (X_i, Y_i, Z_i) = \mathbf{r}_i - \mathbf{R} \qquad i = 1,2 \tag{5-17b}$$

we get

$$\begin{aligned} \frac{\partial}{\partial x_i} &= \frac{m}{M + 2m}\frac{\partial}{\partial \rho_X} + \frac{\partial}{\partial X_i} \qquad i = 1,2 \\ \frac{\partial}{\partial X} &= \frac{M}{M + 2m}\frac{\partial}{\partial \rho_X} - \frac{\partial}{\partial X_1} - \frac{\partial}{\partial X_2} \end{aligned} \tag{5-18}$$

and similarly for the y and z components. Substituting in (5-16) the kinetic energy becomes

$$-\frac{\hbar^2}{2}\left[\frac{1}{M + 2m}\nabla_\rho^2 + \frac{1}{m}\left(\nabla_{R_1}^2 + \nabla_{R_2}^2\right) + \frac{1}{M}\sum_{i,k}\nabla_{R_i}\cdot\nabla_{R_k}\right] \tag{5-19}$$

Separating the motion of the center of mass and introducing the reduced mass

$$\mu = \frac{mM}{M + m} \tag{5-20}$$

Schrödinger's equations becomes

$$\left[-\frac{\hbar^2}{2\mu}\left(\nabla_{R_1}^2 + \nabla_{R_2}^2\right) - \frac{\hbar^2}{M}\nabla_{R_1}\cdot\nabla_{R_2} + V(R_1, R_2\ |\mathbf{R}_1 - \mathbf{R}_2|)\right]\psi = E\psi \tag{5-21}$$

Thus the motion of the nucleus modifies the Schrödinger equation in two ways. In the first place, the effective mass of the electron μ replaces the actual mass m. This is taken into account when we express the energy in terms of the reduced Rydberg unit,

$$R_M = \frac{M}{M + m}R_\infty \approx R_\infty\left(1 - \frac{m}{M}\right) \tag{5-22}$$

The second effect is the addition of a perturbation term $-(\hbar^2/M) \times \nabla_{R_1}\cdot\nabla_{R_2}$ to the energy and can be evaluated by perturbation theory (Bethe and Salpeter, pp. 166–170).

There are also relativistic corrections and further corrections due to the interaction of the electron with its own field (Lamb shift).

Pekeris gives for the nuclear motion plus relativistic correction the result $-5.348 \pm 0.0005\ \text{cm}^{-1}$. The Lamb shift was calculated by Salpeter and Zaidi to be $1.360 \pm 0.02\ \text{cm}^{-1}$. The corrected ionization potential is then

$$I_{\text{theor}}^{\text{tot}} = 198310.665 \pm 0.04\ \text{cm}^{-1} \tag{5-23}$$

The phenomenal agreement of (5-23) with (5-15) is one of the most striking proofs of the validity of wave mechanics, in a definitely nontrivial problem.

Kinoshita gives an estimate of the accuracy of the trial wave function in the following way. He writes the trial function ψ as

$$\psi = \sqrt{1 - \eta^2}\ \psi_0 + \eta f \tag{5-24}$$

where ψ_0 is the exact wave function and f is defined by

$$\int \psi_0 f\ d\tau = 0 \qquad \int |f|^2\ d\tau = 1 \tag{5-25}$$

In this case it can be verified that $\langle H \rangle$ differs from E by terms of order η^2. Kinoshita finds $\eta = 1.1 \times 10^{-3}$. Hence η^2 is about 10^{-6}.

We can now see why the Heisenberg perturbation theory fails to give the correct ground-state energy. A symmetrized wave function of the sort we were using for the perturbation calculations could never depend on $u = r_{12}$. However, we see from the variation calculations that ψ must depend on u. Specifically for $s = 1$, $t = 0$, the Kinoshita wave function behaves as

$$\psi \sim 1 + 0.498u + \cdots \tag{5-26}$$

It can also be shown that in the approximation r_1, r_2 large, r_{12} small, Schrödinger's equation leads to a solution of the form $\psi \sim 1 + 0.5u$, which agrees very well with (5-26) (Slater, Vol. II, p. 38).

HIGHER Z

The variation method can be used to obtain the ground-state energies of helium-like ions. For large Z we use the following procedure. In our Schrödinger equation (4-1) we change variables:

$$\begin{aligned} \rho &= 2Zr \qquad \sigma = 2Zs \qquad \tau = 2Zt \\ \nu &= 2Zu \qquad \epsilon = \frac{E}{2Z^2} \end{aligned} \tag{5-27}$$

Then we write Schrödinger's equation in the form

$$(H^0 + \lambda H^1 - \epsilon)U = 0$$

$$H^0 = -\left(\nabla_1^2 + \nabla_2^2 + \frac{1}{\rho_1} + \frac{1}{\rho_2}\right)$$

$$H^1 = \frac{1}{\rho_{12}} \qquad \lambda = \frac{1}{Z} \tag{5-28}$$

$$\epsilon = \epsilon^0 + \frac{\epsilon^1}{Z} + \frac{\epsilon^2}{Z^2} + \cdots$$

$$U = U^0 + \frac{U^1}{Z} + \frac{U^2}{Z^2} + \cdots$$

Then

$$U^0 = \tfrac{1}{2} e^{-1/2\,\sigma}$$

$$\epsilon^0 = -\tfrac{1}{2} \tag{5-29}$$

$$\epsilon^1 = \tfrac{5}{16}$$

To obtain ϵ^2, we write

$$U^1 = U^0 \Phi$$

or

$$U \approx \tfrac{1}{2} e^{-Zs}(1 + \Phi/Z) \tag{5-30}$$

Φ is obtained by variational methods, and $\epsilon^2 = -0.0788278$ (Bethe and Salpeter, pp. 151–153).

In principle one can calculate higher-order corrections also. Unfortunately the variational procedures become very cumbersome. Nevertheless, we now have exact values for ϵ^0 and ϵ^1 and a very accurate (variational) estimate for ϵ^2. One can then get an excellent semiempirical expansion for ϵ by using these values of ϵ^0 to ϵ^2 and by fitting ϵ^3 to ϵ^6 to the values determined directly for Z = 1, 2, 3, and 8 by Hylleraas. Then the ionization potential in Rydberg is, according to Hylleraas,

$$I = Z^2 - \tfrac{5}{4}Z + 0.315311 - 0.01707\frac{1}{Z} + 0.00068\frac{1}{Z^2} + 0.00164\frac{1}{Z^3} + 0.00489\frac{1}{Z^4} \tag{5-31}$$

EXCITED STATES

The energies for the excited states of helium can be calculated by the variation method provided the trial functions of the excited state are orthogonal to the eigenfunctions of all lower states. In general, this subsidiary condition makes the calculation quite difficult. However, cases do exist in which the subsidiary condition is satisfied automatically if the form of the wave function is prescribed by the character of the term to be calculated. A case in point is the $2\,^3S$ term. Every trial function must be chosen to be antisymmetric in the two electron space coordinates. This in itself is sufficient to assure orthogonality to the symmetric ground-state eigenfunction. In general, the eigenfunctions belonging to two states of an atom are automatically orthogonal if either the total orbital angular momentum **L** or the total spin **S** (or both) have different values for the two states. Hence the $2\,^3S$, $2\,^1P$, $2\,^3P$, etc., states of helium can be treated by the Ritz procedure without additional conditions. However, for the $2\,^1S$ term one must specifically provide for the orthogonality of the eigenfunction to that of the ground state 1^1S.

Table 5-3 lists the theoretical and experimental values for the energy of various helium states, as calculated by Hylleraas and Undheim for the 2S states, and by Breit and Eckart for the 2P states. The degree of agreement is directly related to the amount of calculational labor expended on each of these states.

Table 5-3
Energy Levels for Helium in Rydbergs

State	Theoretical	Experimental
$2\,^3S$	0.35044	0.35047
$2\,^1S$	0.2898	0.2920
$2\,^3P$	0.262	0.266
$2\,^1P$	0.245	0.247

Chapter 6

SELF-CONSISTENT FIELD

INTUITIVE PRELIMINARIES

We assume with Hartree that each electron in a multielectron system is described by its own wave function. This implies that each electron is subject to an equivalent potential due to the other electrons and to the nucleus. This equivalent potential is obtained by postulating that there is a charge density associated with each electron which is e times its position probability density. The equivalent potential for the jth electron is then

$$V(\mathbf{r}_j) = \sum_{k \neq j} \int |u_k(\mathbf{r}_2)|^2 \frac{1}{r_{j2}} \, d\tau_2 - \frac{Z}{r_j} \tag{6-1}$$

Here the subscript k indicates a set of quantum numbers describing the state of the kth electron. The summation extends over all the electrons except the jth.

If there are N electrons, this leads to N simultaneous nonlinear integrodifferential equations of the form

$$\left[-\tfrac{1}{2}\nabla_j^2 + V(\mathbf{r}_j)\right] u_i(\mathbf{r}_j) = \epsilon_i u_i(\mathbf{r}_j) \tag{6-2}$$

The next approximation is made by replacing $V(\mathbf{r}_j)$ by its average over the angles of $\mathbf{r}_j$, thus making it spherically symmetric:

$$V(r_j) = \frac{1}{4\pi} \int V(\mathbf{r}_j) \, d\Omega_j \tag{6-3}$$

This is the so-called *central field approximation*. (We shall see below that this is in fact a very mild approximation.) The solutions of (6-2) can then be expressed as products of radial functions and spherical harmonics.

$$u_n(\mathbf{r}) = u_{n\ell m}(\mathbf{r}) = \frac{\mathcal{R}_{n\ell}(r)}{r} \, Y_{\ell m}(\Omega) \tag{6-4}$$

$\mathcal{R}_{n\ell}(r)$ satisfies the differential equation

$$\frac{1}{2}\frac{d^2\mathcal{R}_{n\ell}}{dr^2} + \left[\epsilon_{n\ell} - V(r) - \frac{\ell(\ell+1)}{2r^2}\right]\mathcal{R}_{n\ell} = 0 \tag{6-5}$$

n is defined by the statement that $\mathcal{R}_{n\ell}$ has $n - \ell - 1$ nodes, not counting the nodes at $r = 0$ and $r = \infty$. This also gives an ordering for the $\epsilon_{n\ell}$; i.e., $\epsilon_{n\ell}$ increases with increasing n.

It is clear that even with all these assumptions we cannot solve the N equations of the form (6-2) exactly. Hartree's procedure is to solve this system by successive approximations, subject to the requirement of self-consistency. That is, the final wave functions must determine a final equivalent potential which agrees with the initial equivalent potential to a high order of accuracy.

It is apparent that the Hartree method neglects correlations between the positions of the electrons. This is inherent in assuming single-particle wave functions; that is, the entire wave function for the system is assumed to be a product of one-electron wave functions. This also means that symmetry considerations are ignored in Hartree's method. The Pauli principle can be included by choosing the quantum numbers of the one-electron orbitals appropriately.

VARIATION DERIVATION

Hartree arrived at (6-2) and (6-5) by physically reasonable, intuitive arguments. We shall now show how one can obtain similar results from a variation principle. We shall generalize Hartree's results by including the symmetry requirements. This generalization is known as the *Hartree-Fock theory* and is due to Fock and Slater.

For the variational trial function we choose a determinantal wave function of the form

$$\Psi = (N!)^{-1/2} \begin{vmatrix} u_1(1) & u_1(2) & \cdots & u_1(N) \\ u_2(1) & u_2(2) & \cdots & u_2(N) \\ & & \cdots & \\ u_N(1) & u_N(2) & \cdots & u_N(N) \end{vmatrix} \tag{6-6}$$

Each orbital occurring in (6-6) is a product of a space part and a spin part, which is either α or β. We require that all orbitals be orthonormal:

$$u_i(j) = u_i(\mathbf{r}_j)\chi_i(\sigma_j)$$
$$\int u_i^*(1)u_j(1)\, d\tau_1 = \delta_{ij} \tag{6-7}$$

where the integration is over space and spin coordinates. Since orbitals of different spins are automatically orthogonal, (6-7) reduces to the condition that space orbitals corresponding to the same spin function be orthonormal. This assures that Ψ is normalized and the variation condition becomes

$$\delta \int \Psi^* H \Psi \, d\tau = 0 \tag{6-8}$$

MATRIX ELEMENTS BETWEEN DETERMINANTAL WAVE FUNCTIONS

It is of general interest to calculate the matrix elements of an arbitrary operator F, involving all the electrons, between determinantal wave functions. We recall that (6-6) can be written as

$$\Psi = (N!)^{-1/2} \sum_P \epsilon_P \prod_{i=1}^{N} u_{Pi}(i)$$

$$= (N!)^{-1/2} \sum_P \epsilon_P \prod_{i=1}^{N} u_i(Pi) \tag{6-9}$$

The sum extends over all permutations, and ϵ_P is + or − depending on whether P1, P2, . . . , PN is an even or odd permutation of 1, 2, . . . , N. In order to calculate $\int \Psi_b^* F \Psi_a \, d\tau$, we assume that the orbitals corresponding to Ψ_b are $u_i(j)$; and to Ψ_a, $v_i(j)$. Then

$$\langle F \rangle = \frac{1}{N!} \int \sum_Q \epsilon_Q \prod_{i=1}^{N} u_i^*(Qi) F \sum_P \epsilon_P \prod_{j=1}^{N} \left[v_{Pj}(j)\, d\tau_j \right] \tag{6-10}$$

Note that for the final wave function we permute the electrons; for the initial wave function we permute the states. We can simplify (6-9) by observing that F must be symmetric in the coordinates of all the electrons, since these electrons are identical.

To simplify (6-10) it is convenient to group the terms referring to the same electron coordinates together. We therefore set j = Qi in the product over j; this does not change anything, since Qi will run over all values 1 to N when i does. Therefore,

$$\langle F \rangle = \frac{1}{N!} \int \sum_Q \sum_P \epsilon_Q \epsilon_P \prod_{i=1}^{N} u_i^* (Qi) F v_{PQi}(Qi) \, d\tau_{Qi} \qquad (6\text{-}10a)$$

We note that $\epsilon_Q \epsilon_P = \epsilon_{PQ}$. Now Qi is only a dummy variable of integration; therefore the integral (for each given P and Q) is not changed if we change the label Qi into i. (Here the symmetry of F in all electron coordinates is important.) Also we can sum over all permutations PQ, for given Q, and thus cover all permutations P. Then

$$\langle F \rangle = \frac{1}{N!} \sum_Q \sum_{PQ} \epsilon_{PQ} \int \prod_{i=1}^{N} u_i^*(i) F v_{PQi}(i) \, d\tau_i \qquad (6\text{-}10b)$$

Now the integral (and the coefficient ϵ_{PQ}) is entirely independent of Q, for each PQ; therefore each Q gives the same contribution, and the total is N! times the contribution of the simplest permutation, the identity. This eliminates the normalization factor $N!^{-1}$. Replacing now again the label PQ by P we get

$$\langle F \rangle = \sum_P \epsilon_P \int \prod_{i=1}^{N} u_i^*(i) F v_{Pi}(i) \, d\tau_i \qquad (6\text{-}11)$$

We now consider particular forms of F.

1. F = 1. Owing to the orthogonality of the one-electron wave functions, we get $\langle F \rangle = 0$, unless for some one P $v_{Pi} = u_i$ for *all* i. There can be at most one such P, since (6-7) holds. We shall assume here, and in everything that follows, that the ordering of the determinant Ψ_a is such that the v's that are identical with the u's are arranged in the same order. Then P is the identity permutation, and

$$\langle F \rangle = 1 \qquad (6\text{-}12)$$

2. $F = \Sigma_{j=1}^{N} f_j$, where f_j is a one-electron operator, operating on electron j. If $u_i \neq v_i$ for more than one i, we get $\langle F \rangle = 0$. If $u_i \neq v_i$ for some i, but $u_j = v_j$ for all j except j = i, we get

$$\langle F \rangle = \langle i | f | i \rangle = \int u_i^*(1) f_1 v_i(1) \, d\tau_1 \qquad (6\text{-}13)$$

If $u_i = v_i$ for all i,

$$\langle F \rangle = \sum_i \langle i | f | i \rangle \tag{6-14}$$

Only the identity permutation P = I contributes to (6-13) and (6-14).

3. $F = \Sigma_{i<j} g_{ij}$. The summation extends over all different pairs $i \neq j$ and g_{ij} is an operator operating on electrons i and j. If $u_i \neq v_i$ for more than two i's we get $\langle F \rangle = 0$. Suppose now $u_i = v_i$ for all i. Then

$$\langle F \rangle = \sum_{i<j} [\langle ij | g | ij \rangle - \langle ij | g | ji \rangle] \tag{6-15}$$

where the sum goves over all pairs, and

$$\langle ij | g | k\ell \rangle = \int u_i^*(1) u_j^*(2) g_{12} v_k(1) v_\ell(2) \, d\tau_1 \, d\tau_2 \tag{6-16}$$

The first term in (6-15) comes from P = I, the second from $P = P_{ij}$, i.e., the interchange of electrons i and j; this is, of course, an odd permutation, $\epsilon_P = -1$. In (6-16), the integration is over space and spin coordinates, and 1 and 2 are dummy variables. If for some i $u_i \neq v_i$, but for all j except j = i, we have $u_j = v_j$; then

$$\langle F \rangle = \sum_{j \neq i} [\langle ij | g | ij \rangle - \langle ij | g | ji \rangle] \tag{6-17}$$

If for some i and j $u_i \neq v_i$, $u_j \neq v_j$, but for all k except k = i, k = j, we have $u_k = v_k$; then

$$\langle F \rangle = \langle ij | g | ij \rangle - \langle ij | g | ji \rangle \tag{6-18}$$

DERIVATION OF THE HARTREE-FOCK EQUATIONS

We return now to the specific problem of evaluating $\int \Psi^* H \Psi \, d\tau$. Here $\Psi_a = \Psi_b = \Psi$. Hence $u_i = v_i$ for all i. We write $H = F_1 + F_2$, where

$$F_1 = \sum_i f_i \qquad f_i = -\tfrac{1}{2} \nabla_i^2 - \frac{Z}{r_i}$$
$$F_2 = \sum_{i<j} g_{ij} \qquad g_{ij} = \frac{1}{r_{ij}} \tag{6-19}$$

Then from (6-14) and (6-15)

$$\langle F_1 \rangle = \sum_i \langle i | f | i \rangle \tag{6-20a}$$

$$\langle F_2 \rangle = \sum_{i<j} [\langle ij | g | ij \rangle - \langle ij | g | ji \rangle] \tag{6-20b}$$

We shall write (6-20b), indicating explicitly the space integrations and spin summations.

$$\langle F_2 \rangle = \sum_{i<j} \Bigg[\sum_{\sigma_1,\sigma_2} \int d\tau_1\, d\tau_2\, u_i^*(\mathbf{r}_1) u_j^*(\mathbf{r}_2) g_{12} u_i(\mathbf{r}_1) u_j(\mathbf{r}_2)$$

$$\times |\chi_i(\sigma_1)|^2 \, |\chi_j(\sigma_2)|^2$$

$$- \sum_{\sigma_1,\sigma_2} \int d\tau_1\, d\tau_2\, u_i^*(\mathbf{r}_1) u_j^*(\mathbf{r}_2) g_{12} u_i(\mathbf{r}_2) u_j(\mathbf{r}_1)$$

$$\times \chi_i^*(\sigma_1) \chi_j^*(\sigma_2) \chi_i(\sigma_2) \chi_j(\sigma_1) \Bigg] \tag{6-21}$$

[We have taken $u_i(j) = u_i(\mathbf{r}_j)\chi_i(\sigma_j)$.] Recalling that

$$\sum_\sigma \chi_i^*(\sigma) \chi_j(\sigma) = \delta(m_{si}, m_{sj})$$

we obtain

$$\langle H \rangle = \sum_i \int d\tau\, u_i^*(\mathbf{r}) \left(-\tfrac{1}{2}\nabla^2 - \frac{Z}{r} \right) u_i(\mathbf{r})$$

$$+ \sum_{i<j} \Bigg[\int d\tau_1\, d\tau_2\, |u_i(\mathbf{r}_1)|^2 \, |u_j(\mathbf{r}_2)|^2 \, \frac{1}{r_{12}} - \delta(m_{si}, m_{sj})$$

$$\times \int d\tau_1\, d\tau_2\, \frac{1}{r_{12}}\, u_i^*(\mathbf{r}_1) u_j^*(\mathbf{r}_2) u_j(\mathbf{r}_1) u_i(\mathbf{r}_2) \Bigg] \tag{6-22}$$

The first term in the second sum is called the direct term, the second the exchange term. We notice that the exchange term is 0, unless the spins are the same for the two states of each pair. (This is another example of the fact that exchange effects do not exist for identical particles if their state functions are nonoverlapping; see p. 21).

According to (6-8) and (6-7) we require

$$\delta \langle H \rangle = 0 \tag{6-8a}$$

with the subsidiary conditions for orbitals with the same spin

$$\int u_i^*(\mathbf{r}_1)\, u_j(\mathbf{r}_1)\; d\tau_1 = \delta_{ij} \tag{6-7a}$$

To satisfy these conditions we use the method of Lagrange's undetermined multipliers. We demand that

$$\delta\Bigg(\langle H\rangle + \sum_i \lambda_{ii} \int |u_i|^2\, d\tau + \sum_{i<j} \delta(m_{si}, m_{sj}) \times \left[\lambda_{ij} \int u_i^* u_j\, d\tau + \lambda_{ji} \int u_j^* u_i\, d\tau\right]\Bigg) = 0 \tag{6-23a}$$

We choose $\lambda_{ij} = \lambda_{ji}^*$. Then the two terms of the second sum are complex conjugates of each other.

We now vary a particular u_i. Since $\langle H\rangle$ is stationary, it will be stationary for the variation of any u_i. Proceeding in a straightforward application of the variation techniques, then making use of the hermiticity and symmetry of the operators, we arrive at

$$\delta\langle H\rangle = \int \delta u_i^*(\mathbf{r}_1)\Bigg\{f_1 u_i(\mathbf{r}_1) + \sum_j \int u_j^*(\mathbf{r}_2)\, g_{12} \times [u_i(\mathbf{r}_1)\, u_j(\mathbf{r}_2) - \delta(m_{s1}, m_{s2})\, u_i(\mathbf{r}_2)\, u_j(\mathbf{r}_1)]\; d\tau_2\Bigg\}\, d\tau_1 + (\text{complex conjugate of previous term}) \tag{6-23b}$$

Combining this with the variation of the remaining terms in (6-23a) we get an expression of the form

$$\int \delta u_i^*(\mathbf{r}_1) R\; d\tau_1 + (\text{complex conjugate}) = 0 \tag{6-23c}$$

We satisfy this by requiring that each term be identically zero. Then, since the variation is arbitrary, the integrand must be zero. We thus obtain

$$-\tfrac{1}{2}\nabla_1^2 u_i(\mathbf{r}_1) - \frac{Z}{r_1} u_i(\mathbf{r}_1) + \left(\sum_j \int |u_j(\mathbf{r}_2)|^2 \frac{1}{r_{12}}\; d\tau_2\right) u_i(\mathbf{r}_1) - \sum_j \delta(m_{si}\, m_{sj})\left(\int u_j^*(\mathbf{r}_2)\, u_i(\mathbf{r}_2)\, \frac{1}{r_{12}}\; d\tau_2\right) u_j(\mathbf{r}_1) = -\sum_j \lambda_{ij}\; \delta(m_{si}, m_{sj})\, u_j(\mathbf{r}_1) \tag{6-24}$$

This is called the *Hartree-Fock equation* (Slater, Vol. II, p. 4).

We now make a unitary transformation of the u_i's. This obviously does not change the minimization results, since such transformations leave determinants (hence also determinantal wave functions) unchanged. Let

$$u'_j = \sum_k c^*_{kj} u_k \qquad u_k = \sum_j c_{kj} u'_j \tag{6-25}$$

Further, not to mix spins, we require $c_{kj} = 0$ if $m_{sk} \neq m_{sj}$. We multiply (6-24) by c^*_{ik} and sum over i, thus obtaining a Hartree-Fock equation for u'_k. We make use of the relations (Slater, Vol. II, p. 6)

$$\sum_j \delta(m_{si}, m_{sj}) u^*_j(2) u_j(1) = \sum_p \delta(m_{si}, m_{sp}) u'^*_p(2) u'_p(1)$$

$$\sum_j u^*_j(2) u_j(2) = \sum_p u'^*_p(2) u'_p(2) \tag{6-26}$$

$$\sum_i c^*_{ik} \sum_j \lambda_{ij} u_j(1) \delta(m_{si}, m_{sj}) = \sum_p \lambda'_{kp} u'_p(1) \delta(m_{sk}, m_{sp})$$

$$\lambda'_{ij} = \sum_{k\ell} c^*_{ki} \lambda_{k\ell} c_{\ell j}$$

Applying the above results to the transformed Hartree-Fock equation we observe that the form is unaltered and the λ_{ij} transform as matrix elements. Since the matrix $\{\lambda_{ij}\}$ is Hermitian $(\lambda_{ij} = \lambda^*_{ji})$ we can choose that unitary transformation which diagonalizes $\{\lambda_{ij}\}$. Defining $-\epsilon_i = \lambda'_{ii}$, the transformed Hartree-Fock equation reads (suppressing the prime and setting $k = i$),

$$-\tfrac{1}{2}\nabla_1^2 u_i(\mathbf{r}_1) - \frac{Z}{r_1} u_i(\mathbf{r}_1) + \left[\sum_j \int d\tau_2 \, |u_j(\mathbf{r}_2)|^2 \frac{1}{r_{12}}\right] u_i(\mathbf{r}_1)$$

$$-\sum_j \delta(m_{si}, m_{sj}) \left[\int u^*_j(\mathbf{r}_2) \frac{1}{r_{12}} u_i(\mathbf{r}_2)\, d\tau_2\right] u_j(\mathbf{r}_1)$$

$$= \epsilon_i u_i(\mathbf{r}_1) \tag{6-27}$$

The Hartree-Fock equation differs from the Hartree equation (6-1) and (6-2) by

$$\int \frac{|u_i(\mathbf{r}_2)|^2}{r_{12}}\, d\tau_2\, u_i(\mathbf{r}_1) - \sum_j \delta(m_{si}\, m_{sj}) \left[\int \frac{u_j^*(\mathbf{r}_2)\, u_i(\mathbf{r}_2)}{r_{12}}\, d\tau_2\right] u_j(\mathbf{r}_1)$$

$$= -\sum_{j \neq i} \delta(m_{si}, m_{sj}) \left[\int \frac{u_j^*(\mathbf{r}_2)\, u_i(\mathbf{r}_2)}{r_{12}}\, d\tau_2\right] u_j(\mathbf{r}_1) \qquad (6\text{-}28)$$

The second term on the left-hand side is the *exchange integral.* The expression (6-28) arises from the fact that we used determinantal trial functions [see (6-15)]. Had we used a product trial wave function this term would be missing and we would have obtained Hartree's equation. We shall discuss the physical significance of the exchange term below.

DISCUSSION OF THE EXCHANGE TERM

That part of the Hartree-Fock equation which agrees with the Hartree equation has the same physical significance; i.e., it represents an electron moving in an equivalent potential due to the other electrons and to the nucleus.

The exchange term, which we write as

$$-\int \sum_j u_j^*(\mathbf{r}_2)\, \frac{1}{r_{12}}\, u_j(\mathbf{r}_1)\, u_i(\mathbf{r}_2)\, d\tau_2 \qquad (6\text{-}29)$$

is a special case of a nonlocal potential. [We have suppressed the factor $\delta(m_{si}, m_{sj})$ for convenience. This means that all subsequent sums run over orbitals corresponding to the same spin.] A term, occurring in the Schrödinger equation for u_i, of the form

$$\int U(\mathbf{r}_1, \mathbf{r}_2)\, u_i(\mathbf{r}_2)\, d\tau_2$$

with (6-30)

$$U(\mathbf{r}_1, \mathbf{r}_2) = U^*(\mathbf{r}_2, \mathbf{r}_1)$$

is called a *nonlocal potential.* In our case

$$U(\mathbf{r}_1, \mathbf{r}_2) = -\frac{1}{r_{12}} \sum_j u_j^*(\mathbf{r}_2)\, u_j(\mathbf{r}_1) \qquad (6\text{-}31)$$

Any local potential $V(\mathbf{r}_1)$ can be considered as a nonlocal potential if we set

$$U(\mathbf{r}_1, \mathbf{r}_2) = V(\mathbf{r}_1)\, \delta(\mathbf{r}_1 - \mathbf{r}_2) \qquad (6\text{-}32)$$

We define an *average potential*

$$\overline{V}(\mathbf{r}_1) = \int U(\mathbf{r}_1,\mathbf{r}_2)\ d\tau_2 \tag{6-33}$$

and an *effective potential*

$$V_{\text{eff}}(\mathbf{r}_1)u_i(\mathbf{r}_1) = \int U(\mathbf{r}_1,\mathbf{r}_2)u_i(\mathbf{r}_2)\ d\tau_2 \tag{6-34}$$

The Schrödinger equation reads

$$\tfrac{1}{2}\nabla^2 u_i(\mathbf{r}_1) + [\epsilon_i - V(\mathbf{r}_1)]u_i(\mathbf{r}_1) - \int U(\mathbf{r}_1,\mathbf{r}_2)u_i(\mathbf{r}_2)\ d\tau_2 = 0 \tag{6-35}$$

The general properties of the solutions of (6-35) are as follows. The Laplacian is no longer necessarily zero when $u_i = 0$. Hence the inflection points of u_i need not coincide with the zeros of u_i.

The ϵ_i's are real and solutions of (6-35) belonging to different ϵ_i's are orthogonal. To see this we proceed with the usual proof; i.e., we multiply the equation for u_i by u_k^*, the equation for u_k^* by u_i, and subtract. We obtain

$$\left(\epsilon_i - \epsilon_k^*\right) \int u_k^* u_i\ d\tau = \int \Big[u_k^*(\mathbf{r}_1)\,U(\mathbf{r}_1,\mathbf{r}_2)\,u_i(\mathbf{r}_2) - u_i(\mathbf{r}_1)\,U^*(\mathbf{r}_1,\mathbf{r}_2)\,u_k^*(\mathbf{r}_2)\Big]\ d\tau_1\ d\tau_2 \tag{6-36}$$

Using the hermiticity of U and relabeling dummy variables in the second term of the right-hand integral we obtain the desired result. This also indicates that our method of Lagrange multipliers was successful, as they were explicitly introduced to make the functions orthogonal, and the ϵ_i's are real.

We define a quantity called the *density matrix*, $\rho(\mathbf{r}_1,\mathbf{r}_2)$,

$$\rho(\mathbf{r}_1,\mathbf{r}_2) = \sum_j u_j^*(\mathbf{r}_2)\,u_j(\mathbf{r}_1) \tag{6-37}$$

If all the j's were occupied, we would have by closure

$$\rho(\mathbf{r}_1,\mathbf{r}_2) = \delta(\mathbf{r}_1 - \mathbf{r}_2) \tag{6-38}$$

and

$$\int \rho(\mathbf{r}_1,\mathbf{r}_2)\ d\tau_2 = 1 \tag{6-39}$$

Even when the states are not all occupied, we shall show that (6-39) still holds.

In terms of the density matrix we have

$$U(\mathbf{r}_1,\mathbf{r}_2) = -\frac{1}{r_{12}}\,\rho(\mathbf{r}_1,\mathbf{r}_2) \qquad (6\text{-}40)$$

Thus we interpret $\overline{V}(\mathbf{r}_1)$ as the potential at $\mathbf{r}_1$ due to charge density $-\rho(r_1,r_2)$. Since $\int\rho(\mathbf{r}_1,\mathbf{r}_2)\,d\tau = 1$, $\overline{V}$ is the potential at $\mathbf{r}_1$ arising from the absence of one electron. The complete, equivalent potential energy in the Hartree-Fock theory arises from the nuclear interaction, from the interaction with all electrons of spin opposite to that of the electron considered, and from an interaction with a charge distribution of electrons of the same spin as the electron considered. This charge distribution of electrons of the same spin adds up to 1 less than the total number of electrons in this spin state. It is as if the electron under consideration carried a hole with it. This so-called *Fermi hole* is a result of the Pauli principle (antisymmetry of the wave function), which keeps electrons of the same spin separated. The potential energy is lower in the Hartree-Fock model than in the Hartree model, since in the former the other electrons stay further away from the electron in question than in the latter.

PHYSICAL SIGNIFICANCE OF THE EIGENVALUE

We now inquire into the physical significance of the ϵ_i occurring in the Hartree-Fock equations. We multiply (6-27) by $u_i^*(\mathbf{r})$ and integrate, obtaining

$$\epsilon_i = \langle i|\,f\,|i\rangle + \sum_j [\langle ij|\,g\,|ij\rangle - \langle ij|\,g\,|ji\rangle] \qquad (6\text{-}41a)$$

This is the expectation value of that part of the energy which involves electron i.

Furthermore, from (6-22) we see that

$$E = \sum_i \epsilon_i - \sum_{i<j} [\langle ij|\,g\,|ij\rangle - \langle ij|\,g\,|ji\rangle] \qquad (6\text{-}41b)$$

Let us consider the removal energy of electron i, which equals the energy of the ion minus the energy of the atom. If we assume that the orbitals for the ion are the same as for the atom, this energy difference is just the expectation value of those terms in the Hamiltonian which involve the removed electron i. Then, by (6-41a) we obtain $-\epsilon_i$ for the removal energy. This result is known as *Koopman's theorem*.

If the ion wave function when built up out of atomic orbitals is in error by δ, the ion energy is in error by an amount of order δ^2, since the variation method gives a stationary value for the energy. For many-electron atoms δ will be quite small. Even for helium the error committed in the energy is less than 0.1 Ry.

One should realize that the removal energy so calculated is no longer an upper bound for the exact removal energy. This is because we have taken the difference of two upper bounds. This difference is of course still a good approximation.

SPHERICAL SYMMETRY AND THE HARTREE-FOCK EQUATIONS

We shall prove that atoms with closed shells lead to a spherically symmetric theory. By a closed shell is meant that all the $4\ell + 2$ states corresponding to a given $n\ell$ are occupied. We prove this by assuming a solution of the form $[\mathcal{R}_{n\ell}(r)/r]\, Y_{\ell m}(\Omega)$. This will determine the equivalent potential, which we shall find to be spherically symmetric. This shows the self-consistency of the claim that for closed shells the effective potential is spherically symmetric. We write

$$u_i(\mathbf{r}) = \frac{\mathcal{R}_{n\ell}(r)}{r}\, Y_{\ell m}(\Omega) \tag{6-42}$$

Then, using the addition theorem of the spherical harmonics,

$$\sum_{m=-\ell}^{\ell} |Y_{\ell m}(\theta,\varphi)|^2 = \frac{2\ell + 1}{4\pi}$$

we get

$$\sum_{m_s} \sum_{m=-\ell}^{\ell} |u_i(\mathbf{r})|^2 = \frac{\mathcal{R}^2_{n\ell}(r)}{r^2}\, \frac{2(2\ell + 1)}{4\pi} \tag{6-43}$$

$$\begin{aligned} V_{\text{Coulomb}} &= \sum_j \int |u_j(\mathbf{r}_2)|^2 \frac{1}{r_{12}}\, d\tau_2 \\ &= \sum_{n\ell} \int \frac{\mathcal{R}^2_{n\ell}(r_2)}{r_2^2}\, \frac{2(2\ell + 1)}{4\pi}\, \frac{1}{r_{12}}\, d\tau_2 \\ &= \sum_{n\ell} \int_0^\infty \mathcal{R}^2_{n\ell}(r_2)\, 2(2\ell + 1)\, \frac{1}{r_>}\, dr_2 \end{aligned} \tag{6-44}$$

where the factor 2 comes from the fact that we have two spin orientations. This shows that the Coulomb potential is spherically symmetric. For the exchange term

$$\sum_{m=-\lambda}^{\lambda} u_j^*(\mathbf{r}_2)\, u_j(\mathbf{r}_1) = \frac{\mathcal{R}_{n\lambda}(r_2)\,\mathcal{R}_{n\lambda}(r_1)}{r_2 r_1} \times \sum_{m=-\lambda}^{\lambda} Y_{\lambda m}^*(\theta_2 \varphi_2)\, Y_{\lambda m}(\theta_1 \varphi_1)$$

$$= \frac{\mathcal{R}_{n\lambda}(r_2)\,\mathcal{R}_{n\lambda}(r_1)}{r_2 r_1}\, \frac{2\lambda + 1}{4\pi}\, P_\lambda(\cos\theta_{12}) \qquad (6\text{-}45)$$

Here there is no factor 2 because the exchange term is summed only over the electrons with one spin. Then

$$\int \sum_m \frac{u_j^*(\mathbf{r}_2)\, u_j(\mathbf{r}_1)\, u_i(\mathbf{r}_2)}{r_{12}}\, d\tau_2$$

$$= \int_0^\infty \frac{\mathcal{R}_{n\lambda}(r_2)\,\mathcal{R}_{n\lambda}(r_1)\,\mathcal{R}_{n'\ell}(r_2)}{r_1}\, dr_2 \times \int \frac{d\Omega_2}{r_{12}}\, \frac{2\lambda + 1}{4\pi}\, P_\lambda(\cos\theta_{12})\, Y_{\ell m}(\Omega_2) \qquad (6\text{-}46)$$

We first consider the integral over Ω_2. We expand $1/r_{12}$ in terms of $P_k(\cos\theta_{12})$. The terms $P_k(\cos\theta_{12})\, P_\lambda(\cos\theta_{12})$ are polynomials of $\cos\theta_{12}$ and therefore can be expanded in $P_{\ell'}(\cos\theta_{12})$

$$P_k(\cos\theta_{12})\, P_\lambda(\cos\theta_{12}) = \sum_{\ell' = |\lambda - k|}^{\ell' = \lambda + k} \sqrt{\frac{(2\ell' + 1)}{(2\lambda + 1)}}\; c^k(\lambda 0, \ell' 0)\, P_{\ell'}(\cos\theta_{12}) \qquad (6\text{-}47)$$

$$c^k(\lambda 0, \ell' 0) = \tfrac{1}{2}\sqrt{(2\ell' + 1)(2\lambda + 1)} \int_{-1}^{1} P_\lambda(w)\, P_k(w)\, P_{\ell'}(w)\, dw \qquad (6\text{-}48)$$

These coefficients are special cases of

$$c^k(\ell m, \ell' m') = \sqrt{\frac{4\pi}{2k + 1}} \int d\Omega \times Y_{\ell m}^*(\Omega)\, Y_{\ell' m'}(\Omega)\, Y_{k, m - m'}(\Omega) \qquad (6\text{-}49)$$

It is seen that for them to be nonzero we must have

$$\begin{aligned} &|\ell - \ell'| \le k \le \ell + \ell' \\ &\ell + \ell' + k = \text{even integer} \end{aligned} \tag{6-50}$$

We now expand,

$$P_{\ell'}(\cos\theta_{12}) = \frac{4\pi}{2\ell' + 1} \sum_{m'} Y^*_{\ell' m'}(\Omega_2) Y_{\ell' m'}(\Omega_1) \tag{6-51}$$

When we integrate (6-46) over Ω_2, only $\ell' = \ell$, $m' = m$ will give a nonvanishing result.

Collecting terms, the angular integral becomes

$$\sqrt{\frac{2\lambda + 1}{2\ell + 1}} \sum_k \frac{r_<^k}{r_>^{k+1}} c^k(\lambda 0, \ell 0) Y_{\ell m}(\Omega_1) \tag{6-52}$$

We see that the angular dependence of the exchange term is such that it becomes equivalent to a central potential. Substituting these results into the Hartree-Fock equation, we obtain for the radial wave equation,

$$\begin{aligned} &\mathcal{R}''_{n\ell}(r_1) - \frac{\ell(\ell + 1)}{r_1^2} \mathcal{R}_{n\ell}(r_1) + \left(2\epsilon_{n\ell} - 2V_C\right)\mathcal{R}_{n\ell}(r_1) \\ &\quad = 2 \sum_{n'\lambda} \sum_k \sqrt{\frac{2\lambda + 1}{2\ell + 1}}\, c^k(\lambda 0, \ell 0) \\ &\qquad \times \int \mathcal{R}_{n'\lambda}(r_2)\mathcal{R}_{n\ell}(r_2) \frac{r_<^k}{r_>^{k+1}}\, dr_2\, \mathcal{R}_{n'\lambda}(r_1) \\ &V_C = -\frac{Z}{r_1} + \int \sum_{n'\lambda} 2(2\lambda + 1)\mathcal{R}^2_{n'\lambda}(r_2) \frac{dr_2}{r_>} \\ &\qquad |\ell - \lambda| \le k \le |\ell + \lambda| \end{aligned} \tag{6-53}$$

For closed shells the *central field approximation* is not an approximation but is exact. For noncomplete shells it is justified by noticing that mostly there is only one incomplete shell. Also, in the lowest-energy state of the atom, electrons tend to go into a shell with their spins oriented in one direction as long as this is permitted by the

Pauli principle (see Chapter 8). Thus even a half-complete shell leads to a spherically symmetric equivalent potential. The most unfavorable case is then when we have ℓ electrons in a shell. The shells occurring in actual atoms are $\ell = 1,2,3$. For $\ell = 1$, and one electron in the shell, the potential acting on this electron is obviously spherically symmetric, because the electron does not act on itself (Coulomb and exchange term cancel). For $\ell = 2$ and 2 electrons, only the one interaction between these two needs to be considered, so the assumption of spherical symmetry should still be very good; and even for $\ell = 3$ it should be acceptable, especially because $\ell = 3$ occurs only for very large Z. Thus the central field assumption is only a very mild approximation for atoms. (It is different for nuclei where the values of ℓ are much larger, and nuclear spins tend to be opposite.)

APPROXIMATE TREATMENT OF EXCHANGE TERM

We can obtain an estimate for the exchange term in the Hartree-Fock theory by using electron wave functions given by the Thomas-Fermi model of the atom. The principal results of this model, which we discuss in detail in Chapter 7, are the following. We assume the electrons move in a constant potential and hence the wave functions are plane waves. All momenta $k \leq k_F$ are present where $\hbar k_F$ is the Fermi momentum.

$$k_F = (3\pi^2 \rho)^{1/3} \tag{6-54}$$

in which ρ is the density of electrons at the point considered. We then find that

$$\begin{aligned} \rho(\mathbf{r}_1, \mathbf{r}_2) &= \frac{1}{2\pi^2 r^3} (\sin k_F r - k_F r \cos k_F r) \\ r &= r_{12} = |\mathbf{r}_1 - \mathbf{r}_2| \end{aligned} \tag{6-55}$$

$$\int \rho(\mathbf{r}_1, \mathbf{r}_2)\, d\tau_2 = \frac{4\pi}{2\pi^2} \int_0^\infty \frac{dx}{x} (\sin x - x \cos x) \tag{6-56}$$

To evaluate the integral, we must introduce a convergence factor such as $e^{-\alpha x}$ and take the limit $\alpha \to 0$. Then $\int \rho(\mathbf{r}_1, \mathbf{r}_2)\, d\tau_2 = 1$, which verifies (6-39). The average potential is

$$\begin{aligned} -\bar{V}(\mathbf{r}_1) &= \frac{4\pi k_F}{2\pi^2} \int_0^\infty \frac{dx}{x^2} (\sin x - x \cos x) \\ &= \frac{2}{\pi} k_F = 2\left(\frac{3}{\pi}\rho\right)^{1/3} \end{aligned} \tag{6-57}$$

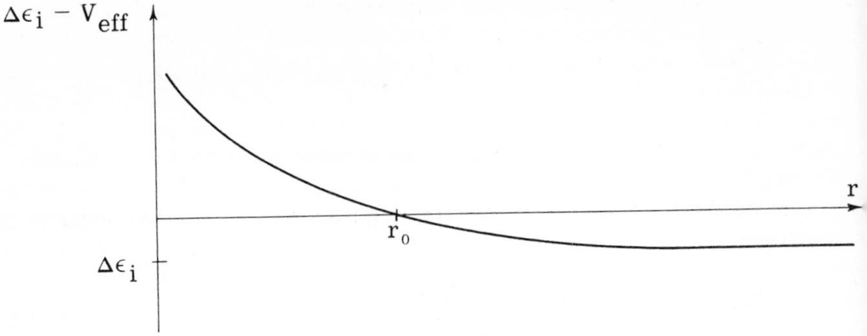

Figure 6-1

We shall also show in Chapter 7 that

$$V_{eff}(\mathbf{r}_2) = \tfrac{3}{4}\,\overline{V}(\mathbf{r}_1) = -\frac{3}{2}\left(\frac{3}{\pi}\rho\right)^{1/3} \tag{6-58}$$

$V_{eff}(\mathbf{r}_1)$ is expected to be smaller than $\overline{V}(\mathbf{r}_1)$, since the integral defining the former has an oscillating term $u_i(\mathbf{r}_2)$ present [see (6-34)]. Equation (6-58) is known as the *simple Slater approximation.*

As we mentioned before, the exchange term lowers the value of ϵ_i and modifies the curvature of the Hartree-Fock wave function as compared to the Hartree wave function. We can represent this graphically as follows. If $\Delta\epsilon_i$ is the increase of the Hartree-Fock relative to the Hartree energy, then $\Delta\epsilon_i - V_{eff}$ is the term which tends to increase the curvature of the Hartree-Fock relative to the Hartree wave functions. Now $-V_{eff} \sim \rho^{1/3}$; ρ falls off with increasing r. Hence if we plot $\Delta\epsilon_i - V_{eff}$ versus r (assuming V_{eff} has been averaged over angles) we obtain Figure 6-1. Therefore for $r < r_0$ the curvature of the Hartree-Fock wave function is increased over the Hartree function, and for $r > r_0$ it is decreased. This means that for $r \to 0$ the wavelength is shorter, for $r \to \infty$, longer. The first loop of the Hartree-Fock wave function is compressed, the last loop extended.

RESULTS OF CALCULATIONS

The expression for the exchange potential occurring in (6-53),

$$\sum_{n'\lambda k} \sqrt{\frac{2\lambda + 1}{2\ell + 1}}\; c^k \int \mathcal{R}_{n'\lambda}(r_2)\,\mathcal{R}_{n\ell}(r_2) \times \frac{r_<^k}{r_>^{k+1}}\;\mathcal{R}_{n'\lambda}(r_1)\,dr_2 \tag{6-59}$$

is seen to be largest for $k = 0$. This is because

$$\left(\frac{r_<}{r_>}\right)^k < 1 \qquad c^0 = 1 \qquad c^k \text{ for } k \neq 0 \text{ is generally} < 1$$

Now $|\ell - \lambda| \leq k \leq \ell + \lambda$. Hence the largest contribution is from terms $\lambda = \ell$.

In the Hartree model the total charge inside a spherical shell of radius r is

$$Z(r) = Z - 4\pi \int_0^r r'^2 \rho(r')\, dr' \tag{6-60}$$

where $\rho(r)$ is the total electronic charge density, so that $Z(r)$ is a decreasing function of r. For small r, $\mathcal{R}_{n\ell} \sim r^{\ell+1}$. Electrons with small ℓ can get closer to the nucleus than those with large ℓ; they "see" a larger effective charge. Therefore the binding energy, which is largely determined by the average of $Z(r)/r$, is larger for small ℓ than for large ℓ.

Table 6-1 gives a comparison of the Hartree-Fock results for Ag^+ with observation. The observed energies are the X-ray absorption limits. Two values are generally given, for $j = \ell - \frac{1}{2}$ and $j = \ell + \frac{1}{2}$.

Table 6-1
Removal Energies of Ag^+ (in Ry)

	Calculated	Observed
1s	1828	1879.7
2s	270	282.0
2p	251	260.1, 247.2
3s	52.2	53.4
3p	44.3	46.0, 43.6
3d	29.8	27.8, 27.4
4s	8.46	7.3
4p	5.82	5.8, 4.9
4d	1.69	1.57

Table 6-2

Ratio of the Binding Energies of Successive Shells for Various Atoms

Ratio of principal quantum numbers	Ag^+	Hg	H
1 : 2	7	6.2	4
2 : 3	$5\frac{1}{2}$	4.4	2.25
3 : 4	7	5.1	1.78
4 : 5		7.8	1.56

The observed energy for 4d is the ionization potential of Ag^+. Other calculations can be found in *Proceedings of the Royal Society,* **247**, 390 (1958); **157**, 490 (1936); **149**, 210 (1935); **141**, 292 (1933). References to other calculations are given in *Reports of the Progress of Physics,* **11**, 113 (1948); and in Hartree's book *The Calculation of Atomic Structure*, Wiley, 1957.

The observed removal energies are generally larger than the calculated ones. This is mainly due to the relativistic corrections which increase the removal energies. This increase is greatest for $j = \frac{1}{2}$; therefore the s states and the (first-listed) $p_{1/2}$ states show appreciably higher observed than calculated energies. For the $p_{3/2}$ states, the second-listed number, the relativity correction is small and the agreement is good.

The d states are very sensitive to small changes in the trial function. This is because it is found that the Coulomb potential and the centrifugal potential very nearly cancel each other over a large range of r. Therefore it is likely that the ion wave function after removal of a 3d electron is not well represented by the atom orbitals. This may explain why the observed removal energy of 3d is substantially (8 per cent) lower than the Hartree eigenvalue.

Table 6-2 lists the *ratios* of the binding energies of successive shells for Ag^+, Hg, and H. The weighted average of s and p shells

Table 6-3

	Zr_1	r_2/r_1	r_3/r_2
H	1.87	3.7	2.25
Hg	1.93	3.8	2.6
Ag^+	1.95	3.9	3.75
Ca	2.04	4.5	3.4

Table 6-4
Screening Constant for Various Z

Z =	11	14	17	19	26	29
σ (2s)	3.29	3.30	3.42	3.48	3.30	3.74
σ (2p)	4.72	4.57	4.67	4.68	4.43	4.89

has generally been taken for each n. It is seen that the ratios for hydrogen are completely different from the ratios for the more complicated atoms. Hydrogen gives no approximation at all for the more complicated atoms. For these the outer electrons are strongly screened by the inner ones so that they "see" a much smaller effective nuclear charge. It is a useful approximation to say that the binding energy for successive n decreases on the average by about a factor of 6 for complex atoms.

It is instructive to calculate the quantities Zr_1, r_2/r_1, and r_3/r_2, where r_i is the ith node of the radial wave function for a 4s electron. Table 6-3 lists these for several Z. It is seen that they vary rather slowly with Z. But we see again the tendency, repeatedly pointed out, that the innermost loop gets shorter and the outer loop longer in going from H to the other atoms. The effect is most pronounced for Ca because here the 4s electron is least strongly bound.

Hartree has defined a screening constant $\sigma(n, \ell)$ by

$$\langle r \rangle = \int \mathcal{R}_{n\ell}^2 \, r \, dr = \frac{\langle r_H \rangle}{Z - \sigma} \tag{6-61}$$

where r_H is the radius of the corresponding hydrogen orbital and $\mathcal{R}_{n\ell}$ is normalized. Table 6-4 lists $\sigma(n\ell)$ for various Z. The σ(2p) is just slightly higher than σ(2s). Hartree has shown that $\mathcal{R}_{n\ell}$, plotted against $r/\langle r \rangle$, is a slowly variable function of Z which can easily be interpolated.

Slater [*Phys. Rev.*, **36**, 57 (1930)] has given a useful, general, though somewhat crude, set of rules for calculating screening constants. For the n = 2 states he would get $\sigma = 4.15$. He also gives rules for the application of these constants.

HIGH n

Calculations for *high n*, i.e., for optically excited states, are facilitated by two simplifications. First of all, the position probability density for a highly excited state is small near the nucleus. Therefore to a very good approximation the wave functions for the nonexcited electrons are the ion wave functions. Second, the optical electron moves in an equivalent potential, which is $-1/r$ for r greater than some radius R. Hence for $r > R$, we have a hydrogenic wave function which is shifted in phase. The phase shift $\pi\delta(E_n)$ is a slowly varying function of the energy. The energy dependence is weak because the E_n for various n are not much different from each other, and because each E_n is much less than the potential energy.

If we use the WKB approximation we get the wave function to be $\Phi^{-1/4} \cos \alpha(r)$, where $\Phi^{1/4}$ is the usual square root of the momentum and $\alpha(r)$ is some function of r. $\alpha(r)$ equals $\alpha_H(r) + \delta\pi$, where $\alpha_H(r)$ is the phase in the hydrogen wave function of the same energy. At the outer turning point r_2 the WKB conditions require that $\alpha = (n' + \frac{1}{4})\pi$, where $n' = n - \ell - 1$ is the number of nodes in $\mathcal{R}_{n\ell}$; hence $\alpha_H = (n' - \delta + \frac{1}{4})\pi$. But α_H can also be obtained as a function of the energy E_n by evaluating the phase integral of the form (4-33); setting $E_n = -Ry/n^{*2}$, this gives $\alpha_H = (n^* - \ell - 1 + \frac{1}{4})\pi$. Hence we get

$$n - \delta = n^* \tag{6-62}$$

with δ independent of n. This is the original *Rydberg formula*.

PERIODIC SYSTEM

Combining the Pauli principle with the Hartree-Fock calculation, we can understand the periodic system. Electron shells get filled in order of increasing energy, with the Pauli principle limiting the number of electrons in a given shell.

Table 6-5 lists the ionization potentials for the first electron (1st and 2nd columns) and for the second electron (3rd column) of various atoms. We see that the alkalis (Li, Na) and the corresponding ions like Ca^+, having one electron outside closed shells, have the lowest binding energy. The second s electron (Be, Mg) is bound more strongly than the first. The next electron must go into a p shell and has again lesser binding energy (B, Al). As we build up the p shell, the binding increases, as might be expected. But we note that there is a break in the ionization potential after three electrons have been put into the p shell (i.e., just before O, S). This is due to the fact that the first three electrons can be put in with the same spin, whereas the fourth electron must go in with opposite spin. The system with three electrons of the same spin is a symmetric spin state, thus an antisymmetric space state. The antisymmetry keeps the electrons apart, hence decreases their electrostatic interaction and yields a greater binding energy (see p. 24).

In the third column we list the ionization potentials of ions which

Table 6-5
Ionization Potentials (in eV) for the First Electron (1st and 2nd Columns) and for the Second Electron (3rd Column) of Various Atoms

Li	5.40	Na	5.14	Ca^+	11.9
Be	9.32	Mg	7.64	Sc^+	12.8
B	8.28	Al	5.97	Ti^+	13.6
C	11.27	Si	8.15	V^+	14.1
N	14.55	P	10.9	Cr^+	16.7
O	13.62	S	10.36	Mn^+	15.6
F	17.47	Cl	12.90	Fe^+	16.5
Ne	21.56	A	15.76	Co^+	17.4
				Ni^+	18.2
				Cu^+	20.2
				Zn^+	18.0
				Ga^+	20.5
				Ge^+	16.0

have an outer 3d shell. We do not choose neutral atoms, because for these there is competition between 3d and 4s. The binding energy increases until it breaks after five electrons have been put in (just before Mn) for the same reason as before. The shell is completed at Cu^+. In Zn^+, the 4s shell is started, which shows in a smaller binding energy. The first 4p electron (Ge^+) again has less binding than the second 4s (Ga^+).

The order of filling of all the shells is determined as above, by the Pauli principle and by energy considerations. Madelung formulated the following heuristic rule for remembering the order of filling of levels in neutral atoms. Fill up in order of increasing $n + \ell$. For each $n + \ell$ fill up in order of increasing n. Each shell is closed after the p electrons have been filled up, except for the first shell, which is closed at $1s^2$. Table 6-6 lists the order of filling of levels according to this rule.

The d shells are always very sensitive, and compete with the s shell of the same $n + \ell$. Schiff's table, p. 280, shows this competition. The 4s shell is first filled by two electrons (Ca); then three electrons are put into the 3d shell (V). The next atom, Cr, has one 4s electron replaced by an extra 3d, giving the configuration $4s3d^5$, and showing

Table 6-6

$n + \ell$	Level	Shell
1	1s	1
2	2s	2
	2p	
3	3s	
	3p	3
4	4s	
	3d	4
5	4p	
	5s	
	4d	5
6	5p	
	6s	
	4f	
	5d	6
7	6p	
	7s	

again the special stability of a half-filled shell. Mn has again $4s^2$, together with the stable $3d^5$, and $4s^2$ persists through Ni. In Cu, the extra stability of the complete shell $3d^{10}$ again leads to a single 4s electron, which is responsible for the fact that Cu is often monovalent, often divalent. In the next transition period, the equilibrium is generally shifted in favor of the 4d shell, a single 5s electron being the rule from $5s4d^4$ (Nb) to $4s4d^8$ (Rh). In the last similar period, the shift is in the opposite direction; we have $6s^2 5d^X$ up to $x = 6$ (Os). The change of pattern from 3d to 4d is probably due to the increased nuclear charge, from 4d to 5d to the intervening 4f shell, which effectively screens the 5d.

It should be remembered that the antisymmetrization of the wave function makes it impossible to assign a particular set of quantum numbers to a definite electron. Such statements as "the $n\ell$ electron" refer merely to the occurrence in the Slater determinant of an orbital with quantum numbers n and ℓ.

Chapter 7

THE THOMAS-FERMI STATISTICAL MODEL

In the previous chapter we discussed the self-consistent field method for finding energy levels and wave functions for atoms. We saw that any numerical calculation is very cumbersome, especially for atoms with many electrons. For these, there exists a simpler method to obtain at least a fair approximation. It is due to Thomas (1927) and Fermi (1928), and is based on Fermi-Dirac statistics. The results admittedly are less accurate than those of the Hartree-Fock calculations. The Thomas-Fermi method nevertheless is very useful for calculating form factors and for obtaining effective potentials which can be used as initial trial potentials in the self-consistent field method. It is also applicable to the study of nucleons in nuclei and electrons in a metal.

The goal of the Thomas-Fermi statistical method is to obtain the effective potential energy which is experienced by an infinitesimal test charge, and to find the electron density $\rho(r)$ about an atom. We shall use ordinary units throughout.

Consider a number of electrons moving in a volume Ω_0, subject to a spherically symmetric potential energy $V(r)$ which varies sufficiently slowly with r so that the system can be treated by Fermi-Dirac free-particle statistics. The electrons are supposed to interact with each other sufficiently to establish statistical equilibrium but still so little that we can speak of the kinetic and potential energy of each individual electron. We assume $\lim_{r \to \infty} V(r) = 0$. The distribution function is

$$f = \frac{1}{e^{(E-\zeta)/kT} + 1} \tag{7-1}$$

where ζ is the chemical potential. If we assume that $T = 0$,

$$f = \begin{cases} 1 & E < \zeta \\ 0 & E > \zeta \end{cases} \tag{7-2}$$

In the zero-temperature limit, therefore, ζ is the energy of the most energetic electrons; the Pauli principle forces the electrons to occupy all states from the ground state to the state of energy ζ. ζ is not a function of r; if it were, electrons would migrate to that region of space where ζ is smallest, because this would make the total energy of the system decrease. By this process, ζ would tend to equalize. Clearly

$$\zeta = V(r) + \frac{p_F^2(r)}{2m} \tag{7-3}$$

where $p_F(r)$ is the maximum momentum of the electrons, the so-called Fermi momentum, which must depend on r to make ζ constant.

We can obtain an expression connecting p_F with ρ by considering the number of quantum states of translational motion of a completely free electron with a momentum whose absolute value lies between p + dp. For this purpose we consider the electron as moving in a box of volume Ω without any forces. Then the number of quantum states (cf. Schiff, p. 49) is equal to

$$2\frac{\Omega}{(2\pi)^3}\, 4\pi k^2\, dk \tag{7-4}$$

where $\hbar k = p$ and the factor 2 is due to the two spin orientations that an electron can have. We integrate (7-4) from 0 to k_F and this must equal N, the total number of electrons.

$$2\frac{\Omega}{(2\pi)^3}\frac{4\pi}{3}k_F^3 = N \qquad k_F^3 = 3\pi^2\rho \qquad \rho = \frac{N}{\Omega} \tag{7-5}$$

It is then assumed that we can construct a box Ω, within the big volume Ω_0 originally considered, which is large enough to make (7-5) valid, and yet small enough that the potential energy does not vary too much within the box. Then we may consider (7-5) and (7-3) simultaneously valid. We now perform a gauge transformation on the potential energy

$$V - \zeta \rightarrow V_1 \tag{7-6}$$

From (7-3) and (7-5) it then follows that

$$\rho = \frac{1}{3\pi^2}\frac{(2m)^{3/2}}{\hbar^3}(-V_1)^{3/2} \tag{7-7}$$

The Poisson equation connects the electrostatic potential $-(1/e)V$ with the charge density $-e\rho$. With suitable rearrangement this is

$$\nabla^2 V_1 = -4\pi e^2 \rho \tag{7-8}$$

Combining (7-7) with (7-8) we get.

$$\frac{1}{r}\frac{d^2}{dr^2}(rV_1) = -\frac{4e^2}{3\pi\hbar^3}(2m)^{3/2}(-V_1)^{3/2} \tag{7-9}$$

For $r \to 0$ the leading term of V must be $-Ze^2/r$. Hence (7-9) satisfies the boundary condition

$$\lim_{r \to 0}(rV_1) = -Ze^2 \tag{7-10}$$

We make the change of variable

$$r = xb \qquad rV_1 = -Ze^2\Phi$$
$$b = \frac{(3\pi)^{2/3}}{2^{7/3}} \qquad \frac{\hbar^2}{me^2} Z^{-1/3} = 0.885\, a_0 Z^{-1/3} \tag{7-11}$$

with $a_0 = \hbar^2/me^2$, the first Bohr radius. Therefore the equation we must solve is

$$\frac{d^2\Phi}{dx^2} = \frac{\Phi^{3/2}}{\sqrt{x}}$$
$$\Phi(0) = 1 \tag{7-12}$$

SOLUTIONS OF THE THOMAS-FERMI EQUATION

Equation (7-12) is a second-order nonlinear differential equation. It is important to notice that it is independent of Z. Apparently we shall obtain a whole family of solutions, since we have specified only one boundary condition. These solutions can be classified according to the initial slope, which is clearly arbitrary in the differential equation (7-12). Numerical integrations of this equation for various initial slopes has been done by Feynman, Metropolis, and Teller [*Phys. Rev.*, **75**, 1561 (1949)]. They found that the solutions can be expressed in a semiconvergent series

$$\Phi = 1 - a_2 x + a_3 x^{3/2} + a_4 x^2 + \cdots \tag{7-13}$$

with

$$a_3 = \tfrac{4}{3} \qquad a_4 = 0$$

Examining (7-12) we see that all solutions are initially concave upward. Hence if a particular solution doesn't become zero, it will remain concave upward and will either diverge for large x or approach the x axis asymptotically. If it becomes zero for a finite $x = x_0$, then the differential equation stops being valid. Indeed physically (7-12) holds only for positive Φ; for negative Φ the electron density becomes zero because there is then no state with $E > \zeta$, cf. (7-2) and (7-7). The correct differential equation for negative Φ is therefore $d^2\Phi/dx^2 = 0$ ($\Phi < 0$). $\Phi = A(x - x_0)$, where A is a constant, which by continuity is equal to $\Phi'(x_0)$. Thus the solution is completely determined if we know it for $\Phi > 0$, and we therefore consider only this portion of it. The behavior of the various solutions is illustrated in Figure 7-1.

For neutral free atoms (i.e., not subject to external pressure) we can obtain a second boundary condition and thus determine a unique solution. At the surface of a free atom (or ion) we must have $V = \zeta$; i.e., $\rho = 0$. For a neutral atom, $V = 0$ at the surface, hence $\zeta = 0$ everywhere. Therefore for an atom $\lim_{r\to\infty} rV_1 = 0$. Thus the second boundary condition which defines a (neutral) atom is

$$\lim_{x\to\infty} \Phi = 0 \tag{7-14}$$

The atom corresponds to a solution which is asymptotic to the x axis. Numerical integration gives $\Phi'(0) = -a_2 = 1.58875$. Since the function Φ vanishes only at infinity, the neutral atom has no boundaries in the Thomas-Fermi model.

Sommerfeld showed that $144x^{-3}$, which is a solution of the differential equation but does not satisfy the boundary condition at $x = 0$, is the asymptotic form of the correct solution for an atom.

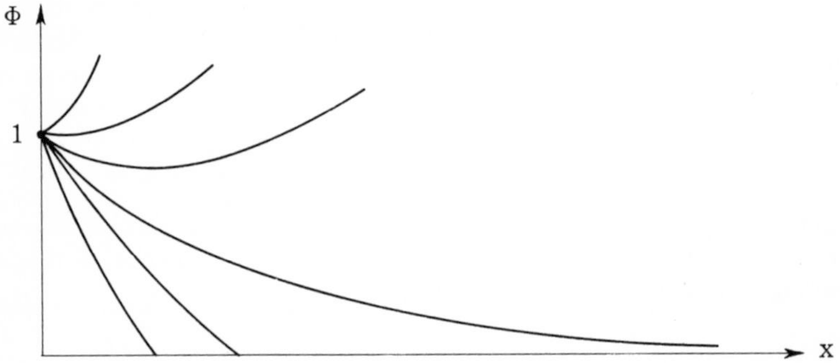

Figure 7-1 Solutions of (7-12)

For an ion one can obtain a condition at the surface. Let r_0 define the surface. Then the total number of electrons N is given by

$$4\pi \int_0^{r_0} \rho r^2 \, dr = -\frac{1}{e^2} \int_0^{r_0} r \frac{d^2}{dr^2}(rV_1) \, dr$$

$$= Z \int_0^{x_0} x\Phi'' \, dx = N$$

$$(\Phi' x - \Phi) \Big|_0^{x_0} = \frac{N}{Z} \tag{7-15}$$

$$\Phi(x_0) - x_0 \Phi'(x_0) = \frac{Z - N}{Z} = \frac{z}{Z}$$

where z is the net charge of the ion.

For a free ion, $\rho = 0$ at $r = r_0$, which implies

$$\Phi(x_0) = 0$$

$$x_0 \Phi'(x_0) = -\frac{z}{Z} \tag{7-16}$$

Hence the solutions of (7-12) which vanish for finite $x = x_0$ correspond to ions of radius r_0. Since the slope of Φ must be negative at x_0 (see Figure 7-1), (7-16) implies that the theory cannot handle negative free ions.

For neutral atoms, (7-16) gives $\Phi(x_0) = \Phi'(x_0) = 0$. This shows that no solution with finite radius x_0 can exist. However, for Sommerfeld's asymptotic solution, $\Phi = 144x^{-3}$; in the limit of $x \to \infty$, we have both Φ and $x\Phi' = 0$.

If the atom is under pressure‡ then $\rho(x_0)$ no longer equals 0. The solutions that do not vanish for finite x correspond to this case. Equation (7-15) determines x_0 and therefore the radius of such systems. Since atoms are neutral,

$$\frac{\Phi(x_0)}{x_0} = \Phi'(x_0) \tag{7-17}$$

which defines the point x_0 at which the tangent to Φ passes through the origin. For $x > x_0$ the differential equation (7-12) is no longer a description of the physical situation.

‡An assembly of many ions under pressure would lead to physical difficulties, because of the large, cumulative Coulomb forces.

APPLICATIONS

All atoms in the Thomas-Fermi model have the same electron distribution, except for a different scale of length and total number of electrons. Equations (7-11) show that the length scale for any atom is proportional to $Z^{-1/3}$. Thus the radius of the entire atom decreases as $Z^{-1/3}$. However it can be shown that the radius of the sphere which contains all but one electron is roughly proportional to $Z^{1/6}$.

An interesting application of the Thomas-Fermi method is to calculate for which Z bound atomic states with a given angular momentum first appear (Fermi). We consider the reduced radial equation

$$\frac{d^2 \mathcal{R}}{dr^2} + \frac{2m}{\hbar^2}(E - V_r)\mathcal{R} = 0$$
$$V_r = V(r) + \frac{\hbar^2}{2m}\frac{(\ell + \frac{1}{2})^2}{r^2} \qquad (7\text{-}18)$$

[We have made the usual WKB substitution $\ell(\ell + 1) \to (\ell + \frac{1}{2})^2$.] Bound states exist only if $E - V_r > 0$ for some range of r. Since $E < 0$, this means we must have

$$-\frac{2m}{\hbar^2} V(r)\, r^2 > (\ell + \tfrac{1}{2})^2$$
$$\frac{2me^2}{\hbar^2} Zr\Phi = 0.885\, Z^{2/3}\, 2x\Phi > (\ell + \tfrac{1}{2})^2 \qquad (7\text{-}19)$$

for some range of r.

The following broad maximum is found in $2x\Phi$, using the tables of Feynman et al.:

$\sqrt{2x}$	1	1.96	2.04	2.12	2.20	3.0
$2x\Phi$	0.607	0.972	0.973	0.968	0.968	0.829

A necessary condition for (7-19) to hold is that

$$0.885Z^{2/3}\ \mathrm{Max}(2x\Phi) > (\ell + \tfrac{1}{2})^2$$
$$0.861Z^{2/3} > (\ell + \tfrac{1}{2})^2 \qquad (7\text{-}20)$$
$$Z > 0.157(2\ell + 1)^3$$

This formula determines the value of Z for which an electron with a given ℓ is first bound. We should expect that we can change the "greater" sign in (7-20) to an "equal" sign if we increase the coefficient somewhat. If we take 0.17 instead of 0.157:

$$Z = 0.17(2\ell + 1)^3 \tag{7-21}$$

we get

for ℓ =	1	2	3	4
Z =	4.6	21.25	58.3	123.9

Rounding to the nearest integer we obtain 5, 21, 58, 124. Comparing with experiment, we find the first three results to be correct and the last one predicting that g electrons can appear only in the 124th element. This is six places beyond the predicted noble gas Z = 118, with the heaviest element so far discovered having Z = 103.

The maximum of Vr^2 was found above to be quite flat. We expect therefore that there will be close cancellation between V(r) and the centrifugal potential term for the largest ℓ which can be bound by a given atom. In this situation a small change in Z would effect a large change in the wave function. This is exactly what Hartree found for d electrons (see p. 58).

CORRECTION FOR EXCHANGE; THE THOMAS-FERMI-DIRAC EQUATION

The Thomas-Fermi equation (7-12) does not take into account the exchange interaction. This was done by Dirac (1930). We shall here give a simple derivation of this correction.

We recall the exchange term in the Hartree-Fock theory,

$$\int U(\mathbf{r}_1,\mathbf{r}_2)\, u_i(\mathbf{r}_2)\, d\tau_2 \tag{6-30}$$

$$U(\mathbf{r}_1,\mathbf{r}_2) = -\frac{\rho(\mathbf{r}_1,\mathbf{r}_2)e^2}{r_{12}} \tag{6-31}$$

$$\rho(\mathbf{r}_1,\mathbf{r}_2) = \sum_j u_j^*(\mathbf{r}_2)\, u_j(\mathbf{r}_1) \tag{6-37}$$

In the spirit of the Thomas-Fermi method we consider the electrons to be free (subject to a constant potential). Thus we set

$$u_j(\mathbf{r}_1) = \Omega^{-1/2}\, e^{i\mathbf{k}_j \cdot \mathbf{r}_2} \tag{7-22}$$

$$\rho(\mathbf{r}_1,\mathbf{r}_2) = \Omega^{-1} \sum_j e^{i\mathbf{k}_j\cdot(\mathbf{r}_1-\mathbf{r}_2)}$$

$$\approx \frac{1}{(2\pi)^3} \int e^{i\mathbf{k}\cdot\mathbf{r}_{12}}\, d^3k \qquad (\mathbf{r}_{12} = \mathbf{r}_1 - \mathbf{r}_2)$$

$$= \frac{4\pi}{(2\pi)^3} \int_0^{k_F} \frac{\sin kr_{12}}{kr_{12}}\, k^2\, dk$$

$$= \frac{1}{2\pi^2}\frac{1}{r_{12}^3} (\sin k_F r_{12} - k_F r_{12} \cos k_F r_{12}) \tag{7-23}$$

which verifies (6-55).

$$\rho(0,0) = \frac{k_F^3}{6\pi^2} = \tfrac{1}{2}\rho \tag{7-24}$$

We recall that for the ith electron

$$V_{eff}(\mathbf{r}_1) = -\int e^2 \frac{\rho(\mathbf{r}_1,\mathbf{r}_2)}{r_{12}} \frac{u_i(\mathbf{r}_2)}{u_i(\mathbf{r}_1)}\, d\tau_2 \tag{6-34}$$

Hence

$$V_{eff}(\mathbf{r}_1) = -e^2 \int \frac{\rho(\mathbf{r}_1,\mathbf{r}_2)}{r_{12}}\, e^{i\mathbf{k}_i\cdot\mathbf{r}_{21}}\, d\tau_2 \tag{7-25}$$

This integral is evaluated to be

$$V_{eff}(\mathbf{r}_1) = -2\left(\frac{3}{\pi}\rho\right)^{1/3} e^2 F(\eta)$$

$$= -\frac{2}{\pi} e^2 k_F F(\eta) \tag{7-26}$$

(Slater, Vol. II, Appendix 22), where

$$\eta = \frac{k_i}{k_F}$$

$$F(\eta) = \frac{1}{2} + \frac{1-\eta^2}{4\eta} \log\frac{1+\eta}{1-\eta} \tag{7-27}$$

$F(0) = 1$, $F(1) = \frac{1}{2}$, and F decreases from 1 to $\frac{1}{2}$ monotonically as η goes from 0 to 1.

Equation (7-26) gives the effective exchange potential for the ith electron. We now average it over all electrons.

$$\text{Average } V_{eff} = \frac{\int_0^{k_F} V_{eff}\, d^3k_i}{\int_0^{k_F} d^3k_i} \qquad (7\text{-}28)$$

We substitute V_{eff} from (7-25) and obtain

$$\text{Average } V_{eff} = \frac{-\frac{e^2}{(2\pi)^3}\int_0^{k_F} d^3k_i \int \frac{\rho(\mathbf{r}_1,\mathbf{r}_2)}{r_{12}}\, e^{i\mathbf{k}_i\cdot\mathbf{r}_{21}}\, d\tau_2}{k_F^3/6\pi^2}$$

$$= -\frac{2}{\rho}\frac{e^2}{(2\pi)^3}\int_0^{k_F} e^{i\mathbf{k}_i\cdot\mathbf{r}_{21}}\, d^3k_i \int \frac{\rho(\mathbf{r}_1,\mathbf{r}_2)}{r_{12}}\, d\tau_2$$

$$= -\frac{2e^2}{\rho}\int \frac{\rho^2(\mathbf{r}_1,\mathbf{r}_2)}{r_{12}}\, d\tau_2 \qquad (7\text{-}29)$$

This can be interpreted as the electrostatic self-energy of the "hole" in the charge distribution, $\rho(\mathbf{r}_1,\mathbf{r}_2)$. Substituting for $\rho^2(\mathbf{r}_1,\mathbf{r}_2)$ from (7-23), the integral can be evaluated in a straightforward fashion and yields

$$\text{Average } V_{eff} = -\frac{3e^2}{2\pi} k_F \qquad (7\text{-}30)$$

We now must determine a relation between V, the electrostatic potential energy, and ρ. The simplest argument is that the total energy of the most energetic electron is now, instead of (7-3),

$$V(r) - \frac{2}{\pi} e^2 k_F F(1) + \frac{p_F^2}{2m} = \zeta \qquad (7\text{-}31)$$

Here the effective exchange potential energy has been added to V(r); this V_{eff} depends on the momentum according to (7-26). In our case of the most energetic electron, $\eta = 1$ and $F(1) = \frac{1}{2}$, according to (7-27). The result (7-31) is identical with (7-34) to be derived below.

For variety, we shall now derive (7-31) in another fashion. We shall consider the total energy E of the system of electrons, vary this quantity as a function of ρ, and obtain the desired relations from the requirement that E be stationary. This approach is due to Lenz (1932). This could have been done also in deriving the Thomas-Fermi model.

The total energy is the sum of the kinetic energy E_k and potential energy E_p. The total kinetic energy of the electrons can be obtained by multiplying the number of states (7-4) by $\hbar^2 k^2/2m$, integrating over all momenta from 0 to k_F, and then integrating over all volume. The result is easily found to be

$$E_k = \int d\tau \left[\frac{3}{5}\,\frac{\hbar^2\pi^2}{2m}\left(\frac{3}{\pi}\,\rho\right)^{2/3} \rho\right] \tag{7-32}$$

The potential energy is

$$E_p = \int \left[\left(-\frac{Ze^2}{r}\right)\rho + \left(\tfrac{1}{2}\int d\tau_2\,\frac{e^2}{r_{12}}\,\rho(r_2)\right)\rho - \tfrac{3}{4}\,e^2\left(\frac{3\rho}{\pi}\right)^{1/3}\rho\right] d\tau \tag{7-33}$$

The first term is due to the nuclear charge; the second term is due to the interelectron interaction, the factor $\frac{1}{2}$ being inserted to avoid counting the electron pairs twice. The third term is the exchange energy (the averaged V_{eff}), with a factor $\frac{1}{2}$ for the same reason as before. If we now set the arbitrary variation of E with respect to ρ equal to 0 we obtain

$$a_0 e^2\,\frac{\pi^2}{2}\left(\frac{3}{\pi}\,\rho\right)^{2/3} + V - e^2\left(\frac{3\rho}{\pi}\right)^{1/3} = 0$$

$$V = -\frac{Ze^2}{r} + \int \frac{e^2}{r_{12}}\,\rho(r_2)\,d\tau_2 \qquad a_0 = \frac{\hbar^2}{me^2} \tag{7-34}$$

[In point of fact, the variation of E is not totally unrestricted, since we must also have $\int\rho\,d\tau = N$, the total number of electrons. We can introduce this subsidiary condition by the Lagrange multiplier method. This adds a term λ to (7-34), where λ is the multiplier. We now can make a gauge transform $V + \lambda \to V$ and obtain (7-34).]

The use of the average effective exchange potential, (7-30), in the potential energy (7-33) is correct. We are here concerned with the total exchange potential for all electrons. In the Hartree-Fock method, where we consider specific electrons, it was only an *approximation* to replace the exchange potential by (7-30).

We now solve (7-34) for the density. Setting $y = a_0(3\rho/\pi)^{1/3} = (a_0/\pi)k_F$,

$$y = \frac{1}{\pi^2}\left(1 + \sqrt{1 - 2\pi^2\,\frac{Va_0}{e^2}}\right) \tag{7-35}$$

The plus sign is chosen in front of the radical to assure agreement with the Thomas-Fermi theory and to avoid negative density. With

$$\Psi = \frac{1}{2\pi^2} - \frac{Va_0}{e^2} \tag{7-36}$$

we obtain

$$y = \frac{\sqrt{2}}{\pi}\left(\sqrt{\Psi} + \frac{1}{\pi\sqrt{2}}\right) \tag{7-37}$$

Poisson's equation now gives

$$\frac{d^2}{dr^2}(r\Psi) = 4\pi a_0 \rho r = \frac{4\pi^2}{3a_0^2} y^3 r$$
$$\frac{d^2}{dr^2}(r\Psi) = \frac{2^{7/2}}{3a_0^2\pi} r\left(\sqrt{\Psi} + \frac{1}{\pi\sqrt{2}}\right)^3 \tag{7-38}$$

Finally, changing variables as in (7-11),

$$r = xb \qquad r\Psi = a_0 Z\Phi \qquad b = 0.885a_0 Z^{-1/3}$$

we obtain

$$\Phi'' = x\left(\sqrt{\frac{\Phi}{x}} + \beta\right)^3$$
$$\beta = \sqrt{\frac{b}{a_0 Z}}\ \frac{1}{\pi\sqrt{2}} = 0.2118Z^{-2/3} \tag{7-39}$$

This is the Thomas-Fermi-Dirac equation. This, unlike (7-12), depends on Z through β. We see that for $Z \to \infty$, (7-39) becomes (7-12).

The boundary conditions for the Thomas-Fermi-Dirac equation are the following:

$$\Phi(0) = 1$$
$$\Phi(x_0) - x_0\Phi'(x_0) = \frac{Z-N}{Z} = \frac{z}{Z} \tag{7-40}$$

For free atoms and ions we can no longer define the surface by $\rho(x_0) = 0$, since it is seen from (7-37) that ρ never vanishes. However, we can define x_0 by requiring that the pressure vanish there. To do this we write the specific energy (energy per particle) from

(7-32) and (7-33). [There is actually some problem about the electrostatic interaction of the electrons, but (7-41) gives the correct result.]

$$\epsilon = \frac{3}{5}\,\frac{\pi^2}{2}\,\frac{e^2}{a_0}\,y^2 + V(r) - \frac{3}{4}\,\frac{e^2}{a_0}\,y \tag{7-41}$$

The pressure $P = -\partial\epsilon/\partial v)_S$, where v is the specific volume and S is the entropy. Since (7-41) has been derived for $T = 0$, the entropy is equal to zero, hence already constant, so we merely need to differentiate with respect to v. Recalling $y = [(3/\pi)\rho]^{1/3} a_0$, $v = 1/\rho$, we obtain

$$P = \rho\,\frac{e^2}{a_0}\left[\frac{\pi^2 y^2}{5} - \frac{y}{4}\right] \tag{7-42}$$

This vanishes at

$$y = \frac{5}{4\pi^2}$$

or (7-43)

$$\rho(x_0) = 2.13 \times 10^{-3} a_0^{-3}$$

Had we not included the exchange effect, P would vanish at $y = 0$, implying $\rho(x_0) = 0$ as before. A lower density than (7-43) is unphysical in the Thomas-Fermi-Dirac model since this would correspond to negative pressure. Substituting (7-43) in (7-37) we find with some algebra that

$$\frac{\Phi(x_0)}{x_0} = \frac{\beta^2}{16} \tag{7-44}$$

These results imply that in the Thomas-Fermi-Dirac theory atoms as well as ions have a finite radius. Equation (7-44) does not apply of course to systems under external pressure, since then the density can be larger than that given in (7-43). [No solution which goes to zero at $x = \infty$ exists, as can be seen from (7-39). This causes no difficulty since atomic solutions no longer satisfy (7-14).] As before the differential equation applies only to $x \leq x_0$.

Numerical calculations have been performed by Feynman et al. (*op. cit.*) and others. It is found that in the Thomas-Fermi-Dirac model negative free ions are not treated.

The Fermi model is useful for calculating properties that depend on the average electron such as form factor, total energy of all electrons, electrostatic potential produced by all electrons at the nucleus, and average excitation potential. The latter occurs in the theory of atomic stopping power and is defined by

$$\log E_{av} = (1/Z) \sum_j \log E_j \tag{7-45}$$

where E_j is the average excitation potential of the jth orbital. The Thomas-Fermi method, even with exchange, is very poor for calculating properties that depend on the outer electrons, such as the ionization potential, or the mean-square radius of the atom, which is important for diamagnetism. Any such calculations should be viewed with suspicion.

Extensions of the above theory to cases with nonzero temperature have been made by Cowan and Ashkin [*Phys. Rev.*, **105**, 144 (1957)]. Latter [*Phys. Rev.*, **99**, 510 (1955)] has solved the radial, one-electron Schrödinger equation for all normally occupied orbitals n, ℓ for many atoms, using as the potential V(r) that given by the Thomas-Fermi-Dirac method. This gives both energy levels and wave functions for these orbitals. From these wave functions, one could then construct a potential using the Hartree-Fock prescription, and this should be very good starting data for a Hartree-Fock calculation. For atoms for which no Hartree-Fock solution is available, Latter's are the best wave functions existing. That they are indeed very good is shown by comparing Latter's eigenvalues with the Hartree-Fock results. We list these for a few orbitals in Ag for which both types of calculation exist in Table 7-1.

Table 7-1

Comparison of Energy Levels of Ag as Calculated by Hartree-Fock Method and Thomas-Fermi-Dirac Method
(Values are given in Ry)

	Hartree-Fock	Thomas-Fermi-Dirac
1s	1828	1805
2s	270	268
2p	251	245
3d	29.8	29.6
4s	8.46	7.95

Chapter 8

THEORY OF MULTIPLETS, ADDITION OF ANGULAR MOMENTUM

A consequence of the central field approximation which we used in Chapters 6 and 7 is that an atom with an incomplete shell is a highly degenerate system with respect to energy. For the ℓth shell there are $g = 2(2\ell + 1)$ orbitals (states) with the same energy. If the shell is occupied by $k \leq g$ electrons, then $\binom{g}{k} = \frac{g!}{k!(g-k)!}$ is the number of different ways the electrons can be distributed in this shell. Hence the degeneracy is $\binom{g}{k}$. For example, phosphorus with 15 electrons has the electron configuration $1s^2\,2s^2\,2p^6\,3s^2\,3p^3$. The degeneracy therefore is 20. Only for complete shells is there no degeneracy: $\binom{g}{g} = 1$.

Some of this degeneracy is removed when we take the electrostatic interaction of the electrons, $\Sigma_{i<j}\,(e^2/r_{ij})$ into account. We consider this interaction, minus a suitable average of it, as the perturbation Hamiltonian. We further consider the determinantal Hartree-Fock wave equations as zero-order approximations in a perturbation expansion. Accordingly we must find proper linear combinations of these, such that the $\binom{g}{k} \times \binom{g}{k}$ Hamiltonian submatrix is diagonal. To facilitate this, we shall consider the vectors of the total orbital and spin angular momentum of all electrons in the atom. Each cartesian component of these two vectors we shall show to be a constant of motion.

ANGULAR MOMENTUM

We consider $[H,\mathbf{L}]$, where H is given by (1-4) and $\mathbf{L}$ by (2-8). For simplicity let us consider a two-electron system. Clearly $\mathbf{L}$ commutes with p_i^2 and $1/r_i$ since $\mathbf{L}_i$ does. But since $\mathbf{L}_i$ is proportional to the rotation operator on $\mathbf{r}_i$, it cannot commute with $1/r_{12}$. However we now show that $[\mathbf{L},1/r_{12}] = 0$. Consider

$$[\mathbf{L}, f(r_{12}^2)] = [\mathbf{L}_1, f(r_{12}^2)] + [\mathbf{L}_2, f(r_{12}^2)] \tag{8-1}$$

where f is an arbitrary differentiable function.

$$[L_{1x}, f(r_{12}^2)] = \left(y_1 \frac{\partial}{\partial z_1} - z_1 \frac{\partial}{\partial y_1}\right)$$

$$\times\ f((x_1 - x_2)^2 + (y_1 - y_2)^2 + (z_1 - z_2)^2)$$

$$= y_1 f'(r_{12}^2)\, 2(z_1 - z_2) - z_1 f'(r_{12}^2)\, 2(y_1 - y_2)$$

$$= -2(y_1 z_2 - z_1 y_2) f'(r_{12}^2) \tag{8-2}$$

By symmetry,

$$[L_{2x}, f(r_{12}^2)] = 2(y_1 z_2 - z_1 y_2) f'(r_{12}^2) \tag{8-3}$$

Combining (8-2) with (8-3) we obtain

$$[L_x, f(r_{12}^2)] = 0 \tag{8-4}$$

This must hold for all components of $\mathbf{L}$, hence

$$[\mathbf{L}, f(r_{12}^2)] = 0 \tag{8-5}$$

Choosing $f(w) = 1/\sqrt{w}$ we conclude that

$$\left[\mathbf{L}, \frac{1}{r_{12}}\right] = 0 \tag{8-6}$$

This obviously generalizes to more than two electrons, and we conclude

$$[H,\mathbf{L}] = 0 \tag{8-7}$$

The same result can be obtained by using a general theorem about commutators. Let A be a hermitian, linear operator with a complete set of eigenvalues $A|A'\rangle = A'|A'\rangle$. A function f of A is defined as follows. f(A) is that operator which satisfies

$$f(A) \mid A' \rangle = f(A') \mid A' \rangle \tag{8-8}$$

Equation (8-8) is clearly consistent for any function that has a Laurent expansion. For other functions, (8-8) serves as a definition. Of course we must require that f be defined for all A′. Suppose $[A,B] = 0$, then $[f(A), g(B)] = 0$ for all f,g that are defined for all the eigenvalues of A and B, respectively. This follows from the fact that the commutation of A with B allows us to express them as diagonal matrices in an appropriate representation. In this representation f(A) and g(B) are also diagonal with elements f(A′), g(B′), respectively, and clearly commute. (For a more careful proof see Dirac, p. 76.)

To establish (8-7) we first see that straightforward differentiation gives $[\mathbf{L}, r_{12}^2] = 0$. By the above theorem this immediately gives (8-6) and hence (8-7).

The total spin angular momentum is also a constant of the motion. A common mistake is to "prove" the above statement by invoking the fact that the Hamiltonian does not depend on spin. This is wrong since the use of antisymmetric wave functions couples the spins to the symmetry of the spatial wave function and thus to the electrostatic energy (see pp. 24 and 49). For example, the above argument would also lead to the conclusion that the individual $\mathbf{S}_i$'s are constants of motion, which is not true. To see that this is not so we consider a two-electron atom and form $S_{1x} u_E(\alpha_1 \alpha_2)$, where $u_E(\alpha_1 \alpha_2)$ is an ortho eigenfunction of He corresponding to the eigenvalue E. We have

$$S_{1x} u_E(\alpha_1 \alpha_2) = \frac{\hbar}{2} u_E(\beta_1 \alpha_2) \tag{8-9}$$

But $u_E(\beta_1 \alpha_2)$ is unsymmetric in the two electrons. Hence it cannot be expanded in terms of antisymmetric eigenfunctions, which are the only ones admissible. It can certainly not be expanded in antisymmetric eigenfunctions belonging to the energy E, which would be required if S_{1x} were a constant of motion.

The proof that **S** commutes with H proceeds as follows: We wish to study the effect of $[H, S_x]$ on an arbitrary function f. Since this function f can be expanded in eigenfunctions of H, it suffices to consider the effect of $[H, S_x]$ on Ψ_E where

$$H\Psi_E = E\Psi_E \tag{8-10}$$

and Ψ_E is a space-spin function with the proper symmetry.

$$\begin{aligned} [H, S_x]\Psi_E &= HS_x\Psi_E - S_x H\Psi_E \\ &= HS_x\Psi_E - ES_x\Psi_E \end{aligned} \tag{8-11}$$

But S_x is a symmetric operator in all the electrons, hence $S_x\Psi_E$ retains the proper symmetry and is an admissible wave function, in contrast to $S_{x1}\Psi_E$ above. Since S_x does not affect the space coordinates, the spatial functions occurring in $S_x\Psi_E$ will be the same as in Ψ_E. We may write

$$\Psi_E = \sum_k c_k \chi_k(\text{spin})\, U_{Ek}(\mathbf{r}_0, \ldots, \mathbf{r}_N) \qquad (8\text{-}12)$$

where the χ_k are all possible spin functions for N electrons and the U_{Ek} certain spatial functions. Then our statement is that

$$S_x \Psi_E = \sum_k c_k \chi_k' U_{Ek} \qquad (8\text{-}13)$$

where χ_k' is a different spin function but U_{Ek} is the same spatial function as before. Now, since H operates only on the space coordinates, the equation (8-10) must hold for each of the spatial functions U_{Ek}. Therefore (8-10) must hold also for the function $S_x \Psi_E$ with the same eigenvalues E, and, from (8-11), $[H,S_x] = 0$. This holds for all components of **S** and

$$[H,\mathbf{S}] = 0 \qquad (8\text{-}14)$$

Inasmuch as L^2, L_z, S^2, and S_z all commute with each other, we can find a representation in which they are diagonal. In this representation, the matrix elements of H, labeled by L, M_L, S, and M_S are, in view of (2-1),

$$\langle L'M_L'S'M_S' \mid H \mid LM_LSM_S\rangle$$
$$= \delta_{LL'}\, \delta_{M_LM_L'}\, \delta_{M_SM_S'}\, \delta_{SS'}\, h \qquad (8\text{-}15)$$

That is H breaks up into submatrixes between states of equal L, M_L, S, M_S, since all these operators are constants of the motion.

ADDITION OF ANGULAR MOMENTA

We now must construct the eigenfunctions of L^2, L_z, S^2, and S_z. We do this from products of single-particle orbitals which are eigenfunctions of L_i^2, L_{iz}, S_i^2, and S_{iz}. For example, suppose we have two spinless particles with angular momenta ℓ_1 and ℓ_2 (we suppress $\hbar$); z-component $m_{\ell 1}$ and $m_{\ell 2}$, respectively. The product $|\ell_1 m_{\ell 1}\rangle|\ell_2 m_{\ell 2}\rangle = |\ell_1 m_{\ell 1}\ell_2 m_{\ell 2}\rangle$ is an eigenfunction of the

Table 8-1
Addition of Angular Momenta

$m_{\ell 1}$	$m_{\ell 2}$	M_L	L
ℓ_1	ℓ_2	$\ell_1 + \ell_2$	$\ell_1 + \ell_2$
$\ell_1 - 1$	ℓ_2	$\ell_1 + \ell_2 - 1$	$\ell_1 + \ell_2$
ℓ_1	$\ell_2 - 1$	$\ell_1 + \ell_2 - 1$	$\ell_1 + \ell_2 - 1$
$\ell_1 - 2$	ℓ_2	$\ell_1 + \ell_2 - 2$	$\ell_1 + \ell_2$
$\ell_1 - 1$	$\ell_2 - 1$	$\ell_1 + \ell_2 - 2$	$\ell_1 + \ell_2 - 1$
ℓ_1	$\ell_2 - 2$	$\ell_1 + \ell_2 - 2$	$\ell_1 + \ell_2 - 2$

operator L_z with eigenvalue $M_L = m_{\ell 1} + m_{\ell 2}$. However L^2 is not in general diagonal. But out of all the possible product wave functions which are eigenfunctions belonging to M_L, we can form linear combinations such that L^2 is diagonalized. To illustrate this we list in the first three columns of Table 8-1 $m_{\ell 1}$, $m_{\ell 2}$, and M_L for a few values of M_L.

We conclude the following: Since there is only one possible combination for $M_L = \ell_1 + \ell_2$, L^2 must be diagonal for this wave function, its eigenvalue being $L(L+1)$, with $L = \ell_1 + \ell_2$. Next, the two states with $M_L = \ell_1 + \ell_2 - 1$ lead to a secular equation to diagonalize L^2, the eigenvalues being of course of the form $L(L+1)$, with $L = \ell_1 + \ell_2$ and $\ell_1 + \ell_2 - 1$. Similarly for $M_L = \ell_1 + \ell_2 - 2$ one linear combination of the product wave functions will lead to $L = \ell_1 + \ell_2$, another to $L = \ell_1 + \ell_2 - 1$, and the third to $L = \ell_1 + \ell_2 - 2$. In the fourth column of Table 8-1 we have listed the values of L that can result from the linear combinations. If we assume $\ell_1 \geq \ell_2$, Table 8-1 continues until $M_L = \ell_1 - \ell_2$. For this M_L, $m_{\ell 2}$ will take all values from $-\ell_2$ to ℓ_2, with $m_{\ell 1} = M_L - m_{\ell 2}$. This leads to a $(2\ell_2 + 1) \times (2\ell_2 + 1)$ secular problem, giving all values of L from $\ell_1 + \ell_2$ to $\ell_1 - \ell_2$. After this the next case would be

$$M_L = \ell_1 - \ell_2 - 1$$

with

$$m_{\ell 1} = \ell_1 - 1, \ldots, \ell_1 - 2\ell_2 - 1 \qquad (8\text{-}16)$$

$$m_{\ell 2} = -\ell_2, \ldots, +\ell_2$$

Since $|m_{\ell 2}| \leq \ell_2$ we can go no further with $m_{\ell 2}$, and obtain again a $(2\ell_2 + 1) \times (2\ell_2 + 1)$ secular problem. Thus we get no new values for L. All the wave functions obtainable by linear combination of the functions listed in (8-16) are needed for the values of L already obtained. As M_L decreases further to $-\ell_1 - \ell_2$ we never get any further values for L. Hence the possible values of L are

$$L = \ell_1 + \ell_2,\ \ell_1 + \ell_2 - 1,\ \ldots,\ |\ell_1 - \ell_2| \tag{8-17}$$

where the absolute-value sign takes care of the eventuality $\ell_2 > \ell_1$. Equation (8-17) is a result of the vector addition of angular momenta known from the old quantum theory.

To add three angular momenta, we first add two of them, and then add the third one to $(\ell_1 + \ell_2)$. Spin behaves the same way and we can add spin angular momenta and orbital angular momenta indiscriminately.

CLEBSCH-GORDAN COEFFICIENTS

We shall now develop the formal theory of addition of angular momenta and derive a method for obtaining the eigenvectors of L^2 and L_z. We write

$$|L,M\rangle = \sum_{m_{\ell 1} m_{\ell 2}} C(\ell_1 m_{\ell 1} \ell_2 m_{\ell 2}, LM) \times |\ell_1 m_{\ell 1}, \ell_2 m_{\ell 2}\rangle \tag{8-18}$$

The above is a transformation equation connecting the eigenvectors of L^2 and L_z with those of L_1^2, L_{1z}, L_2^2, L_{2z}. The summation is carried out only over $m_{\ell 1}$ and $m_{\ell 2}$, for ℓ_1 and ℓ_2 are assumed fixed. The problem of adding angular momenta reduces to determining the elements of the transformation matrix, called the Clebsch-Gordan coefficients (also known as vector addition or Wigner coefficients). An immediate simplification occurs when we operate with $L_z = L_{1z} + L_{2z}$ on (8-18) and recall

$$L_z |L,M\rangle = M |L,M\rangle$$

$$(L_{1z} + L_{2z}) |\ell_1 m_{\ell 1}, \ell_2 m_{\ell 2}\rangle = (m_{\ell 1} + m_{\ell 2}) |\ell_1 m_{\ell 1}, \ell_2 m_{\ell 2}\rangle \tag{8-19}$$

Therefore $C(\ell_1 m_{\ell 1} \ell_2 m_{\ell 2}, LM)$ is 0 unless $M = m_{\ell 1} + m_{\ell 2}$, and the summation in (8-18) is actually over $m_{\ell 1}$ or $m_{\ell 2}$.

Aside from looking them up in tables, there are three methods of obtaining Clebsch-Gordan coefficients. The first is the *step-down* method. We start with $L = \ell_1 + \ell_2$, $M = L$. We know that there is only one term in the sum

$$|L,M\rangle = |\ell_1 + \ell_2, \ell_1 + \ell_2\rangle$$

$$= |\ell_1 m_{\ell 1}, \ell_2 m_{\ell 2}\rangle = |\ell_1\ell_1, \ell_2\ell_2\rangle \tag{8-20}$$

If we operate with $L_- = L_{1-} + L_{2-}$ on (8-20) we obtain

$$L_-|L,M\rangle = \sqrt{(L+M)(L-M+1)}\ |L, M-1\rangle$$

$$= \sqrt{(\ell_1 + m_{\ell 1})(\ell_1 - m_{\ell 1} + 1)}\ |\ell_1 m_{\ell 1} - 1, \ell_2 m_{\ell 2}\rangle$$

$$+ \sqrt{(\ell_2 + m_{\ell 2})(\ell_2 - m_{\ell 2} + 1)}\ |\ell_1 m_{\ell 1}, \ell_2 m_{\ell 2} - 1\rangle$$

or

$$\sqrt{\ell_1 + \ell_2}\ |L, M-1\rangle$$

$$= \sqrt{\ell_1}\ |\ell_1\ell_1 - 1, \ell_2\ell_2\rangle + \sqrt{\ell_2}\ |\ell_1\ell_1, \ell_2\ell_2 - 1\rangle$$

or

$$|L, M-1\rangle = \sqrt{\frac{\ell_1}{\ell_1 + \ell_2}}\ |\ell_1\ell_1 - 1, \ell_2\ell_2\rangle$$

$$+ \sqrt{\frac{\ell_2}{\ell_1 + \ell_2}}\ |\ell_1\ell_1, \ell_2\ell_2 - 1\rangle$$

$$\equiv |\ell_1 + \ell_2, \ell_1 + \ell_2 - 1\rangle \tag{8-21}$$

There is another eigenfunction of $M = \ell_1 + \ell_2 - 1$, namely, the one corresponding to $L = \ell_1 + \ell_2 - 1$. It must be orthonormal to (8-21).

$$|\ell_1 + \ell_2 - 1, \ell_1 + \ell_2 - 1\rangle$$

$$= \sqrt{\frac{\ell_2}{\ell_1 + \ell_2}}\ |\ell_1\ell_1 - 1, \ell_2\ell_2\rangle$$

$$- \sqrt{\frac{\ell_1}{\ell_1 + \ell_2}}\ |\ell_1\ell_1, \ell_2\ell_2 - 1\rangle \tag{8-22}$$

We can now use lowering operators on equations (8-21) and (8-22) and obtain new linear combinations for $M = \ell_1 + \ell_2 - 2$ and so on.

A second method is due to Racah, who obtained a closed formula.

$$C(LM_L SM_S, JM)$$

$$= (-1)^{J+M} \sqrt{2J+1}\ V(L,S,J; M_L, M_S, -M) \tag{8-23}$$

$$V(a,b,c;\alpha,\beta,\gamma)$$

$$= \sqrt{\frac{(a+b-c)!\,(a-b+c)!\,(-a+b+c)!}{(a+b+c+1)!}}$$

$$\times \sqrt{(a+\alpha)!\,(a-\alpha)!\,(b+\beta)!\,(b-\beta)!\,(c+\gamma)!\,(c-\gamma)!}$$

$$\times (-1)^{c-\gamma} \sum_z (-1)^z / [z!\,(a+b-c-z)!\,(a-\alpha-z)!\,(b+\beta-z)!\,(-b+c+a+z)!\,(-a+c-\beta+z)!] \tag{8-24}$$

where z runs through the integers for as long as the arguments of all factorials are nonnegative. (We have made the following relabeling:

$\ell_1 \to L \qquad m_{\ell 1} \to M_L$

$\ell_2 \to S \qquad m_{\ell 2} \to M_S$

$L \to J \qquad M \to M$)

For the particular case $J = L + S$, (8-23) and (8-24) reduce to

$$C(LM_L SM_S,\ L+S\ \ M_L + M_S)$$

$$= \sqrt{\frac{(2L)!\,(2S)!}{(2J)!}} \sqrt{\frac{(J+M)!}{(L+M_L)!\,(S+M_S)!}}$$

$$\times \sqrt{\frac{(J-M)!}{(L-M_L)!\,(S-M_S)!}} \tag{8-25}$$

The third method of obtaining the Clebsch-Gordan coefficients is the *projection operator* method. We define the projection operator

$$P^k_{op} = \prod_{i \neq k} \left[\frac{(\mathbf{L} + \mathbf{S})^2_{op} - J_i(J_i + 1)}{J_k(J_k + 1) - J_i(J_i + 1)} \right] \tag{8-26}$$

The product includes all the J_i's that can result from the addition of

L and S, except that J_k for which we are trying to find the coefficient. Equation (8-18) can be inverted to give

$$|LM_L, SM_S\rangle = \sum_{J,M} D(JM, LM_L SM_S)\,|J, M\rangle \tag{8-27}$$

As before, the restriction $M = M_L + M_S$ makes the sum run over J only. Operating on (8-27) with P_{op}^k, we see that all the terms of the series are annihilated except for $J = J_k$. Thus

$$P_{op}^k\,|LM_L, SM_S\rangle = D(J_k M, LM_L SM_S)\,|J_k, M\rangle \tag{8-28}$$

By unitarity we have

$$D(J_k M, LM_L SM_S) = C^*(LM_L SM_S, JM) \tag{8-29}$$

Substituting (8-18) and (8-29) in (8-28) we obtain

$$\begin{aligned} P_{op}^k\,|LM_L, SM_S\rangle &= |C(LM_L SM_S, J_k M)|^2\,|LM_L, SM_S\rangle \\ &\quad + C^*(LM_L SM_S, J_k M) \\ &\quad \times \sum_{M_L' \neq M_L} C(LM_L' SM_S', J_k M)\,|LM_L', SM_S'\rangle \end{aligned} \tag{8-30}$$

Hence if we operate with P_{op}^k on $|LM_L, SM_S\rangle$ we obtain a series of terms in which $|LM_L, SM_S\rangle$ occurs. If we divide this series by the square root of the coefficient of $|LM_L, SM_S\rangle$ we obtain immediately an expansion for $|J_k, M\rangle$ with the proper Clebsch-Gordan coefficients

A useful recursion relation is obtained if we operate with J_- or J_+ on (8-18)

$$\begin{aligned} &\sqrt{(J \mp M)(J \pm M + 1)}\; C(LM_L SM_S, JM \pm 1) \\ &\quad = \sqrt{(L \mp M_L)(L \pm M_L + 1)}\; C(LM_L \pm 1 SM_S, JM) \\ &\quad + \sqrt{(S \mp M_S)(S \pm M_S + 1)}\; C(LM_L SM_S \pm 1, JM) \end{aligned} \tag{8-31}$$

It is clear that the Clebsch-Gordan coefficients have an arbitrary phase factor common to all of them. It is common to choose $C(LLS\; J - L, JJ)$ real and positive. Then all the coefficients will be real.

Since (8-18) represents a unitary transformation, the usual orthogonality relations hold:

$$\sum_{M_L} C(LM_L SM_S, JM)C^*(LM_L SM_S, J'M') = \delta_{MM'}\,\delta_{JJ'}$$

$$\sum_{J} C(LM_L SM_S, JM)C^*(LM_L' SM_S', JM) = \delta_{M_L M_L'}\,\delta_{M_S M_S'} \tag{8-32}$$

We observe that the number of eigenvectors in the JM representation must be equal to the number in the $LM_L SM_S$ representation. That this is indeed so follows from the fact that in the $LM_L SM_S$ representation there are $(2L + 1)$ possible M_L's, $(2S + 1)$ possible M_S's, a total of $(2L + 1)(2S + 1)$ vectors. In the JM representation there are $2J + 1$ states for each value of J which runs from $L + S$ to $|L - S|$ and

$$\sum_{|L-S|}^{L+S} (2J + 1) = (2L + 1)(2S + 1)$$

SPECIAL CASES

We shall now discuss several useful special cases. For fermions we wish to obtain the total angular momentum $\mathbf{J} = \mathbf{L} + \mathbf{S}$, where $S = \frac{1}{2}$. J can equal either $L + \frac{1}{2}$ or $L - \frac{1}{2}$. The following formulas are then true.

$$|L + \tfrac{1}{2}, M\rangle = \sqrt{\frac{L + \frac{1}{2} + M}{2L + 1}}\;|LM - \tfrac{1}{2}, \tfrac{1}{2}\tfrac{1}{2}\rangle + \sqrt{\frac{L + \frac{1}{2} - M}{2L + 1}}\;|LM + \tfrac{1}{2}, \tfrac{1}{2}\; -\tfrac{1}{2}\rangle \tag{8-33}$$

$$|L - \tfrac{1}{2}, M\rangle = -\sqrt{\frac{L + \frac{1}{2} - M}{2L + 1}}\;|LM - \tfrac{1}{2}, \tfrac{1}{2}\tfrac{1}{2}\rangle + \sqrt{\frac{L + \frac{1}{2} + M}{2L + 1}}\;|LM + \tfrac{1}{2}, \tfrac{1}{2}\; -\tfrac{1}{2}\rangle \tag{8-34}$$

We prove (8-33) by induction. We observe that it holds for $M = L + \frac{1}{2}$. We then operate on (8-33) with J_- and the result, when divided by $\sqrt{(L + \frac{1}{2} + M)(L + \frac{3}{2} - M)}$ can be shown to be of the form (8-33), with M replaced by $M - 1$. To verify (8-34) we merely need to observe that it is orthonormal to (8-33). Since the vector space is two-dimensional (8-34) must be correct.

We next consider the addition to two angular momenta equal in magnitude, $L = S$. Then J can equal $2L, 2L - 1, \ldots, 0$. The wave function for the highest $M = 2L$, corresponding to $J = 2L$ and $M_L = M_S = L$, must be given by

$$|2L,2L\rangle = |L,L\rangle \tag{8-35}$$

(We abbreviate $|LM_L, SM_S\rangle$ as $|M_L, M_S\rangle$.) Equation (8-35) is clearly symmetric in the two angular momenta. In the particular case of two equivalent electrons, the wave function will be symmetric in their spatial coordinates. Since J_- is a symmetric operator, $J_- = L_- + S_-$, $J_-|2L,2L\rangle$ is again symmetric. Hence all the eigenkets with $J = 2L$ are symmetric in the two angular momenta. For $M = 2L - 1$ we have two possibilities $M_L = L$, $M_S = L - 1$; or $M_L = L - 1$, $M_S = L$. Out of the corresponding kets we form linear combinations corresponding to $J = 2L$, $J = 2L - 1$. Since

$$2^{-1/2}(|L-1, L\rangle + |L, L-1\rangle) \tag{8-36}$$

is the only normalized, symmetric state that can be constructed, it must correspond to $J = 2L$. Accordingly,

$$2^{-1/2}(|L-1, L\rangle - |L, L-1\rangle) \tag{8-37}$$

which is orthonormal to (8-36) corresponds to $J = 2L - 1$. By the same argument as before we see that all eigenvectors with $J = 2L - 1$ are antisymmetric.

For lower M the argument is similar. If $M = 2L - 2n$, where n is an integer, the possible pairs of M_L, M_S are

$$\begin{array}{llllll} M_L = L & L-1 & \ldots & L-n & \ldots & L-2n \\ M_S = L-2n & L-2n+1 & \ldots & L-n & \ldots & L \end{array} \tag{8-38}$$

In the cases where $M_S \neq M_L$, we can form a symmetric and an antisymmetric combination of kets, viz.,

$$2^{-1/2}(|M_L, M - M_L\rangle \pm |M - M_L, M_L\rangle) \tag{8-39}$$

while for $M_L = L - n$ we can form only a symmetric ket, $|L-n, L-n\rangle$ Thus there are $n + 1$ symmetric and n antisymmetric kets. On the other hand, if $M = 2L - 2n + 1$, there are n symmetric and n antisymmetric kets, since there is no state $M_L = M_S$. Applying the lowering operator $L_- + S_-$ to the antisymmetric kets for $M = 2L - 2n + 1$ will make n linearly independent, antisymmetric kets for $M = 2L - 2n$ this uses up all the antisymmetric kets available. Doing the same for the symmetric kets, gives n linear combinations of symmetric kets of the type (8-39); but we know there are actually $n + 1$ symmetric kets for $M = 2L - 2n$, so that one is left over. This must belong to $J = 2L - 2n$, and we thus find that the wave function for $J = 2L - 2n$ must be symmetric. Conversely, going from $M = 2L - 2n$ to $2L - 2n - 1$, one antisymmetric wave function is added; therefore the wave function for $J = 2L - 2n - 1$ is antisymmetric. All states with $J = 2L, 2L - 2, \ldots, 0$ (or 1 if L is half-integral) will have eigenvectors symmetric in L and S; all states with $J = 2L - 1, 2L - 3, \ldots, 1$ (or 0) have antisymmetric ones.

This rule can be applied, e.g., to the compounding of the isotopic spins of two π-mesons. The isotopic spin of one π-meson is 1, hence the two-π states of total isotopic spin $I = 2$ and 0 are symmetric in the isotopic spin coordinates of the two π-mesons, while the state $I = 1$ is antisymmetric.

ADDITION OF ANGULAR MOMENTA FOR EQUIVALENT ELECTRONS

In describing the possible resultant angular momenta for a collection of equivalent electrons (i.e., electrons described by orbitals with the same n and ℓ) the Pauli principle will limit the allowable combinations. Table 8-2 exhibits the addition of orbital and spin angular momenta for two equivalent electrons. The orbital angular momenta are $\ell_1 = \ell_2 = \ell$. The components, $m_{\ell 1}$, $m_{\ell 2}$ are listed in columns 1 and 3. The spin is $\frac{1}{2}$ for each electron. The components m_{s1}, m_{s2} are listed in columns 2 and 4; + signifying $+\frac{1}{2}$, − signifying $-\frac{1}{2}$. $M_L = m_{\ell 1} + m_{\ell 2}$, $M_S = m_{s1} + m_{s2}$ are listed in columns 5 and 6. Columns 7 and 8 list the possible total orbital and total spin angular momenta that can be obtained by the linear combinations of states with a given M_L, M_S. The quantum numbers $n\ell$ are suppressed, since they are the same throughout. Each state described by n_1, n_2; ℓ_1, ℓ_2; $m_{\ell 1}, m_{\ell 2}$; s_1, s_2; m_{s1}, m_{s2}; ($n_1 = n_2 = n$, $\ell_1 = \ell_2 = \ell$, $s_1 = s_2 = \frac{1}{2}$) is a Slater determinant of space-spin orbitals.

The entries in columns 1 to 4 of Table 8-2 are determined by the Pauli principle and by the requirement that electrons are indistinguishable. Thus for $m_{\ell 1} = m_{\ell 2} = \ell$, m_{s1} and m_{s2} must be different by the Pauli principle, and it does not matter whether we set $m_{s1} = +$, $m_{s2} = -$, or vice versa. On the other hand, for $m_{\ell 1} = \ell$ and $m_{\ell 2} = \ell - 1$ it is possible to have $m_{s1} = m_{s2}$. If $m_{s1} \neq m_{s2}$, it now matters whether $m_{s1} = +$, $m_{s2} = -$, or vice versa, because orbitals 1 and 2 are distinguished by having different values of m_ℓ.

The entries in columns 7 and 8 are determined by the following arguments. In the first line L clearly is 2ℓ, since $M_L = 2\ell$. S in principle can be 1 or 0. In our case, it cannot be 1, because then the

Table 8-2

Addition of Angular Momenta for Two Equivalent Electrons

$m_{\ell 1}$	m_{s1}	$m_{\ell 2}$	m_{s2}	M_L	M_S	L	S
ℓ	+	ℓ	−	2ℓ	0	2ℓ	0
ℓ	+	$\ell - 1$	+	$2\ell - 1$	1	$2\ell - 1$	1
ℓ	−	$\ell - 1$	−	$2\ell - 1$	−1	$2\ell - 1$	1
ℓ	+	$\ell - 1$	−	$2\ell - 1$	0 }	2ℓ	0
ℓ	−	$\ell - 1$	+	$2\ell - 1$	0 }	$2\ell - 1$	1
ℓ	+	$\ell - 2$	+	$2\ell - 2$	1	$2\ell - 1$	1
ℓ	−	$\ell - 2$	−	$2\ell - 2$	−1	$2\ell - 1$	1
ℓ	+	$\ell - 2$	−	$2\ell - 2$	0 }	$2\ell - 1$	1
ℓ	−	$\ell - 2$	+	$2\ell - 2$	0 }	2ℓ	0
$\ell - 1$	+	$\ell - 1$	−	$2\ell - 2$	0 }	$2\ell - 2$	0

lowering operator S_- would generate three allowable states $M_S = +1, 0, -1$ but we only have one state available. Hence $S = 0$. In the next set there are four possibilities with $m_{\ell 1} = \ell$, $m_{\ell 2} = \ell - 1$ and various values of m_{s1} and m_{s2}. The first and second lines correspond to $S = 1$, since $M_S = \pm 1$. Since linear combinations are allowed only between states of a given M_S and M_L no linear combinations of these two are possible. Each one therefore is an eigenstate of L and S with the appropriate eigenvalues.

The next two entries have the same M_L and M_S and linear combinations are possible. One linear combination will correspond to $L = 2\ell$, $S = 0$, the other to $L = 2\ell - 1$. The next set, with $M_L = 2\ell - 2$ has five possible states enumerated. Some linear combinations of these states must correspond to $L = 2\ell - 1$, $S = 1$. Immediately we conclude that the states in the first two lines are eigenstates of L and S with the indicated eigenvalues. The remaining three states can combine linearly, since they have the same M_L and M_S. One of the linear combinations must correspond to $L = 2\ell - 1$, $S = 1$; another to $L = 2\ell$, $S = 0$. The third state must then have a different L from the previous ones, and we conclude that it is $L = 2\ell - 2$. Since there is only one such state, $S = 0$.

The L and S values have been assigned by enumerating the states of given M_L M_S. Another method depends on considerations of symmetry. The entire wave function must be antisymmetric under interchange of electrons. Thus in the $\ell_1 m_{\ell 1} \ell_2 m_{\ell 2} s_1 m_{s1} s_2 m_{s2}$ representation the wave function is a Slater determinant:

$$R_{n\ell}(r_1) R_{n\ell}(r_2) Y_{\ell m_{\ell 1}}(\Omega_1) Y_{\ell m_{\ell 2}}(\Omega_2) \chi_1(1) \chi_2(2) - R_{n\ell}(r_2) R_{n\ell}(r_1) Y_{\ell m_{\ell 1}}(\Omega_2) Y_{\ell m_{\ell 2}}(\Omega_1) \chi_1(2) \chi_2(1) \tag{8-40}$$

where $R_{n\ell}$ is the radial function of an electron; $Y_{\ell m_{\ell i}}$ is the spherical harmonic and χ_i the spin function of the ith electron.

In the $LM_L SM_S$ representation the wave function $|LM_L SM_S\rangle$ is a linear combination of terms of the form (8-40), with $m_{\ell 1} + m_{\ell 2} = M_L$; $m_{s1} + m_{s2} = M_S$. We see that $R_{n\ell}(r_1) R_{n\ell}(r_2)$ will be a common factor of $|LM_L SM_S\rangle$. Since $R_{n\ell}(r_1) R_{n\ell}(r_2)$ is symmetric the remaining part of $|LM_L SM_S\rangle$, i.e., the angular and spin part, must be antisymmetric. If this angular and spin part is a product of two factors, one angular and the other spin, these two factors must have opposite symmetry under interchange. For $M_S = 1$ or $M_S = -1$ the desired factorization will occur, since then $\chi_1 = \alpha$, $\chi_2 = \alpha$ or $\chi_1 = \beta$, $\chi_2 = \beta$, respectively, and $\alpha_1\alpha_2$ or $\beta_1\beta_2$ can be factored out of the entire expression. For $M_S = 0$ we can have $\chi_1 = \alpha$, $\chi_2 = \beta$ or $\chi_1 = \beta$, $\chi_2 = \alpha$. Then the angular-spin part of $|LM_L SM_S\rangle$ can be written as

$$f(\Omega_1, \Omega_2)\alpha_1\beta_2 + g(\Omega_1, \Omega_2)\beta_1\alpha_2 \tag{8-41}$$

Here f and g are sums of products of spherical harmonics. Since (8-41) is an eigenfunction of L^2 and M_L, f and g independently must also be eigenfunctions. But we proved above that, for $\mathbf{L} = \boldsymbol{\ell} + \boldsymbol{\ell}$, the spatial eigenfunctions and hence f and g, are either symmetric or antisymmetric, depending on the value of L. But (8-41) is antisymmetric, hence

$$\begin{aligned} f(\Omega_1, \Omega_2)\alpha_1\beta_2 + g(\Omega_1, \Omega_2)\beta_1\alpha_2 &= -f(\Omega_2, \Omega_1)\alpha_2\beta_1 - g(\Omega_2, \Omega_1)\beta_2\alpha_1 \\ &= \pm(f(\Omega_1, \Omega_2)\alpha_2\beta_1 + g(\Omega_1, \Omega_2)\alpha_1\beta_2) \end{aligned}$$

$$f(\Omega_1, \Omega_2) = \pm g(\Omega_1, \Omega_2) \tag{8-42}$$

Therefore (8-41) can always be written as

$$f(\Omega_1, \Omega_2)(\alpha_1\beta_2 \pm \beta_1\alpha_2) \tag{8-43}$$

We conclude that for two equivalent electrons, $|LM_L SM_S\rangle$ always factors into radial, angular, and spin parts, and the angular and spin parts have opposite symmetries under interchange. This means that whenever L is even, S = 0; when L is odd, S = 1. We see in Table 8-2 that this is obeyed. Indeed this could have been used to derive the entries in Table 8-2.

For three or more electrons it is much more difficult to give any general rules. Table 8-3 exhibits the addition of angular momenta for three equivalent p electrons. There are 20 allowed states (see p. 76). The table can, however, be abbreviated, because for every state with positive M_S, we can obtain a state with $M'_S = -M_S$ by simply changing the signs of all m_{si}. Similarly, we can independently change the signs of all $m_{\ell i}$. Thus we need only list the states of positive or zero M_L, and positive M_S, a total of 7 instead of 20.

The reasoning to establish L and S is again enumerating states. Symmetry arguments do not apply, since we no longer are adding two equal angular momenta. The curly brackets indicate that linear combinations are to be taken. It is seen that one obtains one ^4S, one ^2P, and one ^2D state. The ^4S state has $4 \times 1 = 4$ magnetic substates M_L, M_S; the ^2P state has $2 \times 3 = 6$; the ^2D state $2 \times 5 = 10$ magnetic substates. The total is 20, as expected. This is an important check of the completeness of our table of states.

In all cases we have so far discussed there is only one state for each combination LS (or none). We shall see in the next chapter that this greatly simplifies the calculation of energy levels. The simplest configuration involving only equivalent electrons for which this is no longer true is d^3, three equivalent d electrons. In this case, two ^2D states occur. They cannot be distinguished except by their energy, and the calculation of their energy is more difficult than if there is only one state of given LS. For d^4 there are five pairs of states of the same LS, and for the f shell the occurrence of states of the same LS becomes very common (cf. Slater, Vol. I, p. 304).

Table 8-3

Addition of Angular Momenta for Three Equivalent p Electrons

$m_{\ell 1}$	m_{s1}	$m_{\ell 2}$	m_{s2}	$m_{\ell 3}$	m_{s3}	M_L	M_S	L	S
1	+	1	−	0	+	2	$\frac{1}{2}$	2	$\frac{1}{2}$
1	+	1	−	−1	+	1	$\frac{1}{2}$ }	2	$\frac{1}{2}$
1	+	0	+	0	−	1	$\frac{1}{2}$ }	1	$\frac{1}{2}$
1	+	0	+	−1	+	0	$\frac{3}{2}$	0	$\frac{3}{2}$
1	+	0	+	−1	−	0	$\frac{1}{2}$ }	2	$\frac{1}{2}$
1	+	0	−	−1	+	0	$\frac{1}{2}$ }	1	$\frac{1}{2}$
1	−	0	+	−1	+	0	$\frac{1}{2}$ }	0	$\frac{3}{2}$

Chapter 9

THEORY OF MULTIPLETS, ELECTROSTATIC INTERACTION

In keeping with the program outlined at the beginning of Chapter 8, we shall now calculate the matrix elements of H in a representation in which L^2, L_z, S^2, and S_z are diagonal. We shall want to evaluate terms of the form

$$\langle H \rangle = \langle LM_L SM_S | H | LM_L SM_S \rangle \tag{9-1}$$

Each ket is a linear superposition of determinantal wave functions of a given electron configuration.

$$|LM_L SM_S\rangle = \sum_k C_k |m_{\ell 1} m_{s1}, \ldots, m_{\ell n} m_{sn}(k)\rangle \tag{9-2}$$

$$\langle H \rangle = \sum_j \sum_k C_j^* C_k \times \langle m_{\ell 1} m_{s1}, \ldots, m_{\ell n} m_{sn}(j) | H | m_{\ell 1} m_{s1}, \ldots, m_{\ell n} m_{sn}(k)\rangle \tag{9-3}$$

Each ket represents one Slater determinant. Each of the indices j and k represents a certain choice of the m_ℓ and m_s of the orbitals in the incomplete shell or shells; each such choice defines a Slater determinant. The summation is over all possible choices j, k. It is assumed that there are n electrons in the incomplete shell or shells.

EVALUATION OF MATRIX ELEMENTS

We are thus led to a consideration of matrix elements of H between determinantal wave functions. Since

$$H = F_1 + F_2 \qquad F_1 = \sum_i f_i \qquad F_2 = \sum_{i<j} g_{ij} \tag{9-4}$$

where f_i is a one-electron operator and g_{ij} is a two-electron operator, (6-13) through (6-18) give the appropriate matrix elements. We first consider $f = -(\hbar^2/2m)\nabla^2 - (Ze^2/r)$. According to (6-13) and (6-14) the nonzero contributions in the series (9-3) arise only from two cases: (1) only one orbital different between the initial and final determinants, and (2) all orbitals the same. In the first case, the contribution is still zero for the following reason. Suppose the ith orbital is different. We wish to evaluate

$$\int v_i^* f u_i \, d\tau \tag{6-13}$$

$$f u_i = -\frac{\hbar^2}{2m} \nabla^2 u_i - \frac{Ze^2}{r} u_i$$

$$= +\frac{\hbar^2}{2m} \frac{1}{r}\left[-\frac{d^2}{dr^2} + \frac{\ell_i(\ell_i + 1)}{r^2}\right] \mathcal{R}_{n_i \ell_i} Y_{\ell_i m_{\ell i}} \chi(m_{si})$$

$$- \frac{Ze^2}{r^2} \mathcal{R}_{n_i \ell_i} Y_{\ell_i m_{\ell i}} \chi(m_{si}) \tag{9-5}$$

Since the orbitals v_i and u_i can differ only in the assignment of m_ℓ or m_s, the φ integration or the spin space integration implied in (6-13) will make the integral vanish.

The diagonal contribution

$$\sum_i \int u_i^* f u_i \, d\tau \tag{6-14}$$

is seen to be independent of all $m_{\ell i}$'s and m_{si}'s, when we take note of (9-5).

$$\langle F_1 \rangle = \sum_j |C_j|^2$$

$$\times \langle m_{\ell 1} m_{s1}, \ldots, m_{\ell n} m_{sn}(j) | F_1 | m_{\ell 1} m_{s1}, \ldots, m_{\ell n} m_{sn}$$

$$= \sum_j |C_j|^2 \sum_i \langle i | f | i \rangle \tag{9-6}$$

where the sum over i goes over all the orbitals $m_{\ell i} m_{si}$ occupied in term j. Now from (9-5) it follows that $\langle i | f | i \rangle$ depends only on $n_i \ell_i$ but not on $m_{\ell i} m_{si}$, since the angular integral is simply $\int | Y_{\ell_i m_{\ell i}}(\Omega) |^2 \, d\Omega = 1$. Therefore the sum over i in (9-6) is the same for all Slater determinants j arising from a given electron configuration. Therefore

$$\langle F_1 \rangle = \left(\sum_i \langle i | f | i \rangle \right) \sum_j | C_j |^2$$

$$= \sum_i \langle i | f | i \rangle \qquad (9\text{-}7)$$

for any wave function of type (9-2). As eventually we shall take differences of terms with different m_ℓ or m_s, we ignore the entire contribution of $\langle F_1 \rangle$ to $\langle H \rangle$.

We now evaluate $\langle F_2 \rangle$. According to (6-15), (6-17), and (6-18) the nonzero contributions to the series (9-3) arise only from three cases: (1) only two orbitals different between the initial and final determinants, (2) only one orbital different, and (3) all orbitals the same. Also we see from (6-15) to (6-18) that the relevant expressions involve only two orbitals; we shall want to evaluate expressions of the form

$$\langle ij | \frac{1}{r_{12}} | ij \rangle - \langle ij | \frac{1}{r_{12}} | ji \rangle \qquad (9\text{-}8)$$

For case (1) above, where two orbitals are different, we must have both orbitals describing electrons in incomplete shells, since for complete shells the orbitals in the Slater determinants are the same. For case (2) above, the one different orbital must also describe an electron in an incomplete shell. The contribution given by (6-17) can be written as

$$\sum_{\substack{j \\ \text{complete} \\ \text{shells}}} \left[\langle i'j | \frac{1}{r_{12}} | ij \rangle - \langle i'j | \frac{1}{r_{12}} | ji \rangle \right]$$

$$+ \sum_{\substack{j \neq i \\ \text{incomplete} \\ \text{shells}}} \left[\langle i'j | \frac{1}{r_{12}} | ij \rangle - \langle i'j | \frac{1}{r_{12}} | ji \rangle \right] \qquad (9\text{-}9)$$

where the ith orbital is different in initial and final state, denoted by i and i′, respectively. We now show that the summation over the complete shells is 0.

$$\sum_{\substack{j \\ \text{complete} \\ \text{shells}}} \langle i'j | \frac{1}{r_{12}} | ij \rangle$$

$$= \sum_{\substack{j \\ \text{complete} \\ \text{shells}}} \iint v_{i'}^*(2)\, u_i(2)\, |u_j(1)|^2 \frac{1}{r_{12}}\, d\tau$$

$$= 2\delta(m_{si}, m_{si'}) \sum_{n\ell} \sum_{m_\ell=-\ell}^{\ell} \int \mathcal{R}^2_{n_i\ell_i}(r_2)$$

$$\times\, Y^*_{\ell_i m_{\ell i'}}(\Omega_2)\, Y_{\ell_i m_{\ell i}}(\Omega_2)\, d\Omega_2\, dr_2$$

$$\times \int \frac{1}{r_{12}} \mathcal{R}^2_{n\ell}(r_1)\, |Y_{\ell m_\ell}(\Omega_1)|^2\, d\Omega_1\, dr_1$$

$$= 2\delta(m_{si}, m_{si'}) \sum_{n\ell} \int \mathcal{R}^2_{n_i\ell_i}(r_2)\, Y^*_{\ell_i m_{\ell i'}}(\Omega_2)\, Y_{\ell_i m_{\ell i}}(\Omega_2)$$

$$\times\, d\Omega_2\, dr_2\, (2\ell + 1) \int \mathcal{R}^2_{n\ell}(r_1) \frac{1}{r_>}\, dr_1$$

$$= 2\delta(m_{si}, m_{si'})\, \delta(m_{\ell i}, m_{\ell i'}) \sum_{n\ell} (2\ell + 1) F^0(n\ell; n_i\ell_i)$$

$$= \delta(m_{si}, m_{si'})\, \delta(m_{\ell i}, m_{\ell i'})\, \Phi(n_i, \ell_i) \tag{9-10}$$

where Φ is some function of n_i and ℓ_i and

$$F^0(n\ell; n_i\ell_i) = \iint \mathcal{R}^2_{n\ell}(r_1)\, \mathcal{R}^2_{n_i\ell_i}(r_2) \frac{1}{r_>}\, dr_1\, dr_2 \tag{9-11}$$

Since by hypothesis $v_{i'} \neq u_i$, i.e., $m_{si} \neq m_{si'}$ or $m_{\ell i} \neq m_{\ell i'}$ (or both), this becomes 0. However, the result (9-10) will be useful for the case $v_i = u_i$. The exchange integral can be evaluated by a procedure similar to (6-45) through (6-53).

$$\sum_{\substack{j \\ \text{complete} \\ \text{shells}}} \langle i'j| \frac{1}{r_{12}} |ji\rangle$$

$$= \sum_{\substack{j \\ \text{complete} \\ \text{shells}}} \iint v_{i'}^*(1)\, u_j^*(2) \frac{1}{r_{12}} u_j(1)\, u_i(2)\; d\tau$$

$$= \delta(m_{si'}, m_{si}) \sum_{n\ell} \sum_{m_\ell=-\ell}^{\ell} \iint \mathcal{R}_{n_i\ell_i}(r_1)\mathcal{R}_{n\ell}(r_2)\mathcal{R}_{n\ell}(r_1)$$

$$\times\, \mathcal{R}_{n_i\ell_i}(r_2) \frac{1}{r_{12}} Y^*_{\ell_i m_{\ell i'}}(\Omega_1)\, Y^*_{\ell m_\ell}(\Omega_2)\, Y_{\ell m_\ell}(\Omega_1)$$

$$\times\, Y_{\ell_i m_{\ell i}}(\Omega_2)\; d\Omega_1\; d\Omega_2\; dr_1\; dr_2$$

$$= \delta(m_{si'}, m_{si}) \sum_{n\ell} \sum_{k} \frac{2\ell + 1}{4\pi}\, G^k(n_i\ell_i, n\ell)$$

$$\times \iint Y^*_{\ell_i m_{\ell i'}}(\Omega_1)\, Y_{\ell_i m_{\ell i}}(\Omega_2)$$

$$\times\, P_k(\cos\theta_{12})\, P_\ell(\cos\theta_{12})\; d\Omega_1\; d\Omega_2$$

$$= \delta(m_{si'}, m_{si}) \sum_{n\ell} \sum_{k} \sum_{\ell'} \frac{\sqrt{(2\ell' + 1)(2\ell + 1)}}{4\pi}$$

$$\times\, c^k(\ell 0, \ell' 0)\, G^k(n_i\ell_i, n\ell)$$

$$\times \iint Y^*_{\ell_i m_{\ell i'}}(\Omega_1)\, Y_{\ell_i m_{\ell i}}(\Omega_2)\, P_{\ell'}(\cos\theta_{12})\; d\Omega_1\; d\Omega_2$$

$$= \delta(m_{si'}, m_{si}) \sum_{n\ell} \sum_{k} \sum_{\ell'} \sum_{m'} \sqrt{\frac{2\ell + 1}{2\ell' + 1}}$$

$$\times\, c^k(\ell 0, \ell' 0)\, G^k(n_i\ell_i, n\ell)$$

$$\times \iint Y^*_{\ell_i m_{\ell i'}}(\Omega_1)\, Y_{\ell_i m_{\ell i}}(\Omega_2)$$

$$\times\, Y^*_{\ell' m'}(\Omega_2)\, Y_{\ell' m'}(\Omega_1)\; d\Omega_1\; d\Omega_2 \qquad (9\text{-}12)$$

where

$$G^k(n_i\ell_i, n\ell) = \iint \mathcal{R}_{n_i\ell_i}(r_1)\mathcal{R}_{n\ell}(r_1)\mathcal{R}_{n_i\ell_i}(r_2)\mathcal{R}_{n\ell}(r_2) \times \frac{r_<^k}{r_>^{k+1}}\, dr_1\, dr_2 \tag{9-13}$$

The notation in these expansions is the same as equations (6-48) and (6-49). Integrating over Ω_2 only the terms $\ell' = \ell_i$, $m' = m_{\ell i}$ contribute. Then integrating over Ω_1 we finally get

$$\sum_{\substack{j \\ \text{complete} \\ \text{shells}}} \langle i' j | \frac{1}{r_{12}} | ji \rangle$$

$$= \delta(m_{si'}, m_{si})\,\delta(m_{\ell i}, m_{\ell i'}) \times \sum_{n\ell} \sum_k \sqrt{\frac{2\ell + 1}{2\ell_i + 1}}\; c^k(\ell 0, \ell_i 0)\, G^k(n\ell, n_i\ell_i) \tag{9-14}$$

Since $m_{\ell i} \neq m_{\ell i'}$ or $m_{si} \neq m_{si'}$ (or both), this again is zero.

In the third case, identical initial and final orbitals the contribution is given by (6-15), and for our purposes can be written

$$\tfrac{1}{2} \sum_i \sum_j [\langle ij | g | ij \rangle - \langle ij | g | ji \rangle]$$

$$= \tfrac{1}{2} \sum_i \left(\sum_{\substack{j \\ \text{complete} \\ \text{shells}}} + \sum_{\substack{j \\ \text{incomplete} \\ \text{shells}}} \right) [\langle ij | g | ij \rangle - \langle ij | g | ji \rangle] \tag{9-15}$$

We have made use of the fact that the summand is 0 for $i = j$ and is symmetric in i and j. The sum over the complete shells j is a constant independent of $m_{\ell i}$ and m_{si}, as can be seen from (9-10) and (9-14). As before in (9-7) we disregard this term. Equation (9-15) can now be written

$$\frac{1}{2} \sum_{\substack{j \\ \text{incomplete} \\ \text{shells}}} \left(\sum_{\substack{i \\ \text{complete} \\ \text{shells}}} + \sum_{\substack{i \\ \text{incomplete} \\ \text{shells}}} \right) [\langle ij | g | ij \rangle - \langle ij | g | ji \rangle] \tag{9-16}$$

The sum over i for the complete shells is again disregarded, and the relevant contribution reduces to

$$\frac{1}{2} \sum_{\substack{i \\ \text{incomplete} \\ \text{shells}}} \sum_{j} [\langle ij \mid g \mid ij \rangle - \langle ij \mid g \mid ji \rangle]$$

$$= \sum_{\substack{i<j \\ \text{incomplete} \\ \text{shells}}} [\langle ij \mid g \mid ij \rangle - \langle ij \mid g \mid ji \rangle] \qquad (9\text{-}17)$$

We conclude that we need only consider the case when both orbitals describe electrons in incomplete shells, when evaluating terms of the form (9-8).

EQUIVALENCE OF HOLES AND ELECTRONS

We now prove the important and useful result that the level separations will be the same for a shell lacking $N < 4\ell + 2$ electrons as they will be for a shell with N electrons present. This result is due to Heisenberg (1931).

First of all, a shell $n\ell$ containing k equivalent electrons has the same multiplets as a shell containing $4\ell + 2 - k$ electrons. This follows from our general procedure of obtaining resultant multiplets for equivalent electrons, as outlined at the end of Chapter 8. If we are dealing with a shell containing $4\ell + 2 - k$ electrons we can list the m_ℓ's and m_s's of the occupied orbitals as in Table 8-3. We can equally well describe the situation by listing the unoccupied orbitals and obtain a table like Table 8-3 for k electrons. The only difference is that M_L and M_S of a given state are the negatives of the sums of the m_ℓ's and m_s's for the unoccupied orbitals. But this does not change the permitted values of L and S.

We now examine the energy separations. The diagonal elements (9-15) for a set of $4\ell + 2 - N$ electrons can be written

$$\frac{1}{2}\left(\sum_{\substack{i \\ \text{complete} \\ \text{shells}}} \sum_{j} - \sum_{\substack{j \\ \text{holes}}} \sum_{\substack{i \\ \text{complete} \\ \text{shells}}} - \sum_{\substack{j \\ \text{complete} \\ \text{shells}}} \sum_{\substack{i \\ \text{holes}}} + \sum_{j} \sum_{\substack{i \\ \text{holes}}} \right)$$

$$\times (\langle ij \mid g \mid ij \rangle - \langle ij \mid g \mid ji \rangle) \qquad (9\text{-}18)$$

The first three terms can be neglected as they give a result independent of the magnetic quantum numbers. Hence the contribution of the diagonal elements to the level separation of a set of $4\ell + 2 - k$ electrons in an incomplete shell is the same as the contribution of k electrons.

We now discuss the off-diagonal elements. For one (two) orbitals different, we have an electron shifting from u_i' to u_i (and from u_j' to u_j). This is the same as a hole shifting from u_i to u_i' (and from u_j to u_j'), and will produce the same contribution whether we view it as an electron or as a hole. The desired result is now proved. It is seen that apart from a general displacement in energy due to the over-all number of electrons present, the level structure is quantitatively the same for k electrons as for $4\ell + 2 - k$ electrons.

ANGULAR INTEGRALS

The angular and spin part of the general integral is

$$\langle \ell_1 m_{\ell 1} m_{s1} \ell_2 m_{\ell 2} m_{s2} | \frac{1}{r_{12}} | \ell_3 m_{\ell 3} m_{s3} \ell_4 m_{\ell 4} m_{s4} \rangle$$

$$= \delta(m_{s1} m_{s3})\, \delta(m_{s2} m_{s4}) \int Y^*_{\ell_1 m_{\ell 1}}(\Omega_1)\, Y^*_{\ell_2 m_{\ell 2}}(\Omega_2)$$

$$\times\, Y_{\ell_3 m_{\ell 3}}(\Omega_1)\, Y_{\ell_4 m_{\ell 4}}(\Omega_2)\; d\Omega_1\, d\Omega_2 \qquad (9\text{-}19)$$

Expanding $1/r_{12}$ in terms of spherical harmonics and considering the Ω_1 integral we obtain

$$\int Y^*_{\ell_1 m_{\ell 1}}(\Omega_1)\, Y_{\ell_3 m_{\ell 3}}(\Omega_1)\, Y_{k\mu}(\Omega_1)\; d\Omega_1$$

$$= \sqrt{\frac{2k+1}{4\pi}}\; c^k(\ell_1 m_{\ell 1}, \ell_3 m_{\ell 3})\, \delta(\mu, m_{\ell 1} - m_{\ell 3}) \qquad (9\text{-}20)$$

(definition of c^k). The Ω_2 integration gives

$$\sqrt{\frac{2k+1}{4\pi}}\; c^k(\ell_4 m_{\ell 4}, \ell_2 m_{\ell 2})\, \delta(\mu, m_{\ell 4} - m_{\ell 2}) \qquad (9\text{-}21)$$

(note reversed subscripts). Therefore including the radial part, the entire matrix element is

$$\delta(m_{s1}, m_{s3})\, \delta(m_{s2}, m_{s4})\, \delta(m_{\ell 1} + m_{\ell 2}, m_{\ell 3} + m_{\ell 4})$$

$$\times \sum_{k=0}^{\infty} c^k(\ell_1 m_{\ell 1}, \ell_3 m_{\ell 3})\, c^k(\ell_4 m_{\ell 4}, \ell_2 m_{\ell 2})$$

$$\times\, R^k(12,34) \qquad (9\text{-}22)$$

530.1 B465e cop. 2 Tech
THE CHICAGO PUBLIC LIBRARY

where

$$R^k(12,34) = \iint \mathcal{R}_{n_1\ell_1}(r_1)\mathcal{R}_{n_2\ell_2}(r_2)\mathcal{R}_{n_3\ell_3}(r_1)\mathcal{R}_{n_4\ell_4}(r_4) \times \frac{r_<^k}{r_>^{k+1}}\, dr_1\, dr_2 \tag{9-23}$$

The coefficients c^k, defined in (9-20) and in (6-49), were first evaluated by Gaunt. Still more convenient and symmetrical is a formula due to Racah:

$$c^k(\ell m, \ell' m') = (-1)^m \sqrt{(2\ell + 1)(2\ell' + 1)} \times V(\ell, \ell', k; -m, m', m - m')V(\ell, \ell', k; 0,0,0) \tag{9-24}$$

where V is defined in (8-24).

As previously stated, (6-50) $k + \ell + \ell'$ must be even, and

$$|\ell - \ell'| < k < \ell + \ell' \tag{9-25}$$

Interesting particular cases are

$$c^0(\ell m, \ell' m') = \sqrt{4\pi} \int Y^*_{\ell m}(\Omega)\, Y_{\ell' m'}(\Omega)\, Y_{00}(\Omega)\, d\Omega = \delta_{\ell\ell'}\, \delta_{mm'} \tag{9-26}$$

$$\sum_{m=-\ell}^{\ell} c^k(\ell m, \ell m) = \sum_m \sqrt{\frac{4\pi}{2k+1}} \int |Y_{\ell m}(\Omega)|^2\, Y_{k0}(\Omega)\, d\Omega = \sqrt{\frac{4\pi}{2k+1}}\; \frac{2\ell + 1}{4\pi} \int Y_{k0}(\Omega)\, d\Omega = 0 \quad \text{for } k \neq 0 \tag{9-27}$$

We introduce the further notation

$$F^k\left(n_i\ell_i, n_j\ell_j\right) = R^k(ij,ij)$$
$$G^k\left(n_i\ell_i, n_j\ell_j\right) = R^k(ij,ji) \tag{9-28}$$

with R^k given in (9-23). Evidently G^k is identical with the earlier definition (9-13), and F^0 in (9-11) is a special case of (9-28).

SLATER SUM RULE

A convenient device for calculating the energy levels is the *Slater sum rule* (1929). This rule is a statement of the well-known mathematical result that the trace of a matrix is invariant under similarity transformation. This implies, disregarding spin,

$$\sum_{\substack{m_1, m_2, \ldots, m_n \\ (\Sigma m_i = M)}} \langle m_1, \ldots, m_n | H | m_1, \ldots, m_n \rangle = \sum_{L \geq |M|} E(LM) \tag{9-29}$$

The sum on the left-hand side goes over all possible sets of single-electron, angular-momentum quantum numbers which satisfy the relation $\Sigma_i m_i = M$. The left-hand side is thus the trace of the Hamiltonian matrix in the m_i representation, more accurately of the submatrix corresponding to a given M. The right-hand side is the sum of the energy eigenvalues for those L that are compatible with M. The transformation from the m_i representation to the LM representation is unitary; hence (9-29) must hold. When spin is included we get instead

$$\sum_j \langle m_{\ell 1} m_{s1} \cdots m_{\ell n} m_{sn} | H | m_{\ell 1} m_{s1} \cdots m_{\ell n} m_{sn} \rangle = \sum_{L \geq |M_L|} \sum_{S \geq |M_S|} E(LM_L, SM_S) \tag{9-30}$$

where the sets j on the left-hand side must fulfill the condition

$$\sum m_{\ell i} = M_L \qquad \sum m_{si} = M_S$$

An example of an application of the sum rule follows. Consider a system with two nonequivalent electrons having orbital angular momenta ℓ_1 and ℓ_2 and having $m_{s1} = m_{s2} = \frac{1}{2}$. We enumerate states:

$m_{\ell 1}$	$m_{\ell 2}$	M_L	L
ℓ_1	ℓ_2	$\ell_1 + \ell_2$	$\ell_1 + \ell_2 = L_0$
$\ell_1 - 1$	ℓ_2	$\ell_1 + \ell_2 - 1$	L_0
ℓ_1	$\ell_2 - 1$	$\ell_1 + \ell_2 - 1$	$L_0 - 1$

We evaluate $\langle LM_L | H | LM_L \rangle$ for $L = M_L = L_0$:

$$\langle L_0 L_0 | H | L_0 L_0 \rangle$$

$$= \langle m_{\ell 1} = \ell_1 \quad m_{\ell 2} = \ell_2 | H | m_{\ell 1} = \ell_1 \quad m_{\ell 2} = \ell_2 \rangle$$

$$= \langle m_{\ell 1} m_{\ell 2} | \frac{1}{r_{12}} | m_{\ell 1} m_{\ell 2} \rangle - \langle m_{\ell 1} m_{\ell 2} | \frac{1}{r_{12}} | m_{\ell 2} m_{\ell 1} \rangle$$

$$= \sum_{k=0}^{\infty} \{ c^k(\ell_1 \ell_1, \ell_1 \ell_1)\, c^k(\ell_2 \ell_2, \ell_2 \ell_2)\, F^k(n_1 \ell_1, n_2 \ell_2)$$

$$- [c^k(\ell_1 \ell_1, \ell_2 \ell_2)]^2 G^k(n_1 \ell_1, n_2 \ell_2) \}$$

$$= E(L_0 L_0) \tag{9-31}$$

We now compute the sum of the matrix elements for the two functions corresponding to $M = L_0 - 1$:

$$\langle m_{\ell 1} = \ell_1 - 1 \quad m_{\ell 2} = \ell_2 | H | m_{\ell 1} = \ell_1 - 1 \quad m_{\ell 2} = \ell_2 \rangle$$
$$+ \langle m_{\ell 1} = \ell_1 \quad m_{\ell 2} = \ell_2 - 1 | H | m_{\ell 1} = \ell_1 \quad m_{\ell 2} = \ell_2 - 1 \rangle \tag{9-32}$$

We know by the sum rule that this equals

$$E(L_0, L_0 - 1) + E(L_0 - 1, L_0 - 1) \tag{9-33}$$

But $E(L_0, M) = E(L_0, L_0)$, since E cannot depend on M, because $[L_x, H] = [L_y, H] = 0$; but $[L_x, L_z] \neq 0$. Hence subtracting the result we obtained in (9-31) from (9-33) we get $E(L_0 - 1)$. This procedure can now be continued to get the remaining energies.

In the above we obtained the energies for the triplet states by taking $m_{s1} = m_{s2} = \frac{1}{2}$. To obtain the singlet energies we take $m_{s1} = \frac{1}{2}$, $m_{s2} = -\frac{1}{2}$, or $m_{s1} = -\frac{1}{2}$, $m_{s2} = +\frac{1}{2}$. With different values of m_s the exchange term vanishes. Corresponding to given $M_L = L_0$, M_S will then equal 0 in the two instances. This then corresponds to $S = 1$ and $S = 0$. Knowing the triplet-state energy allows determination of the singlet-state energy from the sum rule. Since the exchange term appears with the negative sign in the triplet energy (9-31), and is absent in the diagonal matrix elements for m_{s1}, m_{s2}, it will appear with a positive sign in the singlet energy. This is in agreement with the result for parahelium.

It should be pointed out that the sum rule is not always a sufficient tool for determining the energies. For example, in the case of three

Table 9-1

$c^k(1m_1, 1m_2)$ for $k = 0$ and $k = 2$

$c^0(1m_1, 1m_2)$

$m_2 \backslash m_1$	1	0	−1
1	1	0	0
0	0	1	0
−1	0	0	1

$c^2(1m_1, 1m_2)$

$m_2 \backslash m_1$	1	0	−1
1	$-1/5$	$-\sqrt{3}/5$	$-\sqrt{6}/5$
0	$\sqrt{3}/5$	$\sqrt{4}/5$	$\sqrt{3}/5$
−1	$-\sqrt{6}/5$	$-\sqrt{3}/5$	$-1/5$

nonequivalent s electrons we have states ^4S, ^2S, and ^2S. For $M_S = \frac{3}{2}$, arising from $m_{s1} = m_{s2} = m_{s3} = \frac{1}{2}$, we can get the energy of the ^4S term readily. However, there are three possibilities for $M_S = \frac{1}{2}$. Hence the sum rule will only give the sum of the energies of the two ^2S multiplets.

We now work out an example for two equivalent p electrons ($\ell_1 = \ell_2 = 1$):

$$\left\langle \frac{1}{r_{12}} \right\rangle = \sum_k \{a^k(\ell_1 m_{\ell 1}, \ell_2 m_{\ell 2}) - \delta(m_{s1}, m_{s2})\, b^k(\ell_1 m_{\ell 1}, \ell_2 m_{\ell 2})\} \times F^k(n\ell_1, n\ell_2) \tag{9-34a}$$

Table 9-2

Multiplet Energies for Two Equivalent p Electrons

$m_{\ell 1}$	m_{s1}	$m_{\ell 2}$	m_{s2}	State	a^2	$\delta(m_{s1}, m_{s2})b^2$	Energy
1	+	1	−	^1D	1/25	0	$1/25\ F^2$
1	+	0	+	^3P	−2/25	3/25	$-5/25\ F^2$
1	+	0	−	$^1D + {^3P}$	−2/25	0	$-4/25\ F^2$
1	−	0	+				
1	+	−1	+	^3P	1/25	6/25	$-5/25\ F^2$
1	+	−1	−	$^1D + {^3P} + {^1S}$	1/25	0	$6/25\ F^2$
1	−	−1	+		1/25	0	
0	+	0	−		4/25	0	

Table 9-3
Multiplet Structure for Various Electron Configurations

p^2	d^2	p^3
^1D: $+1\ F^{2\prime}$	^1S: $14\ F^{2\prime\prime} + 126\ F^{4\prime\prime}$	^2D: $-6\ F^{2\prime\prime}$
^3P: $-5\ F^{2\prime}$	^3P: $7\ F^{2\prime\prime} - 84\ F^{4\prime\prime}$	^2P: 0
^1S: $+10\ F^{2\prime}$	^1D: $-3\ F^{2\prime\prime} + 36\ F^{4\prime\prime}$	^4S: $-15\ F^{2\prime\prime}$
	^3F: $-8\ F^{2\prime\prime} - 9\ F^{4\prime\prime}$	
	^1G: $+4\ F^{2\prime\prime} + 1\ F^{4\prime\prime}$	

$F^{2\prime} = \frac{1}{25} F^2, \quad F^{2\prime\prime} = \frac{1}{49} F_2^2, \quad F^{4\prime\prime} = \frac{1}{441} F^4$

where

$$a^k(\ell_1 m_{\ell 1}, \ell_2 m_{\ell 2}) = c^k(\ell_1 m_{\ell 1}, \ell_1 m_{\ell 1})\, c^k(\ell_2 m_{\ell 2}, \ell_2 m_{\ell 2})$$

$$b^k(\ell_1 m_{\ell 1}, \ell_2 m_{\ell 2}) = [c^k(\ell_1 m_{\ell 1}, \ell_2 m_{\ell 2})]^2 \qquad (9\text{-}34b)$$

Such a term always appears in cases when the initial and final states are the same. We list in Table 9-1 the values of c^k for $k = 0, 2$. [From (6-50) we see that only those two values of k contribute for $\ell_1 = \ell_2 = 1$.]

Table 9-2 lists the possible multiplets and energies. Since $k = 0$ always contributes the same term F^0, we shall suppress this. From Table 9-2 we see that not only can we determine all the energy levels from the sum rules but we get three independent determinations of the ^3P state which are in agreement. This also happens in many other cases. Without evaluating the radial integrals (which must of course be positive) Table 9-2 or similar tables give the order of the various energy levels arising from a configuration and the ratio of their spacings. The results for several configurations are given in Table 9-3.

AVERAGE ENERGY

In what has been done above, the contribution to the multiplet energy which does not depend on m_ℓ or m_s, i.e., the contribution that is the same for all multiplets of a given configuration, has been ignored. We shall now obtain an expression for this energy. The total energy, as will be remembered, is

$$E = \sum_{i} \langle i|\,f\,|i\rangle + \sum_{i<j} \Big[\langle ij\,|\,g\,|\,ij\rangle - \delta(m_{si}, m_{sj})\,\langle ij\,|\,g\,|\,ji\rangle\Big] \qquad (9\text{-}35)$$

where f is the one-electron operator and g is the electron interaction, e^2/r_{12}. The one-electron operator can clearly be expressed in terms of radial wave functions,

$$E_1 = \sum_{n\ell} N_{n\ell} \int_0^\infty \left\{ \frac{\hbar^2}{2m} \mathcal{R}_{n\ell} \left[- \frac{d^2\mathcal{R}_{n\ell}}{dr^2} + \frac{\ell(\ell+1)}{r^2} \mathcal{R}_{n\ell} \right] - \frac{Ze^2}{r} \mathcal{R}^2_{n\ell} \right\} dr \qquad (9\text{-}36)$$

where $N_{n\ell}$ is the number of electrons in the $n\ell$ shell, whether complete or incomplete. The kinetic-energy term in (9-36) can be simplified (see Slater).

The interaction of one electron with a complete shell was considered in the beginning of this chapter. Setting $i' = i$, (9-10) becomes

$$\sum_{\substack{j \\ \text{complete} \\ \text{shell } n\ell}} \langle ij\,|\frac{1}{r_{12}}|\,ij\rangle = 2(2\ell+1)\,F^0(n\ell, n_i\ell_i) \qquad (9\text{-}37)$$

and (9-14) gives

$$\sum_{\substack{j \\ \text{complete} \\ \text{shell } n\ell}} \langle ij\,|\frac{1}{r_{12}}|\,ji\rangle = \sqrt{\frac{2\ell+1}{2\ell_i+1}} \times \sum_k c^k(\ell 0, \ell_i 0)\,G^k(n\ell, n_i\ell_i) \qquad (9\text{-}38)$$

with F^0 and G^k defined in (9-11) and (9-13). This gives all the interactions between electrons inside the complete shells, and also of the electrons in incomplete shells with all electrons in complete ones.

We can also formally apply (9-37) and (9-38) to the interaction of one electron in the incomplete shell‡ with all orbitals in that same shell. Consider first the interaction of the electron with all other electrons if its shell were complete.

‡We assume only one incomplete shell.

$$\sum_{j\,(\text{shell } n_i\ell_i)} \left[\langle ij | \frac{1}{r_{12}} | ij \rangle - \langle ij | \frac{1}{r_{12}} | ji \rangle \right]$$

$$= (4\ell_i + 2)\, F^0 - \sum_{k=0}^{2\ell_i} c^k(\ell_i 0, \ell_i 0)\, F^k(n_i\ell_i, n_i\ell_i)$$

$$= (4\ell_i + 1)\, F^0 - \sum_{k=2}^{2\ell_i} c^k(\ell_i 0, \ell_i 0)\, F^k(n_i\ell_i, n_i\ell_i) \qquad (9\text{-}39)$$

The second line follows from the fact that, by the definition (9-28), $G^k = F^k$ when $n\ell = n_i\ell_i$. The last line follows from $c^0(\ell 0, \ell 0) = 1$, Eq. (9-26). In the sum on the left-hand side of (9-39), the term $j = i$ does not give any contribution, therefore (9-39) may be considered the interaction of orbital i with all the $4\ell_i + 1$ other orbitals in the shell. This is of course independent of $m_{\ell i}, m_{si}$. We may then define the *average* interaction W_{av} of one orbital in the shell with any other, as (9-39) divided by $4\ell_i + 1$. Dropping the subscript i we find

$$W_{av} = F^0 - \frac{1}{4\ell + 1} \sum_{k=2}^{2\ell} c^k(\ell 0, \ell 0)\, F^k(n\ell, n\ell) \qquad (9\text{-}40)$$

Of course, the sum contains only even values of k.

Now assume N electrons in the incomplete shell $n\ell$, and consider all possible distributions of these over the $m_\ell m_s$ states, compatible with the Pauli principle. Then, averaging over all these distributions, every orbital $m_{\ell i} m_{si}$ is equally likely to be occupied. Then each electron actually present will have *on the average* the interaction (9-40) with every other electron. The interaction energy of the N electrons, averaged over all distributions, will therefore be

$$\tfrac{1}{2} N(N - 1)\, W_{av} \qquad (9\text{-}41)$$

since $\frac{1}{2}N(N-1)$ is the number of interacting pairs of electrons. Thus we know the sum of all the diagonal elements of the electron interaction $1/r_{12}$ in the $m_\ell m_s$ representation: It is equal to the average interaction (9-41), multiplied by the number of possible states in the $m_\ell m_s$ representation, which in turn is equal to the number of possible distributions of N electrons over the $4\ell + 2$ orbitals, viz., $\binom{4\ell + 2}{N}$. Now we use the diagonal sum rule: The sum of the diagonal elements of the electron interaction energy in the $m_\ell m_s$ representation is equal to the sum of the eigenvalues of the energy in the LS representation. Therefore the weighted average of these eigenvalues must equal (9-41); thus:

$$\sum_{LS} (2L + 1)(2S + 1)\, E(LS) = \binom{4\ell + 2}{N} \tfrac{1}{2} N(N - 1)\, W_{av} \qquad (9\text{-}42)$$

where of course

$$\sum_{LS} (2L + 1)(2S + 1) = \binom{4\ell + 2}{N} \qquad (9\text{-}43)$$

and E(L,S) denotes the electrostatic energy for the term LS which we have calculated in the earlier parts of this chapter. Using the results in Table 9-2 or Table 9-3 we can easily verify (9-42) and (9-40).

Moreover, we may extend Koopman's theorem (Chapter 6) to the case of incomplete shells. Using (9-36), (9-37), (9-38), (9-40), and (9-42) and the Hartree-Fock equations averaged over angles (6-27), we can easily show that the Hartree-Fock energy eigenvalue is equal to the difference between the average energies of the atom and the ion. The averages are defined in the sense of (9-42) and the Koopman approximation has been made, viz., the eigenfunctions of the ion have been assumed to be identical with those of the atom.

COMPARISON WITH EXPERIMENTAL RESULTS

In Condon and Shortley, pp. 197–207, and Slater, Vol. I, pp. 339–342, are tabulated many comparisons between this theory and experiments. In Table 9-4 we list a typical comparison. It is seen that the agreement is qualitatively good, but quantitatively far from perfect. It is felt that the discrepancy is from an S state lying lower than predicted, owing to interactions with other configurations. The magnitude of the splitting is of the order of 0.1 Rydberg or 1 ev.

A different kind of comparison is to attempt to find a consistent empirical set of values for the radial integrals so that the energy levels can be computed. Slater has deduced for F^2 the value 0.35 Ry for C and 0.88 for O^{+++}. Increasing Z and degree of ionization q tends to increase F^2. This might be expected because F^k is fundamentally the average of $1/r$, albeit with complicated weighting factors. As Z or q increases, the distance r of the electrons from the nucleus tends to decrease. In interpreting the results in the d^2 case, F^4/F^2 has been assigned a value of 0.75 by Condon and Shortley and 0.55 to 0.6 by Slater. The ^3F state is found to be lowest in energy.

From the many calculations that have been performed, several rules have emerged. (1) The lowest energy goes with the highest spin.

Table 9-4
Theoretical and Experimental Energy Separation Ratios for Various Terms

p^2			p^3		
Atom	Configuration	$\frac{^1S-^1D}{^1D-^3P}$	Atom	Configuration	$\frac{^2P-^2D}{^2D-^4S}$
Theory	np^2	1.50	Theory	np^3	0.667
C	$2p^2$	1.13	N	$2p^3$	0.500
N^+	$2p^2$	1.14	O^+	$2p^3$	0.509
O^{++}	$2p^2$	1.14	S^+	$3p^3$	0.651
Si	$3p^2$	1.48	As	$4p^3$	0.715
Ge	$4p^2$	1.50	Sb	$5p^3$	0.908
Sn	$5p^2$	1.39	Bi	$6p^3$	1.121

p^4		
Atom	Configuration	$\frac{^1S-^1D}{^1D-^3P}$
Theory	np^4	1.50
O	$2p^4$	1.14
Te	$5p^4$	1.50

Since the highest spin corresponds to a symmetric combination of the individual spin functions, the space function will be antisymmetric and produces the least Coulomb repulsion (see p. 24). (2) Among the multiplets with the highest spin, the highest L gives the lowest energy. High M_L implies the orbits are near the equatorial plane, which permits the electrons to be far apart in the mean, and makes their interaction energy small.

These two rules are known as *Hund's rule*. They have been tested and confirmed in studying many spectra, including those of the rare earths which involve f electrons. The rules only apply to the lowest energy state. It is *not* true that *all* states of maximum S have lower energy than all states of the next smaller S: E.g., in the d^2 configuration, the ^1D state usually lies lower than ^3P; in the d^4, the state ^1I is always lower than the higher of two ^3F states and also lower than

Table 9-5
Multiplet Energies for the p^n Configuration

n	Lowest multiplet	Energy	Difference
1	^2P	0	
			$F^0 - \frac{5}{25} F^2$
2	^3P	$F^0 - \frac{5}{25} F^2$	
			$2F^0 - \frac{10}{25} F^2$
3	^4S	$3F^0 - \frac{15}{25} F^2$	
			$3F^0$
4	^3P	$6F^0 - \frac{15}{25} F^2$	
			$4F^0 - \frac{5}{25} F^2$
5	^2P	$10F^0 - \frac{20}{25} F^2$	
			$5F^0 - \frac{10}{25} F^2$
6	^1S	$15F^0 - \frac{30}{25} F^2$	

the ^3D state. Similarly, for S less than its maximum value, the state of highest L is not always the lowest: In the simple case of d^2, the lowest singlet state is ^1D, not ^1G. (For the nuclear shell structure, Hund's rule gives the opposite pattern, since the force is attractive.)

Applying this rule we can find the lowest state for a p^n configuration. Table 9-5 lists the lowest multiplet for p^n configurations, interaction between the electrons in the p^n shell for this multiplet, and the difference in energy between n and n − 1 electrons.

Apart from the general increase in the interaction (the F^0 terms) due to the addition of more electrons, there is an increase in binding (more negative contribution from F^2) from the first to second and from the second to third. Then there is a drop, and a repetition of the pattern. Thus we have shown that a half-filled p shell (3 electrons) gives a particularly high ionization potential. The same can be shown for half-complete d- and f-shells. This behavior was observed in the ionization potential of various atoms (see p. 61).

CONFIGURATION INTERACTION

By ignoring all spin effects in the Hamiltonian we found that **L** and **S** commutes with the Hamiltonian. We saw that **L** and **S** can be separately quantized, and this is called Russell-Saunders, or LS, coupling. Strictly speaking, L, S, M_L, and M_S are the only good quantum numbers. Parity is determined by the sum of the individual ℓ's. Hence even though the individual ℓ's are not good quantum numbers, the evenness or oddness of their sum remains a good quantum number. However, since the difference between the energy levels arising from different configurations is in general large compared to the electrostatic interaction energy, we assumed that the Hartree-Fock equations yield suitable zeroth-order wave functions from which to find the interaction energies. More precisely, we should allow for mixing, because several configurations may lead to a multiplet of the same LS. This is the second approximation, the zeroth being the Hartree-Fock, the first, the electrostatic interaction.

We are led to construct the submatrix of the Hamiltonian which connects the configurations contributing to a given LS. We label the rows and columns by the different contributing configurations. In what has gone above we have considered only diagonal elements of this matrix, i.e., elements between the same configuration. Now we take into account the entire Hamiltonian and diagonalize.

If only two configurations contribute, the Hamiltonian is

$$\begin{pmatrix} H_{aa} & H_{ab} \\ H_{ab}^{*} & H_{bb} \end{pmatrix} \tag{9-44}$$

The energy eigenvalues become

$$\epsilon = \tfrac{1}{2}(H_{aa} + H_{bb}) \pm \sqrt{\tfrac{1}{4}(H_{bb} - H_{aa})^2 + |H_{ab}|^2} \tag{9-45}$$

The square root is greater than $\frac{1}{2}(H_{bb} - H_{aa})$. Hence H_{ab}, which represents the degree of mixing, will spread the eigenvalues farther apart. A singlet S state, for example, is depressed by its interaction with higher singlet S states.

Chapter 10

THEORY OF MULTIPLETS, MAGNETIC INTERACTIONS

We have been neglecting magnetic effects in atoms by assuming that the energy is due only to the Coulomb electrostatic interaction. We shall now deal with the orbital and spin magnetic effects. The orbital magnetic effects are readily handled by the present theory. The electron spin, however, can be dealt with only in an *ad hoc* fashion; the correct treatment requiring the Dirac theory we postpone to Chapter 18.

INTERACTION WITH A CONSTANT EXTERNAL MAGNETIC FIELD

The quantum mechanical (nonrelativistic) description of a charged (spinless) mass point in a general external magnetic field, described by a vector potential **A**, can be effected by adding to the Hamiltonian the terms

$$H_{mag} = \frac{ie\hbar}{mc} \mathbf{A} \cdot \nabla + \frac{e^2}{2mc^2} A^2 \tag{10-1}$$

(See Schiff, p. 138. We are in a gauge $\nabla \cdot \mathbf{A} = 0$, $\phi = 0$, which is always possible if the field has no sources. The charge of the particle is taken to be $+e$.)

A solenoidal vector potential for a constant magnetic field $\mathcal{H}$ can be verified to be

$$\mathbf{A} = \tfrac{1}{2}\mathcal{H} \times \mathbf{r} \tag{10-2}$$

The first term of (10-1) then reads

$$-\frac{e}{2mc}\,\mathcal{H}\times\mathbf{r}\cdot\mathbf{p} = -\frac{e}{2mc}\,\mathcal{H}\cdot\mathbf{r}\times\mathbf{p} = -\frac{e}{2mc}\,\mathcal{H}\cdot\boldsymbol{\ell}$$

where $\boldsymbol{\ell}$ is the orbital momentum of the particle. Equation (10-1) becomes

$$H_{mag} = -\frac{e}{2mc}\,\mathcal{H}\cdot\boldsymbol{\ell} + \frac{e^2}{8mc^2}(\mathcal{H}\times\mathbf{r})^2 \qquad (10\text{-}3)$$

We shall estimate the magnitude of the terms in (10-3); using atomic units: $r \approx 1$, and ℓ of an electron is of order 1. $\mathcal{H}$ is at most 30 kilogauss in Zeeman effect measurements, or 1.8×10^{-3} atomic units. The first term is then $\sim 0.65 \times 10^{-5}$ atomic units, $\sim 1.5\ \text{cm}^{-1}$, which is easily measurable. If $\mathcal{H}$ is as high as 200 kilogauss, the second term is $\sim 0.0002\ \text{cm}^{-1}$ and is clearly negligible. Therefore we neglect the quadratic term for the present.

The effect of the magnetic field can now be described by ascribing to the particle a magnetic dipole moment

$$\mathbf{M}_\ell = g_m\boldsymbol{\ell} \qquad (10\text{-}4a)$$

where

$$g_m = \frac{e}{2mc} \qquad (10\text{-}4b)$$

is the gyromagnetic ratio. If we orient our coordinates such that the z axis is along $\mathcal{H}$, the contribution to the Hamiltonian becomes $-g_m\mathcal{H}(\hbar/i)(\partial/\partial\varphi)$. We write the Schrödinger equation

$$H^0\Psi - g_m\mathcal{H}\frac{\hbar}{i}\frac{\partial}{\partial\varphi}\Psi = E\Psi \qquad (10\text{-}5)$$

If the potential occurring in H^0 is spherically symmetric, we set $\Psi = R_{n\ell}Y_{\ell m_\ell}$ and

$$\begin{aligned} E &= E^0 - m_\ell g_m \hbar\mathcal{H} \\ H^0\Psi &= E^0\Psi \end{aligned} \qquad (10\text{-}6)$$

where m_ℓ is the magnetic quantum number. Thus the interaction with the magnetic field shifts the energy by an amount $m_\ell g_m\hbar\mathcal{H}$, $-\ell \le m_\ell \le \ell$, and removes the m_ℓ degeneracy in energy. The last term in (10-6) is obviously the energy which we should expect for the interaction of the magnetic field with the magnetic moment (10-4), viz.,

$$E_{mag} = -\mathcal{H}\cdot\mathbf{M}_\ell \qquad (10\text{-}7a)$$

with $\mathbf{M}_\ell$ given by (10-4). We may consider (10-7a) as the definition of the magnetic moment. It is only correct if E is linear in $\mathcal{H}$; otherwise

$$\mathbf{M}_\ell = -\frac{\partial E}{\partial \mathcal{H}} \tag{10-7b}$$

If the particle is an electron it has spin $\mathbf{s}$, and the spin magnetic moment is found experimentally to be

$$\mathbf{M}_s = 2g_m \mathbf{s} \times (1.00116) \tag{10-8}$$

where the magnetic moment is again defined from the magnetic energy by (10-7). The statements (10-7) and (10-8) are verified by Stern-Gerlach experiments or by analysis of the Zeeman effect. In the Dirac theory the spin magnetic interaction follows naturally. The factor 1.00116 is a radiative correction which has been observed and can be predicted by field theory.

SPIN-ORBIT INTERACTION FOR ATOMS

The spin-orbit interaction is due to the interaction of the magnetic moment of the electron with the magnetic field set up by its motion. Since this effect is entirely relativistic we can expect that only the Dirac theory can give a complete analysis. However, we can give here a pseudo-derivation which gives the correct result.

If one electron is moving with a velocity $\mathbf{v}$ relative to the entire atomic configuration, then viewed from the electron's rest frame, the nucleus and the other electrons are moving with a velocity $-\mathbf{v}$ and so is their effective field $\boldsymbol{\mathcal{E}}$. Associated with the moving electric field is a magnetic field arising from the relativistic transformation equation, which to first order in v/c is

$$\mathcal{H} = \frac{1}{c}\,\boldsymbol{\mathcal{E}} \times \mathbf{v} = -\frac{1}{c}\,\nabla\phi \times \mathbf{v} \tag{10-9}$$

(We keep only terms in first order v/c, since we shall fit this into the nonrelativistic Schrödinger theory.) If ϕ, the effective potential, is spherically symmetric (10-9) gives, with the substitution $e\phi = V$ and further rearrangement:

$$\mathcal{H} = -\frac{1}{mec}\,\frac{dV}{dr}\,\frac{\mathbf{r}}{r} \times \mathbf{p}$$

$$= -\frac{1}{mecr}\,\frac{dV}{dr}\,\boldsymbol{\ell} \tag{10-10}$$

Combining (10-4), (10-7), (10-8), and (10-9) we obtain the interaction energy,

$$H_{so} = \frac{1}{m^2 c^2 r} \frac{dV}{dr} \boldsymbol{\ell} \cdot \mathbf{s} \tag{10-11}$$

(The radiative correction has been suppressed. Notice that in its rest frame the electron has no orbital magnetic moment; hence no ℓ^2 term occurs.) Equation (10-11) also holds in the rest frame of the nucleus, since to first order in v/c the energy is the same. Thomas and Frankel (1926) have shown that from a picture of the electron as a spinning top, (10-11) has to be multiplied by a factor $\frac{1}{2}$. Therefore the correct spin-orbit interaction energy is given by

$$H_{so} = \frac{1}{2m^2 c^2} \left(\frac{1}{r} \frac{dV}{dr} \right) \boldsymbol{\ell} \cdot \mathbf{s} \tag{10-12}$$

This formula is obtained from the Dirac theory. For several electrons this becomes

$$H_{so} = \frac{1}{2m^2 c^2} \sum_i \left(\frac{1}{r} \frac{dV}{dr} \right)_i \boldsymbol{\ell}_i \cdot \mathbf{s}_i \tag{10-13}$$

As long as the spin-orbit interaction is much smaller than the level separation of the various terms, i.e., much smaller than the electrostatic interaction, we can consider (10-13) as a perturbation and evaluate its diagonal elements in a scheme labeled by SLJM, even though **S** and **L** no longer commute with the Hamiltonian. **J** and J_Z of course are still constants of motion. Accordingly the energy states are described by L and S and then for a given LS further splitting occurs corresponding to different resultant J.

We evaluate

$$\int \frac{1}{r} \frac{dV}{dr} \mathcal{R}^2_{n\ell} \, dr = \xi_{n\ell} \tag{10-14}$$

Since dV/dr may be written $Z(r)e^2/r^2$, where Z(r)e is the charge inside a sphere of radius r,

$$\xi_{n\ell} = \left\langle \frac{Z(r)e^2}{r^3} \right\rangle > 0 \tag{10-15}$$

Equation (10-13) is then rewritten as

$$H_{so} = \frac{1}{2m^2 c^2} \sum_i \xi_{n_i \ell_i} \boldsymbol{\ell}_i \cdot \mathbf{s}_i \tag{10-16}$$

When i runs over electrons lying in the same shell, $\xi_{n_i \ell_i}$ does not depend on i. Moreover $\Sigma_i \boldsymbol{\ell}_i \cdot \mathbf{s}_i = 0$ for complete shells. Hence we need only to consider electrons in incomplete shells.

A THEOREM ON MATRIX ELEMENTS

We shall now sketch the proof of a theorem about operators which will permit us to evaluate (10-16), and which is generally important in the quantum mechanical treatment of atoms. We consider any operator **A** which satisfies the commutation relations

$$[A_\alpha, J_\beta] = [J_\alpha, A_\beta] = iA_\gamma \qquad [A_\alpha, J_\alpha] = 0 \tag{10-17}$$

where α, β, γ are cyclic permutations of x, y, z.

There are many operators which satisfy the commutation relations (10-17). The most important type for us is that of an angular momentum **J**, which is the sum of mutually commuting components,

$$\mathbf{J} = \mathbf{J}_1 + \cdots + \mathbf{J}_n \tag{10-18}$$

Then each $\mathbf{J}_i$ may be substituted for **A** in (10-17). This follows from the fact that the components of $\mathbf{J}_i$ satisfy

$$[J_{i\alpha}, J_{i\beta}] = iJ_{i\gamma} \tag{10-19}$$

since $\mathbf{J}_i$ is an angular momentum; and that $J_{i\alpha}$ commutes with $J_{k\beta}$ for $k \neq i$. In particular we shall use the theorem to be derived for $\boldsymbol{\ell}_i$ and $\mathbf{s}_i$ occurring in (10-16): We know that

$$\mathbf{L} = \sum_i \boldsymbol{\ell}_i \qquad \mathbf{S} = \sum_i \mathbf{s}_i \tag{10-20}$$

Then we may choose any $\boldsymbol{\ell}_i$ to be **A** in (10-17) if we identify **L** with **J**, and similarly for $\mathbf{s}_i$ and **S**.

However, A in (10-17) may also be the position vector of an electron and **J** its orbital momentum. Or **J** may be the sum of the orbital momenta of all electrons, or the total angular momentum of the atom, with **A** being either the position vector of one electron, or the sum of the position vectors of all electrons, or the sum of their linear momenta. In this form, the theorem will be applicable to the calculation of optical transition probabilities.

We take matrix elements of (10-17) with respect to states in which J^2 and $J_z = M$ are diagonal, in particular elements leading from a state J to another state with the same J. We indicate that there may be other quantum numbers λ (such as the energy) which may be different in initial and final state:

$$\langle \lambda' JM' | [A_\alpha, J_\beta] | \lambda JM \rangle = i \langle \lambda' JM' | A_\gamma | \lambda JM \rangle \qquad (10\text{-}21)$$

We assume that **J** commutes with whatever variables are represented in λ, e.g., the Hamiltonian, so that J_β has only matrix elements diagonal in λ; and furthermore that these do not depend on λ but only on J and M. Then (10-21) becomes

$$\sum_{M''} \langle \lambda' JM' | A_\alpha | \lambda JM'' \rangle \langle JM'' | J_\beta | JM \rangle - \sum_{M'''} \langle JM' | J_\beta | JM''' \rangle \langle \lambda' JM''' | A_\alpha | \lambda JM \rangle = i \langle \lambda' JM' | A_\gamma | \lambda JM \rangle \qquad (10\text{-}22)$$

Let us first use (10-22) with $\beta = z$, and $A_\alpha = A_x + iA_y$. Then only $M'' = M$, $M''' = M'$ contribute and, from (10-17), $A_\gamma = iA_\alpha$, so that

$$\langle \lambda' JM' | A_x + iA_y | \lambda JM \rangle (M - M') = -\langle \lambda' JM' | A_x + iA_y | \lambda JM \rangle \qquad (10\text{-}23)$$

Therefore $M' = M + 1$, as might be expected. Next we keep the same A_α but replace J_β by $J_x + iJ_y$. Then (10-17) gives

$$[A_x + iA_y, J_x + iJ_y] = A_z - A_z = 0$$

In (10-22) we have $M'' = M''' = M + 1$ and $M' = M + 2$, so that

$$\langle \lambda' J, M+2 | A_x + iA_y | \lambda J, M+1 \rangle \langle J, M+1 | J_x + iJ_y | JM \rangle - \langle \lambda' J, M+1 | A_x + iA_y | \lambda J, M \rangle \langle J, M+2 | J_x + iJ_y | J, M+1 \rangle = 0 \qquad (10\text{-}24)$$

This can be fulfilled for all M only if

$$\langle \lambda' J, M+1 | A_x + iA_y | \lambda JM \rangle = K(\lambda' \lambda J) \langle J, M+1 | J_x + iJ_y | JM \rangle \qquad (10\text{-}25)$$

where K is a constant independent of M but depending on the initial and final states, $\lambda\lambda'$ and J. Thus we have reduced the matrix element of $A_x + iA_y$ to those of $J_x + iJ_y$, which we know.

Next we take still the same A_α but set $J_\beta = J_x - iJ_y$. Then (10-17) gives

$$[A_x + iA_y, J_x - iJ_y] = 2A_z \tag{10-26}$$

Inserting (10-25), and remembering that (10-26) is also true if **A** is replaced by **J**, we find

$$\langle \lambda' JM' | A_z | \lambda JM \rangle = K(\lambda'\lambda J) \langle JM' | J_z | JM \rangle \tag{10-27}$$

A similar argument gives the corresponding relation for $A_x - iA_y$. Hence we have shown that

$$\langle \lambda' JM' | A_\alpha | \lambda JM \rangle = K(\lambda\lambda' J) \langle JM' | J_\alpha | JM \rangle \tag{10-28}$$

for *any* component α. In other words, *the matrix components of the* **A** *vector between states of the same* J *are proportional to the corresponding matrix components of the* **J** *vector.* This is the theorem we wished to prove. Of course it also holds for diagonal elements.

A simple corollary of (10-28) is

$$\langle \lambda' JM' | \mathbf{A} \cdot \mathbf{J} | \lambda JM \rangle = K(\lambda\lambda' J) \langle JM' | J^2_{op} | JM \rangle$$

$$= \delta(M,M') K(\lambda\lambda' J) J(J + 1) \tag{10-29}$$

Thus the scalar product $\mathbf{A} \cdot \mathbf{J}$ is diagonal in M. Frequently, $\mathbf{A} \cdot \mathbf{J}$ is easier to calculate than any component of **A**, and this then serves to determine the constant $K(\lambda\lambda' J)$.

Dirac has proved a more general theorem which permits us to calculate matrix elements of a vector of type **A**, i.e., satisfying (10-17), between states of different J. Some intricate algebra (see Condon and Shortley, pp. 59–73, and Slater, Vol. II, Appendix 31) yields the result

$$[J^2, [J^2, \mathbf{A}]] = 2(J^2\mathbf{A} + \mathbf{A}J^2) - 4(\mathbf{A} \cdot \mathbf{J})\mathbf{J} \tag{10-30}$$

Taking matrix elements between states of the same J, the theorem (10-28) can be recovered. Taking matrix components of (10-30) between states JM; J′M′; J ≠ J′, the last term on the right will be zero since **J** does not have elements between different J values. A little algebra yields

$$[(J + J' + 1)^2 - 1][(J - J')^2 - 1]$$
$$\times \langle \lambda' J'M' | \mathbf{A} | \lambda JM \rangle = 0 \tag{10-31}$$

Hence **A** has nonzero matrix elements only for $J' = J,\ J \pm 1$. Since A_Z commutes with J_Z, A_Z has nonzero matrix elements only for $M = M'$. The elements of **A** are given in Condon and Shortley. We shall use them in Chapter 14.

If $\mathbf{J} = \mathbf{L} + \mathbf{S}$ we see that L and S each satisfy (10-17), hence (10-22). In this case (10-28) and (10-29) give the old vector-model result that the time average of **L** (or **S**) can be replaced by its component along **J**, which is $[(\mathbf{L}\cdot\mathbf{J})\mathbf{J}]/\mathbf{J}^2$, since, in the time average, the perpendicular component cancels out, owing to the "precession" of **L** (or **S**) about **J**.

EVALUATION OF SPIN-ORBIT INTERACTION

Returning now to (10-16) and identifying **J** with **L** (**S**) and **A** with $\boldsymbol{\ell}_i$ ($\mathbf{s}_i$), where $\mathbf{L} = \Sigma_i \boldsymbol{\ell}_i$ ($\mathbf{S} = \Sigma_i \mathbf{s}_i$), we see that $\boldsymbol{\ell}_i$ ($\mathbf{s}_i$) satisfies (10-17). Hence, for the matrix elements of $\boldsymbol{\ell}_i$ ($\mathbf{s}_i$) which are diagonal in LS we have from (10-28)

$$\boldsymbol{\ell}_i = \alpha(i)\,\mathbf{L} \qquad \mathbf{s}_i = \beta(i)\,\mathbf{S} \tag{10-32}$$

where the $\alpha(i)$, $\beta(i)$ are certain constants depending on the multiplet LS. Then (10-16) is replaced by

$$\begin{aligned}\langle \lambda LSM'_L M'_S \mid H_{so} \mid \lambda LSM_L M_S \rangle &= \frac{1}{2m^2c^2}\left(\sum_i \xi_{n_i\ell_i}\,\alpha(i)\,\beta(i)\right)\\ &\quad \times \langle LSM'_L M'_S \mid \mathbf{L}\cdot\mathbf{S} \mid LSM_L M_S \rangle\end{aligned} \tag{10-33}$$

We can now diagonalize the last factor by going from the $M_L M_S$ representation to the JM representation, making use of the fact that

$$2\mathbf{L}\cdot\mathbf{S} = (J^2 - L^2 - S^2)_{op} \tag{10-34}$$

L^2_{op} and S^2_{op} remain quantized, but $L_z = \hbar M_L$ and $S_z = \hbar M_S$ no longer are. If we further assume that only the shell $n\ell$ is incomplete, we get

$$\begin{aligned}H_{so} &= \frac{1}{4}\left(\frac{\hbar}{mc}\right)^2 \xi_{n\ell}\,\gamma_{LS}\\ &\quad \times [J(J+1) - L(L+1) - S(S+1)]\end{aligned} \tag{10-35}$$

where

$$\gamma_{LS} = \sum_i \alpha(i)\beta(i) \tag{10-36}$$

is a numerical coefficient which can be calculated if the wave function of the $LSM_L M_S$ state is known in terms of the $m_{\ell i} m_{si}$ representation.

As the only J dependence of H_{so} is through the term in brackets, we can form the difference

$$H_{so}(J) - H_{so}(J-1) = \left(\frac{1}{2}\frac{\hbar}{mc}\right)^2 \xi_{n\ell}\gamma_{LS}\, 2J \tag{10-37}$$

This is *Landé's interval rule,* which states that the separation of two J states belonging to the same LS is proportional to the larger value of J.

Let us consider k electrons in the $n\ell$ shell with $k \leq 2\ell + 1$. We assume maximum S, i.e., all $m_{si} = \frac{1}{2}$, but L is arbitrary. In (10-16) the diagonal elements arise only from s_{kz}, since s_{kz} and s_{ky} have no diagonal elements. Thus (10-16) can be written

$$\begin{aligned} H_{so} &= \frac{\hbar^2}{2m^2c^2}\,\xi_{n\ell}\sum_k m_{\ell k} m_{sk} \\ &= \frac{\hbar^2}{4m^2c^2}\,\xi_{n\ell}\sum_k m_{\ell k} \\ &= \frac{\hbar^2}{4m^2c^2}\,\xi_{n\ell} M_L \end{aligned} \tag{10-38}$$

Also the diagonal elements of $\mathbf{L}\cdot\mathbf{S}$ equal $\hbar^2 M_L M_S = \hbar^2 M_L S$.

$$\frac{\hbar^2}{4m^2c^2}\,\xi_{n\ell} M_L = \frac{\hbar^2}{2m^2c^2}\,\xi_{n\ell}\gamma_{LS} M_L S$$

or

$$\gamma_{LS} = \frac{1}{2S} \qquad \text{(highest S)} \tag{10-39}$$

Assuming $\xi_{n\ell}$ known, we can calculate H_{so} from (10-35). For lower multiplicities we can use the sum rule as in the electrostatic case and work in the $\ell_k m_{\ell k} m_{sk}$ representation.

For more than half-full shells the following argument is useful. We can write

$$\sum_k \boldsymbol{\ell}_k \cdot \mathbf{s}_k = \left(\sum_{\substack{\text{whole} \\ \text{shell}}} - \sum_{\substack{\text{empty} \\ \text{states}}} \right) \boldsymbol{\ell}_k \cdot \mathbf{s}_k$$

$$= - \sum_{\substack{\text{empty} \\ \text{states}}} \boldsymbol{\ell}_k \cdot \mathbf{s}_k \qquad (10\text{-}40)$$

Hence the spin-orbit energies for a configuration of $4\ell + 2 - k$ electrons are negatives of those for a configuration of k electrons. In particular, for more than half-filled shells,

$$\gamma_{LS} = -\frac{1}{2S} \qquad \text{(highest S)} \qquad (10\text{-}41)$$

If $\gamma_{LS} > 0$, highest energies correspond to highest J; if $\gamma_{LS} < 0$, the reverse is true. The former is called a *regular multiplet*, the latter an *inverted multiplet*. For less than $2\ell + 1$ electrons in the shell, most multiplets are regular, but there are some exceptions, e.g., the ^2F state arising from a d^3 configuration, which has $\gamma_{LS} = -\frac{1}{6}$. For more than half-filled shells, most (but not all) multiplets are inverted. The following rule is only true for regular multiplets, i.e., less than half-filled shells. To obtain the lowest energy, take the highest S, then take the highest L, and finally the lowest J.

For exactly half-filled shells there is no first-order spin-orbit interaction, since a half-filled shell can be viewed two ways, either as $2\ell + 1$ electrons or $2\ell + 1$ holes. The energies of these two cases by (10-40) must be equal in magnitude and opposite in sign. Hence the energy vanishes. The state of highest multiplicity in a half-filled shell has $L = 0$, so no spin-orbit splitting occurs. To obtain the spin-orbit energy for other multiplets for half-filled shells we must use second-order perturbation theory.

H_{so} is of the order $10^{-4}\, \xi_{n\ell}\, \gamma_{LS}$, as can be seen from (10-37). For the Fe group 3d electrons $(\hbar/2mc)^2 \xi_{n\ell}$ is found to be 50 to 1000 cm^{-1}, the value increasing from the beginning to the end of the shell. We recall that the configuration energies were usually of the order of 10^5 cm^{-1}; the electrostatic interaction, 10^4 cm^{-1}; the spin orbit term now is of order 10^2 cm^{-1}; and the effect of an external magnetic field, 1 cm^{-1}. Hence our assumptions about quantum numbers are usually correct.

However, it may happen that the spin-orbit interaction is much larger than the electrostatic interaction. This occurs in X-ray spectra. (Although comparatively rare in atomic theory, in nuclear theory this is quite common.) Each electron is then characterized by $n\ell jm$ rather than $n\ell m_\ell m_s$. A configuration $(n\ell)^k$ then splits up first into subconfigurations, characterized by the number k_1 of electrons having $j = \ell + \frac{1}{2}$; this may be written $(n\ell, \ell + \frac{1}{2})^{k_1}(n\ell, \ell - \frac{1}{2})^{k-k_1}$. The electrostatic energy then splits each subconfiguration into states of different J, with

$$\mathbf{J} = \sum_i \mathbf{j}_i \tag{10-42}$$

This is called jj coupling. The calculation of electrostatic energy is more complicated than for LS coupling and is treated in Condon and Shortley. They also treat the case of intermediate coupling when spin-orbit and electrostatic interaction are of the same order of magnitude. In either case, L and S are no longer good quantum numbers but J is.

ZEEMAN EFFECT

The interaction of an electron with a homogenous magnetic field $\mathcal{H}$ along the z axis is given by

$$H_z = -\frac{e\mathcal{H}}{2mc}(L_z + 2S_z) \tag{10-43}$$

The total Hamiltonian commutes with J_z but not with J^2. Since we now have an externally defined orientation in space, we do not expect the Hamiltonian to be invariant under rotations. The quantity $e\hbar/2mc$ is called the Bohr magneton μ_0 and is equal to 9×10^{-21} cgs units. When the field is sufficiently weak so that the effects are small, we can consider (10-43) as a perturbation in the SLJM scheme. We need to evaluate the diagonal elements $\langle JM | L_z + 2S_z | JM \rangle$. Writing this as $\langle JM | J_z + S_z | JM \rangle$ we apply (10-28) and (10-29) to get

$$S_z = K J_z \tag{10-44}$$

where

$$K = \frac{J(J+1) - L(L+1) + S(S+1)}{2J(J+1)} \tag{10-45}$$

Therefore,

$$H_z = -\frac{e}{2mc}\mathcal{H}\langle JM | J_z | JM \rangle (1 + K)$$

$$= -\mu_0 M \mathcal{H} g \tag{10-46}$$

where

$$g = 1 + K = 1 + \frac{J(J+1) - L(L+1) + S(S+1)}{2J(J+1)} \tag{10-47}$$

g is the Landé g factor.

$$g = \frac{3}{2} + \frac{(S - L)(S + L + 1)}{2J(J+1)} \tag{10-48}$$

$$\begin{aligned} &L = 0,\ J = S:\ g = 2 && J = L + S:\ g = 1 + \frac{S}{J} \\ &J = L - S:\ g = 1 - \frac{S}{J+1} && J = S - L:\ g = 1 + \frac{S+1}{J+1} \end{aligned} \tag{10-49}$$

For one-electron spectra

$$\begin{aligned} &J = L + \tfrac{1}{2}:\ g = 1 + \frac{1}{2L+1} \\ &J = L - \tfrac{1}{2}:\ g = 1 - \frac{1}{2L+1} \end{aligned} \tag{10-50}$$

The splitting of the spectral lines will be given by

$$\hbar\omega = \hbar\omega_0 - \mathcal{H}\mu_0\left[g_i M_i - g_f M_f\right] \tag{10-51}$$

where $\hbar\omega_0$ is the energy without magnetic field, and i and f refer to initial and final states, respectively.

PASCHEN-BACK EFFECT

If the field is sufficiently strong, the Zeeman term in the Hamiltonian may dominate the spin-orbit interaction. This is known as the Paschen-Back effect. In this case we can consider the entire magnetic interaction $H_{SO} + H_Z$ as a perturbation in the $LM_L SM_S$ scheme. The diagonal matrix elements now become

$$H_{mag} = \frac{1}{2}\left(\frac{\hbar}{mc}\right)^2 \xi_{n\ell}\gamma_{LS} M_L M_S - \mu_0\mathcal{H}(M_L + 2M_S) \tag{10-52}$$

In first order M_S cannot change in a transition, and M_L can change only by ± 1 or 0. The spectral line splitting is given by

$$E_i - E_f = \hbar\omega_0 - \mu_0 \mathcal{H}\left(M_{L_i} - M_{L_f}\right) + \frac{M_S}{2}\left(\frac{\hbar}{mc}\right)^2 \times \left(\xi_{n\ell_i}\gamma_{LS_i} M_{L_i} - \xi_{n\ell_f}\gamma_{LS_f} M_{L_f}\right) \tag{10-53}$$

where $\hbar\omega_0$ is the energy change without magnetic effects. The main splitting is, by assumption, given by the term with $\mathcal{H}$, which gives simply the Lorentz triplet, $M_{L_i} - M_{L_f} = +1, 0$, and -1. The last term gives the spin-orbit interaction. For $\Delta M_L = 0$, this becomes

$$\Delta E = \hbar\omega_0 + \frac{M_S}{2}\left(\frac{\hbar}{mc}\right)^2 \xi_{n\ell} M_L \left(\gamma_{LS_i} - \gamma_{LS_f}\right) \tag{10-54}$$

This gives a splitting into $(2L + 1)(2S + 1)$ components. If L is known simple counting of the components will determine the spin S. The nuclear spin of Bi^{209} was determined this way and found to be $\frac{9}{2}$.

For intermediate magnetic field strength, the interaction with the external field and the spin-orbit interaction become comparable. In this case, the secular equation has to be solved explicitly for the energy. M is still a good quantum number but neither M_L, M_S, nor J are. In the case $S = \frac{1}{2}$ (e.g., alkali atoms), there are two values of M_S, $+\frac{1}{2}$ and $-\frac{1}{2}$, for each value of M, except for $M = \pm(L + \frac{1}{2})$. For $M = L + \frac{1}{2}$ we must have $M_S = \frac{1}{2}$, and (10-52) is exact at all values of the field strength. For other M, the lower energy value in the limit of high field, (10-52), is given by $M_S = \frac{1}{2}$, $M_L = M - \frac{1}{2}$. In the limit of low field, and for a regular doublet, the level $J = L - \frac{1}{2}$ has the lower energy. Thus the state $J = L - \frac{1}{2}$, M at low field goes over into the state $M_S = +\frac{1}{2}$, M at high field, and $J = L + \frac{1}{2}$, M into $M_S = -\frac{1}{2}$, M. This transition can easily be followed in detail by explicit solution of the eigenvalue problem for intermediate fields (Schiff, p. 295).

QUADRATIC ZEEMAN EFFECT

For very strong magnetic fields and large values of n (corresponding to large $\langle r^2 \rangle$) the quadratic term in (10-3) may become important Since the magnitude of the spin-orbit interaction is characterized by $\xi_{n\ell} \sim \langle 1/r^3 \rangle \sim 1/n^3$ for large n, we can neglect it. In this case, electron spin becomes a constant of the motion and can be ignored in the discussion. With these approximations the entire magnetic interaction is given by

$$-\frac{e}{2mc}\mathcal{H}\ell_z + \frac{e^2}{8mc^2}\mathcal{H}^2 r^2 \sin^2\theta \tag{10-55}$$

θ being the angle between the radius vector and the z axis. We ha[ve] seen that the effect of the first term is to displace the energy by $m_\ell g_m \hbar \mathcal{H}$. Thus the problem of evaluating the quadratic Zeeman effect (for one electron) reduces to evaluating the effect of the perturbation $(e^2/8mc^2)\mathcal{H}^2 r^2 \sin^2\theta$. [For many electrons the perturbation is $(e^2/8mc^2)\mathcal{H}^2 \Sigma_i r_i^2 \sin^2\theta_i$.] Methods for doing this are discussed by Schiff, pp. 296–298. We shall not pursue the general problem any further.

The diamagnetism of atoms receives its explanation from the quadratic Zeeman effect. In particular, for noble gases L_z and $S_z = 0$, and our approximations become exact. The only magnetic effect is the quadratic Zeeman effect, since there even is no shift in levels with magnetic quantum number. Then for helium, for example,

$$\Delta E = \frac{e^2\mathcal{H}^2}{8mc^2}\langle r_1^2 \sin^2\theta_1 + r_2^2 \sin^2\theta_2\rangle \tag{10-56}$$

Using Hartree's wave functions, which are symmetric in r_1 and r_2 and are spherically symmetric, we obtain

$$\Delta E = 1.05 \times 10^{-5}\,\mathcal{H}^2 \qquad \text{(atomic units)} \tag{10-57}$$

The magnetic susceptibility per mole χ is defined by

$$N_0\,\Delta E = -\tfrac{1}{2}\chi\mathcal{H}^2 \tag{10-58}$$

where N_0 is Avogadro's number. Inserting (10-57) we obtain $\chi = -1.87 \times 10^{-6}$. The measured value of the magnetic susceptibility for helium is $\chi = -1.88 \times 10^{-6}$. The agreement is excellent.

For heavier noble gases available wave functions are less good, so the theory cannot be checked to this accuracy. The term in $\mathcal{H}^2$ is also responsible for the diamagnetism of diatomic molecules. For atoms with a resultant $J \neq 0$, the $\mathcal{H}^2$ term gives a diamagnetic contribution to the susceptibility χ which subtracts from the dominant, paramagnetic contribution.

STARK EFFECT

When an atom is placed in an external electric field the Hamiltonian has a term

$$H_F = -eFz = -eF\sum_k z_k \tag{10-59}$$

added to it, where F is the external field, assumed constant and pointing along the z axis (electron charge taken to be +e). Since

(10-59) is an odd operator, its diagonal elements will vanish because of the definite parity of the eigenfunctions. Therefore the first-order perturbation is always 0. An exception exists for the excited states of hydrogen. Owing to the accidental ℓ degeneracy, linear combinations of the $n\ell$ wave functions can be taken, which no longer possess definite parity and give a nonzero result for the Stark effect (Schiff, p. 158).

In general, however, we must go to second-order perturbation theory. The shift in energy ΔE_a will be given by

$$\Delta E_a = \sum_b{}' \frac{|H_F{}_{ab}|^2}{E_a - E_b} = e^2 F^2 \sum_b{}' \frac{|z_{ab}|^2}{E_a - E_b} \tag{10-60}$$

where the prime in the sum sign indicates that the state $b = a$ is omitted in the sum. This is called the quadratic Stark effect. For a many-electron atom, the results will depend on the mode of angular momentum coupling. We can nevertheless say some general things about (10-60).

Equation (10-60) holds only with the usual stipulation that the energy shift must be small compared to the energy separation of the unperturbed levels. z_{ab} will be nonzero only between states of opposite parity. Since z is the z component of the displacement operator $\mathbf{R}$ which satisfies (10-17), the theorem (10-31) will hold, and z will have nonzero elements only for $J_b = J_a$, $J_a \pm 1$, and $M_a = M_b$. In the case of LS coupling, L is a good quantum number; then the theorem (10-31) holds also for L and we must have $L_b = L_a$, $L_a \pm 1$. In this case, of course, $S_b = S_a$, since z does not depend on S.

Let us calculate the pattern observed in a state described by quantum numbers αJM, where α stands for a whole collection of quantum numbers such that αJM is a complete commuting set of observables. Therefore z_{ab} is nonvanishing only in the following three instances:

$$\begin{aligned}
\langle \alpha JM \,|\, z \,|\, \alpha' J-1M \rangle &= A(J,\alpha,\alpha')\sqrt{J^2 - M^2} \\
\langle \alpha JM \,|\, z \,|\, \alpha' JM \rangle &= B(J,\alpha,\alpha') M \\
\langle \alpha JM \,|\, z \,|\, \alpha' J+1M \rangle &= C(J,\alpha,\alpha')\sqrt{J+1)^2 - M^2}
\end{aligned} \tag{10-61}$$

where A, B, and C are some functions of J, α, and α'. The JJ element follows from (10-27) and the off-diagonal elements from formulas given in Condon and Shortley. Equation (10-60) now reads

$$\Delta E_a = e^2 F^2 \left[\left(\sum_{\alpha'}{}' \frac{|A(J\alpha\alpha')|^2}{E_{\alpha J} - E_{\alpha' J-1}} \right) (J^2 - M^2) \right.$$

$$+ \left(\sum_{\alpha'}{}' \frac{|B(J\alpha\alpha')|^2}{E_{\alpha J} - E_{\alpha' J}} \right) (M^2)$$

$$\left. + \left(\sum_{\alpha'}{}' \frac{|C(J\alpha\alpha')|^2}{E_{\alpha J} - E_{\alpha' J+1}} \right) ((J+1)^2 - M^2) \right]$$

$$= F^2(R - TM^2) \qquad (10\text{-}62)$$

Hence we see that the quadratic Stark effect does not depend on the sign of M. This is because the electric field acts on the charge-probability density, which does not depend on the sign of M.

The ground-state Stark effect will always be negative, this being the general characteristic of any second-order perturbation effect on the lowest state.

For sufficiently excited states any atomic configuration becomes hydrogenic. Then $z \sim n^2$ and $1/(E_a - E_b)$ certainly has a n^3 dependence (see p. 29). Therefore $\Delta E \sim n^7$, and the perturbation treatment no longer applies. Foster (1928) has shown that for very large n the Stark effect is linear in F.

For extremely high electric fields the Stark effect is capable of ionizing the atom. Looking at the one-electron potential energy $-(Ze^2/r) - eFz$ we see that the atomic center is not the only place where the potential is at a relative minimum. In the direction of the negative z, i.e., of the anode, the magnitude of the term $-eFz$ will eventually make the potential even lower than in the atom. It is a well-known quantum mechanical result that whenever two potential troughs exist, an electron can pass from one trough (atom) to the other (anode) by the tunnel effect. Furthermore, once the electron has passed through the potential barrier it will be accelerated to the anode and the atom will be left ionized.

Chapter 11

MOLECULES

The quantum mechanical treatment of molecules is much more complex than that of atoms. The electrons move in a field which can no longer be considered spherically symmetric since there are two or more nuclei acting as sources of the field. The one simplifying feature, which allows for separate calculation of the energy associated with nuclear motion and of the energy of electronic motion, is due to the large ratio of nuclear mass to electron mass. This leads, as we shall see below, to the result that the kinetic energy of the nuclei, E_n, is much smaller than the kinetic energy of the electrons, E_ϵ (Born and Oppenheimer, 1927). Since period of motion is of the order of $\hbar$ divided by energy, the nuclear periods are much larger than the electron periods. Hence it is expected that to a good approximation the nuclei can be considered fixed in calculating electron motion. The nuclear motion is calculated with the approximation that the motion can be classified into translations, vibrations, and rotations of the nuclei.

If R is a molecular dimension, then

$$E_e \sim \frac{\hbar^2}{mR^2} \sim \text{several ev} \tag{11-1}$$

where m is the electronic mass. This follows from the uncertainty principle, which requires a momentum $\hbar/R$ to fix the electron in a distance R.

The translational motion of the system as a whole is the same as that of a free particle. As this has no nonclassical features we shall not consider it any further.

The vibrational energy, E_v, for a fairly low mode of vibration is $\hbar(K_0/M)^{1/2}(v + \frac{1}{2})$, where M is the molecular mass, K_0 is an appropriate stiffness constant, and v is the vibrational quantum number.

One can estimate K_0 by noting that the displacement in a normal mode must be of the order of R if the molecule is to dissociate. The energy of vibration is then about $K_0 R^2$, by definition of the stiffness constant. On the other hand, the energy of dissociation must be of the order of E_e; hence $K_0 R^2 \sim E_e$. Thus the energy difference between two neighboring vibrational levels is about

$$E_v \sim \hbar \left(\frac{E_e}{MR^2} \right)^{1/2} \sim \left(\frac{m}{M} \right)^{1/2} E_e \sim 0.1 \text{ ev} \tag{11-2}$$

m/M is usually in the range 10^{-3} to 10^{-4}.

The rotational energy is calculated from the moment of inertia $\sim MR^2$ of the molecule:

$$E_r \sim \frac{\hbar^2}{MR^2} \sim \frac{m}{M} E_e \sim 0.001 \text{ ev} \tag{11-3}$$

We see that the various energies indeed satisfy the Born-Oppenheimer theory.

The time-independent Schrödinger equation for the molecule is

$$\left[-\frac{\hbar^2}{2m} \sum_{j=1}^{n} \nabla_i^2 - \sum_{j=1}^{N} \frac{\hbar^2}{2M_j} \nabla_j^2 + V(\mathbf{R}_1, \ldots, \mathbf{R}_N; \mathbf{r}_1, \ldots, \mathbf{r}_n) - E \right] \times \Psi(\mathbf{R}_1, \ldots, \mathbf{R}_N; \mathbf{r}_1, \ldots, \mathbf{r}_n) = 0 \tag{11-4}$$

where the R's and M's refer to the positions and masses of the nuclei and the lower-case letters refer to electronic coordinates and masses. The kinetic energy of nuclear motion is of the order m/M and can be neglected according to the Born-Oppenheimer approximation. Then, in the remaining equation, the wave function Ψ depends on the (fixed) $\mathbf{R}_i$'s only parametrically. Therefore Ψ is approximated by

$$\Psi(\mathbf{r}_i, \mathbf{R}_j) = u_{\mathbf{R}_j}(\mathbf{r}_i) w(\mathbf{R}_j) \tag{11-5}$$

The u's satisfy the equation

$$\left[-\frac{\hbar^2}{2m} \sum_i \nabla_i^2 + V(\mathbf{R}_j, \mathbf{r}_i) \right] u_{\mathbf{R}_j}(\mathbf{r}_i) = U(\mathbf{R}_j) u_{\mathbf{R}_j}(\mathbf{r}_i) \tag{11-6}$$

(The symbols $\mathbf{R}_j$ and $\mathbf{r}_i$ are abbreviations for the complete sets $\mathbf{R}_1, \ldots, \mathbf{R}_N$; and $\mathbf{r}_1, \ldots, \mathbf{r}_n$.) That is, to each arrangement of the nuclei indexed by $\mathbf{R}_j$, there corresponds an electron distribution

$|u_{\mathbf{R}_j}(\mathbf{r}_i)|^2$ with energy $U(\mathbf{R}_j)$. Substituting (11-5) in (11-4) gives, with the aid of (11-6) and some algebra,

$$u_{\mathbf{R}_j}(\mathbf{r}_i)\left[-\frac{\hbar^2}{2}\sum_j \frac{1}{M_j}\nabla_j^2 + U(R_j) - E\right] w(R_j)$$

$$= \frac{\hbar^2}{2}\sum_j \frac{1}{M_j}\left[w(\mathbf{R}_j)\nabla_j^2 u_{\mathbf{R}_j}(\mathbf{r}_i) + 2\left(\boldsymbol{\nabla}_j w(\mathbf{R}_j)\right)\cdot\left(\boldsymbol{\nabla}_j u_{\mathbf{R}_j}(\mathbf{r}_i)\right)\right] \tag{11-7}$$

If we assume that $u_{\mathbf{R}_j}(\mathbf{r}_i)$ is real, multiply both sides of (11-7) by $u_{\mathbf{R}_j}(\mathbf{r}_i)$, and integrate over $d\tau_i$, the left-hand side contains the factor $\int u^2_{\mathbf{R}_j}(\mathbf{r}_i)\, d\tau_i = 1$. The second term on the right-hand side is proportional to

$$\boldsymbol{\nabla}_j w(\mathbf{R}_j)\cdot\boldsymbol{\nabla}_j \int u^2_{\mathbf{R}_j}(\mathbf{r}_i)\, d\tau_i = \boldsymbol{\nabla}_j w(\mathbf{R}_j)\cdot\boldsymbol{\nabla}_j(1) = 0$$

The first term on the right-hand side involves

$$\int u_{\mathbf{R}_j}(\mathbf{r}_i)\nabla_j^2 u_{\mathbf{R}_j}(\mathbf{r}_i)\, d\tau_i$$

$$= \tfrac{1}{2}\nabla_j^2 \int u^2_{\mathbf{R}_j}(\mathbf{r}_i)\, d\tau_i - \int\left(\nabla_j u_{\mathbf{R}_j}(\mathbf{r}_i)\right)^2 d\tau_i$$

$$= -\int\left[\nabla_j u_{\mathbf{R}_j}(\mathbf{r}_i)\right]^2 d\tau_i$$

Hence (11-7) can be written

$$\left[-\sum_{j=1}^{N}\frac{\hbar^2}{2M_j}\nabla_j^2 + U(\mathbf{R}_j) + W(\mathbf{R}_j)\right] w(\mathbf{R}_j) = Ew(\mathbf{R}_j) \tag{11-8}$$

where

$$W(R_j) = \sum_{j=1}^{N}\frac{\hbar^2}{2M_j}\int\left(\nabla_j u_{\mathbf{R}_j}(\mathbf{r}_i)\right)^2 d\tau_i \tag{11-9}$$

Equation (11-9) can be evaluated and gives a small correction to the molecular motion potential $U(\mathbf{R}_j)$. More important is the approximation we made of considering only the projection of (11-7) on $u_{\mathbf{R}_j}(\mathbf{r}_i)$.

In an exact solution, it would be necessary to fulfill (11-7) for all R_j and r_i. Born and Oppenheimer have shown that, owing to the smallness of the amplitudes of the nuclear motion in comparison with the equilibrium internuclear distances, the correction terms arising from this can be neglected as long as high vibrational and rotational modes are not excited.

HYDROGEN MOLECULE

As an example, we outline an approximate treatment of the hydrogen molecule. The only nuclear coordinate that occurs in the electronic equation is R, the magnitude of the internucleon distance. The Hamiltonian occurring in (11-6) is

$$-\frac{\hbar^2}{2m}\left[\nabla_1^2 + \nabla_2^2\right] + e^2\left[\frac{1}{R} + \frac{1}{r_{12}} - \frac{1}{r_{1A}} - \frac{1}{r_{2A}} - \frac{1}{r_{1B}} - \frac{1}{r_{2B}}\right] \qquad (11\text{-}10)$$

A, B refer to the two nuclei, 1, 2 to the two electrons. We apply the unsymmetric perturbation theory as developed in Chapter 4.

$$H_a^0 = -\frac{\hbar^2}{2m}\left[\nabla_1^2 + \nabla_2^2\right] - e^2\left[\frac{1}{r_{1A}} + \frac{1}{r_{2B}}\right]$$

$$\lambda H_a^1 = e^2\left[\frac{1}{r_{12}} - \frac{1}{r_{1B}} - \frac{1}{r_{2A}} + \frac{1}{R}\right]$$

$$U_a^0 = u_A(\mathbf{r}_{1A})u_B(\mathbf{r}_{2B})$$

$$H_b^0 = -\frac{\hbar^2}{2m}\left[\nabla_1^2 + \nabla_2^2\right] - e^2\left[\frac{1}{r_{1B}} + \frac{1}{r_{2A}}\right]$$

$$\lambda H_b^1 = e^2\left[\frac{1}{r_{12}} - \frac{1}{r_{1A}} - \frac{1}{r_{2B}} + \frac{1}{R}\right]$$

$$U_b^0 = u_A(\mathbf{r}_{1B})u_B(\mathbf{r}_{2A})$$

$$E^0 = -\frac{e^2}{2a_0}\left[\frac{1}{n_A^2} + \frac{1}{n_B^2}\right] \qquad (11\text{-}11)$$

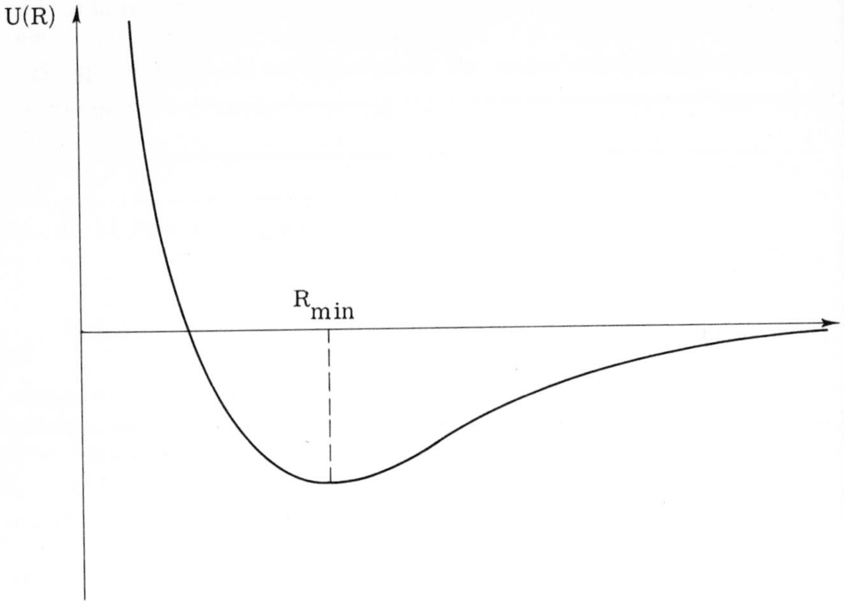

Figure 11-1
Internucleon potential for the hydrogen molecule.

Then, according to (4-19),

$$E^1(R) = \tfrac{1}{2} \int (U_a^0 \pm U_b^0)^* (H_a^1 U_a^0 \pm H_b^1 U_b^0)\, d\tau$$
$$= \int (U_a^0 \pm U_b^0) H_a^1 U_a^0 \, d\tau \qquad (4\text{-}19)$$

because of symmetry, and

$$U(R) = E^0 + E^1(R) \qquad (11\text{-}12)$$

It happens that the exchange term is negative, therefore the energy is lower for the combination $U_a^0 + U_b^0$ (Bethe, "Handbuch der Physik," 24/1, 536). The result that is found for U(R) is plotted in Figure 11-1.

A knowledge of U(R) gives the equilibrium position of the nuclei, R_{min}. $d^2U/dR^2|_{R_{min}}$ gives the vibration frequency of the nuclei. For the antisymmetric combinations the potential function U(R) is found to be repulsive‡ at all R. Hence we conclude that binding can

‡There is, however, a weak attraction at very large R, owing to

Table 11-1
Theoretical and Experimental Results for the Hydrogen Molecule

	Theory		Experiment
Dissociation energy	3.2 ev	(Heitler, London, Sugiura, 1927)	4.73 ev
	4.69 ev	(James & Coolidge, 1933)	
R_{min}	0.72 A	(James & Coolidge, 1933)	0.74 A
Vibrational frequency	4290 cm^{-1}	(Hylleraas)	4270 cm^{-1}

occur only for the antisymmetric combination of spin-wave functions, which corresponds to $S = 0$ (see p. 12). This is called *homopolar binding* and is frequently described by saying that the electrons must have "opposite spin." Detailed results of calculations are listed in Table 11-1.

DIATOMIC MOLECULES

For general diatomic molecules, with nuclear masses M_1 and M_2, the Schrödinger equation for the relative motion follows from (11-8),

$$\left[-\frac{\hbar^2}{2M}\nabla^2 + U(R)\right] w(R,\theta,\varphi) = Ew(R,\theta,\varphi) \tag{11-13}$$

$M = (M_1 M_2)/(M_1 + M_2)$, and W(R) in (11-8) has been included in U(R). The usual central-force separation is possible:

$$w = \frac{w(R)}{R} Y_{Km}(\Omega)$$

$$\left(-\frac{\hbar^2}{2M}\frac{d^2}{dR^2} + U(R) + \frac{\hbar^2}{2M}\frac{K(K+1)}{R^2}\right) w(R) = Ew(R) \tag{11-14}$$

It has been found that for the lowest electronic states the inter-nucleon potential can be represented quite well by (Morse, 1929)

Van der Waals' forces. These forces, which are described, e.g., in Schiff, pp. 176ff., arise from second-order perturbation theory and hence are not included in our present theory.

$$U(R) = U_0 \left[e^{-2(R-R_0)/a} - 2e^{-(R-R_0)/a} \right] \tag{11-15}$$

Equation (11-14) can be rewritten in terms of the effective one-dimensional potential

$$U'(R) = U(R) + \frac{\hbar^2}{2M} \frac{K(K+1)}{R^2}$$

$U'(R)$ can be expanded about its minimum $U_0' = U'(R_1)$ to give

$$U'(R) = U_0' + \tfrac{1}{2} K_0 (R - R_1)^2 + b(R - R_1)^3 + c(R - R_1)^4 \tag{11-16}$$

The third and fourth terms in (11-16) can be considered to be perturbations of a simple harmonic oscillator. By the usual perturbation method we then obtain to second order in v,

$$E = U_0' + \hbar \left(\frac{K_0}{M} \right)^{1/2} (v + \tfrac{1}{2}) - \frac{\hbar^2 b^2}{MK_0^2} \left[\tfrac{15}{4} (v + \tfrac{1}{2})^2 + \tfrac{7}{16} \right] + \frac{3\hbar^2 c}{2MK_0} \left[(v + \tfrac{1}{2})^2 + \tfrac{1}{4} \right] \tag{11-17}$$

where $v = 0, 1, 2, \ldots$ is the vibrational quantum number.

If $U(R)$ is of the form (11-15)

$$R_1 = R_0 + \frac{\hbar^2 K(K+1) a^2}{2MR_0^3 U_0}$$

$$U_0' = -U_0 + \frac{\hbar^2 K(K+1)}{2MR_0^2} - \frac{\hbar^4 K^2 (K+1)^2 a^2}{4M^2 R_0^6 U_0}$$

$$K_0 = \frac{2U_0}{a^2} - \frac{3\hbar^2 K(K+1)}{MR_0^2 a^2} \frac{a}{R_0} \left(1 - \frac{a}{R_0} \right)$$

$$b = -\frac{U_0}{a^3} \qquad c = \frac{7U_0}{12a^4} \tag{11-18}$$

In (11-18) only enough terms were kept to give E correctly to second order in v and K^2.

The first equation in (11-18) shows that the molecule stretches, owing to rotation. The second equation gives the equilibrium energy $-U_0$ and the rotational energy to second order in K^2. It is seen that first-order rotational energy agrees with that of a rigid rotator. The frequency of vibration, $\omega_0 = (K_0/M)^{1/2}$, is found to decrease with

$M = (M_1 M_2)/(M_1 + M_2)$. For H_2, $\omega_0 \sim 4000\ cm^{-1}$; for HX, where X is an arbitrary, heavier atom, $\omega_0 \sim 3000\ cm^{-1}$; for N_2, $\omega_0 \sim 1000\ cm^{-1}$. It is found that for all heavy, tightly bound molecules, K_0 is approximately the same.

Using the expressions for b and c in (11-18), and K = 0, the last two terms in (11-17) can be combined to give

$$-\frac{\hbar^2}{2Ma^2}(v + \tfrac{1}{2})^2$$

neglecting a small term independent of v. Then, for K = 0, all terms in (11-17) can be combined to give

$$E = -\left[\sqrt{U_0} - \frac{\hbar}{a\sqrt{2M}}(v + \tfrac{1}{2})\right]^2 \qquad (11\text{-}19)$$

The pure vibrational spectrum (11-19) is very simple. The spacing between vibrational levels decreases with increasing vibrational quanbum number v, and goes to zero when E = 0. The number of vibrational levels, however, is finite, and can easily be seen to be equal to

$$N = \frac{2U_0}{\hbar\omega_0} \qquad (11\text{-}20)$$

where $\hbar\omega_0$ is the spacing between levels at low v.

SYMMETRY FOR HOMONUCLEAR DIATOMIC MOLECULES

The wave function describing a homonuclear molecule factors into a product of electronic and nuclear spatial and spin wave functions:

$$\Psi = u_{e\ell}\,\chi_{e\ell}\,u_N\,\chi_N \qquad (11\text{-}21)$$

Ψ must be symmetric (antisymmetric) under nuclear interchange if the spin of the nucleus is integral (half-integral). $\chi_{e\ell}$ is symmetric under nuclear interchange, as it does not depend on the nuclei. The electronic spatial wave function $u_{e\ell}$ will depend on the distances r_{ai} and r_{bi} of each electron from the nuclei a and b. Interchange of the two nuclei means interchange of r_{ai} with r_{bi}, simultaneously for all i. Geometrically, this interchange means a reflection of the entire electron system at the mid-plane between the two nuclei. This reflection leaves the Hamiltonian invariant, and therefore $u_{e\ell}$ will have a definite symmetry with respect to it, either symmetric or antisymmetric. (In the simple case of the H_2 molecule, $u_{e\ell}$ is symmetric with respect to the two nuclei, and in this case the symmetry with respect to the nuclei is related to the symmetry of the spatial function between the two electrons. In general, this relation does not hold. In fact, the spatial electron function usually has a complicated symmetry with respect to electron interchange, whereas its symmetry with respect to the nuclei is always simple.) In most molecular ground states, $u_{e\ell}$ is symmetric in the two nuclei.

Therefore, in general, $u_N \chi_N$ must be symmetric (antisymmetric) under nuclear interchange if the nuclear spin is an integer (half-integer). In u_N, nuclear interchange is equivalent to a change in sign of **R**, the relative position vector. (The coordinate system is assumed to be chosen centered at the mid-point of the line joining the two nuclei.) Hence the symmetry of u_N is determined by $(-1)^K$. Thus we conclude that for nuclei of zero or integer spin, the nuclear spin function must be symmetric for even K, antisymmetric for odd K. For nuclei with half-integer spin, the nuclear spin function must be antisymmetric for even K and symmetric for odd K.

From the discussion of addition of equal angular momenta, i.e., addition of the two nuclear spins $I\hbar$, it is seen that the total of $(2I+1)^2$ spin states can be divided into $(I+1)(2I+1)$ symmetric states and $I(2I+1)$ antisymmetric states. It is seen that the ratio of the number of symmetric spin states to antisymmetric spin states is $(I+1)/I$. Thus in a gas of homonuclear diatomic molecules in statistical equilibrium, the ratio of the number of molecules with even K to the number with odd K will be $(I+1)/I$ if I is 0 or an integer, and $I/(I+1)$ if I is a half-integer. This gives rise to alternating intensities in the rotational spectra of molecules. We repeat that this analysis depends on $u_{e\ell}$ being symmetric under interchange of the nuclei. When this is not so, the results are modified in an obvious fashion.

Because of the extremely weak interaction of nuclear spins with the electrons, the probability of changing the spin orientations is very small. Hence gases of molecules differing in total nuclear spin act almost as different gases. For example H_2 can have two states: resultant nuclear spin 1 (ortho) or resultant nuclear spin 0 (para). The statistical weight ratio of ortho to para states is therefore 3 to 1.

Chapter 12

SEMICLASSICAL THEORY OF RADIATION

In the discussion so far, we have dealt only with stationary states of atoms. We shall now treat transitions between these stationary states. We shall want to study the interaction of an atomic system with an electromagnetic radiation field. The Schrödinger equation for a mass point of charge e in an electromagnetic field described by a vector potential **A** is

$$i\hbar \frac{\partial \psi}{\partial t} = \left[-\frac{\hbar^2}{2m} \nabla^2 + \frac{ie\hbar}{mc} \mathbf{A} \cdot \boldsymbol{\nabla} + V \right] \psi \tag{12-1}$$

(Schiff, p. 246). We are in a gauge $\boldsymbol{\nabla} \cdot \mathbf{A} = 0$, $\varphi = 0$, which is always possible when no sources of the electromagnetic field are present, and we have suppressed the term in A^2 which is negligible.

The problem will be treated semiclassically in the sense that although the motion of the particle is quantized, the electromagnetic field will be considered classically. Therefore it is assumed that the vector potential can be specified without any uncertainty at each point of space-time by means of the classical Maxwell equations in a vacuum:

$$\begin{aligned} \boldsymbol{\nabla} \times \boldsymbol{\mathcal{E}} &= -\frac{1}{c} \frac{\partial \boldsymbol{\mathcal{H}}}{\partial t} \\ \boldsymbol{\nabla} \times \boldsymbol{\mathcal{H}} &= \frac{1}{c} \frac{\partial \boldsymbol{\mathcal{E}}}{\partial t} \\ \boldsymbol{\nabla} \cdot \boldsymbol{\mathcal{H}} &= 0 \\ \boldsymbol{\nabla} \cdot \boldsymbol{\mathcal{E}} &= 0 \end{aligned} \tag{12-2}$$

Then

$$\mathcal{H} = \nabla \times \mathbf{A}$$
$$\mathcal{E} = -\frac{1}{c}\frac{\partial \mathbf{A}}{\partial t} \tag{12-3}$$

$$\nabla^2 \mathbf{A} - \frac{1}{c^2}\frac{\partial^2 \mathbf{A}}{\partial t^2} = 0 \tag{12-4}$$
$$\nabla \cdot \mathbf{A} = 0$$

It will be seen that this gives a correct account of the influence of an external radiation field on the particle (absorption and induced emission) but not of the influence of the particle on the field (spontaneous emission). The reason for the correct results for the former phenomena lies in the correspondence principle. When the radiation field is quantized it is regarded as a collection of quantized oscillators, with the nth excited state of the oscillator describing n photons in the electromagnetic field. For high values of n (many photons or intense beam) the correspondence principle allows a classical description of the field. Hence for intense external beams the semiclassical approximate treatment is expected to yield the correct results. But now we observe that (12-1) is linear in **A**. Thus the results that hold for the strong external beam case must also hold for the weak beam. That this is indeed so is related to the happy accident that the correspondence principle for a harmonic oscillator is already valid for low values of n.

These considerations do not hold for spontaneous emission. This emission occurs regardless of the initial presence of an external field; i.e., an accelerated charge radiates regardless whether or not it is in an external field. At least one quantum of radiation must be emitted; thus the effect is not linear in the field, and the correspondence principle cannot be extrapolated in a simple way to the emission of one quantum. For a completely satisfactory theory, we have to quantize the electromagnetic field, i.e., we need quantum field theory. However, we shall be able to obtain the correct probability of spontaneous emission from general conditions of equilibrium, and this result will also be seen to be a plausible extrapolation of the classical theory of emission of radiation.

ABSORPTION AND INDUCED EMISSION

The plane-wave solutions of (12-4) for **A** are of the form

$$\mathbf{A}(\mathbf{r},t) = 2\mathbf{A}_0[\exp\ i(\mathbf{k}\cdot\mathbf{r} - \omega t)] \tag{12-5}$$

where $2\mathbf{A}_0$ is a constant complex vector, describing both the intensity and the polarization, and $\mathbf{k}$ is the propagation vector. $\mathbf{A}_0$ is perpendicular to $\mathbf{k}$ and $kc = \omega$. Physical solutions correspond to the real part of (12-5). The electric and magnetic fields are given by

$$\mathcal{E} = \text{Re } ik2\mathbf{A}_0 \exp i(\mathbf{k}\cdot\mathbf{r} - \omega t) \tag{12-6a}$$

$$\mathcal{H} = \text{Re } 2i\mathbf{k} \times \mathbf{A}_0 \exp i(\mathbf{k}\cdot\mathbf{r} - \omega t) \tag{12-6b}$$

The Poynting vector $(c/4\pi)\,\mathcal{E} \times \mathcal{H}$ is in the direction $\mathbf{k}$. Averaged over a period $2\pi/\omega$ of the oscillation it is

$$I = \frac{\omega^2}{2\pi c} \,|\mathbf{A}_0|^2 \tag{12-7}$$

where $|\mathbf{A}_0|^2 = \mathbf{A}_0 \cdot \mathbf{A}_0^*$. The quantity (12-7) is the intensity of the beam, in ergs/cm² sec. We can also introduce the number of quanta per unit area and time, $N = I/\hbar\omega$, so that (12-7) gives

$$|\mathbf{A}_0|^2 = \frac{2\pi\hbar c}{\omega} N \tag{12-8}$$

PERTURBATION CALCULATION

We consider the term $(ie\hbar/mc)\mathbf{A}\cdot\nabla$ in (12-1) as a time-dependent perturbation with $\mathbf{A}$ given by the real part of (12-5). If the system is initially in the state n, and the perturbation is turned on at time $t = 0$, the first-order amplitude is given by

$$a_f^{(1)}(t) = \frac{1}{i\hbar}\int_0^t H'_{fn}(t')\, e^{i\omega_{fn}t'}\, dt' \tag{1-8}$$

with $\omega_{fn} = (E_f - E_n)/\hbar$. Then

$$\begin{aligned} a_f^{(1)}(t) = &-\frac{H'^0_{fn}}{\hbar}\,\frac{e^{i(\omega_{fn}-\omega)t} - 1}{\omega_{fn} - \omega} \\ &-\frac{H''^0_{fn}}{\hbar}\,\frac{e^{i(\omega_{fn}+\omega)t} - 1}{\omega_{fn} + \omega} \\ H'^0_{fn} = &\ \frac{ie\hbar}{mc}\int u_f^*\, e^{i\mathbf{k}\cdot\mathbf{r}}\, \mathbf{A}_0 \cdot \nabla u_n \, d\tau \\ H''^0_{fn} = &\ \frac{ie\hbar}{mc}\int u_f^*\, e^{-i\mathbf{k}\cdot\mathbf{r}}\, \mathbf{A}_0^* \cdot \nabla u_n \, d\tau \end{aligned} \tag{12-9}$$

The probability that a transition will occur is only appreciable for

$$\omega_{fn} = \pm\omega$$

that is,

$$\begin{aligned} E_f &= E_n + \hbar\omega \\ &= E_n - \hbar\omega \end{aligned} \tag{12-10}$$

The former condition corresponds to an absorption of one quantum from the radiation field, the latter to induced emission. It is quite remarkable that we obtain quantization of the energy emitted or absorbed without having assumed any quantization of the electromagnetic field initially. Energy conservation between particle and field is assured by (12-10). When $\omega_{fn} = \omega$, the probability of finding the system in a state f with higher energy is proportional to $|H_{fn}'^{0}|^2$. When $\omega_{fn} = -\omega$, the probability of finding the system in a state of lower energy is proportional to $|H_{fn}''^{0}|^2$.

To obtain the transition probability per unit time we first assume that transitions can occur to a group of closely spaced or continuously distributed final states of the mechanical system (electron system). The transition will be either an absorption or a stimulated emission of a quantum. We can easily assume that the group of states covers an energy range small compared with $\hbar\omega$; then only one of the two relations $\omega = \pm\omega_{fn}$ is satisfied. In this case, the probability per unit time of transition to this group of final states is given by Fermi's golden rule,

$$w = \frac{2\pi}{\hbar}\,\rho(k)\,|A_{fn}|^2 \tag{12-11}$$

where $\rho(k)$ is the density of states in this region and A_{fn} is $H_{fn}'^{0}$ or $H_{fn}''^{0}$, depending on whether an absorption or an emission is being considered. The final states approach plane waves at distances far from the neighborhood of the perturbation, so that

$$\begin{aligned} \rho(k) &= \frac{V}{(2\pi\hbar)^3}\,\frac{p^2\,dp\,d\Omega}{dE} = \frac{V}{(2\pi\hbar)^3}\,\frac{p^2\,dp\,d\Omega}{v\,dp} \\ &= \frac{V}{(2\pi\hbar)^3}\,\frac{p^2}{v}\,d\Omega \end{aligned} \tag{12-12}$$

where $d\Omega$ is the solid angle into which the ejected electron with momentum $\mathbf{p}$ goes, and V is the quantization volume.

For absorption the transition probability becomes

$$w = \frac{e^2}{(2\pi\hbar c)^2} v |A_0|^2 \left| \int u_f^* e^{i\mathbf{k}\cdot\mathbf{r}} \nabla_{\mathbf{A}} u_n \, d\tau \right|^2 V \, d\Omega \tag{12-13}$$

In (12-13) $\nabla_{\mathbf{A}} u_n$ is the projection of the gradient of u_n on the direction $\mathbf{A}$. The momentum p has been set equal to mv. The final state u_f will asymptotically be a plane wave $V^{-1/2} e^{i\mathbf{k}_f\cdot\mathbf{r}}$, so that the dependence on the normalization volume in (12-13) cancels. The factor $|A_0|^2$ can be expressed by (12-8) in terms of the number of incident quanta N per cm² and sec. The differential cross section for absorption of radiation is then

$$\sigma(\theta,\varphi) = \frac{e^2}{2\pi\hbar c} \frac{v}{\omega} \left| \int u_{f1}^* e^{i\mathbf{k}\cdot\mathbf{r}} \nabla_{\mathbf{A}} u_n \, d\tau \right|^2 \tag{12-14}$$

where u_{f1} is now normalized to unit amplitude at large distance from the atom. Equation (12-14) is the cross section for the photoelectric effect, where the photoelectron is ejected from the atom in the direction θ, φ relative to the incident beam. It will be further evaluated in Chapter 14.

If the final state is in the discrete spectrum, there is no way of calculating $\rho(k)$. Indeed if the radiation is monochromatic, the energy conservation equations (12-10) can in general not be satisfied. It is therefore assumed that the radiation covers a spread of frequencies with no phase relations between different frequency components, so that the radiation can be characterized by an intensity per unit frequency range that is constant in a neighborhood of ω_{fn}. The intensity in the range $\Delta\omega \ll \omega_{fn}$ is taken to be $I(\omega)\Delta\omega$. From (12-7) we have

$$\frac{2\pi c}{\omega^2} I(\omega)\,\Delta\omega = |\mathbf{A}_0|^2 \tag{12-15}$$

The transition probability is then the sum of the probabilities induced by the incident waves of various frequencies. We assume that the number of incident quanta in the frequency interval $\Delta\omega$ is

$$N = N(\omega)\,\Delta\omega$$

and that the number of incident quanta per unit frequency, $N(\omega)$, is constant over the frequency range for which the transition probability $|a_f^{(1)}(t)|^2$ in (12-9) is appreciable. This frequency range is centered at the frequency ω_{fn} and has a width of the order $1/t$; t can easily be chosen $\gg 1/\omega_{fn}$, so that the important frequency range is in fact very small (it needs only to be larger than the natural width of the spectral line $n \rightarrow f$).

To simplify evaluation, it is convenient to rewrite Fermi's golden rule for *one* final state in the form which we have already used in (1-10c):

$$w = \frac{2\pi}{\hbar} |H'_{fn}|^2 \delta(E_{fin} - E_{in}) \tag{12-16}$$

where δ is the Dirac δ function and E_{in} and E_{fin} are the total energies in initial and final state. Thus, in the case of absorption,

$$E_{in} = E_n + \hbar\omega \qquad E_{fin} = E_f \tag{12-17a}$$

while for emission,

$$E_{in} = E_n \qquad E_{fin} = E_f + \hbar\omega \tag{12-17b}$$

With the assumption (12-15) and the golden rule (12-16), the absorption probability leading to one final state is then, using (12-19) and (12-7),

$$w = \frac{2\pi}{\hbar}\left(\frac{e\hbar}{mc}\right)^2 \left| \int u_f^* e^{i\mathbf{k}\cdot\mathbf{r}} \nabla_{\mathbf{A}} u_n \, d\tau \right|^2$$

$$\times \int d\omega \, \frac{2\pi\hbar c}{\omega} N(\omega) \, \delta(E_n + \hbar\omega - E_f) \tag{12-18}$$

The integration over $d\omega$ corresponds to our assumption that the transition probabilities due to the incident waves of different frequency simply add incoherently (no phase relation). The integral over ω can be carried out and gives $1/\hbar$, provided that the frequency ω_{fn} is included in the incident spectrum; otherwise the limits of the integral over ω do not matter. Collecting terms,

$$w = \frac{(2\pi e)^2\hbar}{m^2 c\omega_{fn}} N(\omega_{fn}) \left| \int u_f^* e^{i\mathbf{k}\cdot\mathbf{r}} \nabla_{\mathbf{A}} u_n \, d\tau \right|^2 \tag{12-19}$$

The number of incident quanta can be replaced by the intensity per unit frequency, $N(\omega) = I(\omega)/\hbar\omega$; the resulting expression does not contain $\hbar$ and is thus quasi-classical.

The transition probability per unit time for emission of radiation is the same as (12-19) except that ω_{fn} is replaced by ω_{nf} and the integral is replaced by

$$\int u_f^* e^{-i\mathbf{k}\cdot\mathbf{r}} \nabla_{\mathbf{A}} u_n \, d\tau \tag{12-20}$$

Here we may interchange the labels n and f; this has the advantage that then again f denotes the higher, n the lower energy state. We may then integrate by parts. Now $\nabla_{\mathbf{A}} e^{-i\mathbf{k}\cdot\mathbf{r}} = 0$ because the vector potential **A** is perpendicular to the propagation vector **k**. This results in a transition probability per unit time

$$w = \frac{(2\pi e)^2}{m^2 c\omega_{fn}} \hbar N(\omega_{fn}) \left| -\int u_f e^{-i\mathbf{k}\cdot\mathbf{r}} \nabla_{\mathbf{A}} u_n^* \, d\tau \right|^2 \tag{12-21}$$

It is seen that (12-21) is the same as (12-19); the probabilities of reverse transitions between any pair of states under the influence of the same radiation field are the same. This is the principle of detailed balancing, which is of fundamental importance for statistical mechanics.

MULTIPOLE TRANSITIONS

We expand the exponential in (12-19) and (12-20) and keep only the first term which leads to a nonvanishing integral. This is justified by observing that the ratio of two successive terms is O(ka), with a being a measure of the radius of the atom. Now for optical transitions,

$$ka = \frac{\omega}{c} a = \frac{a\,\Delta E}{\hbar c} \leq \frac{a}{a_0} \frac{e^2}{2\hbar c} \approx \frac{1}{300} \tag{12-22}$$

Here we have assumed that the energy in the optical transition, $\Delta E < 1$ Rydberg $= e^2/2a_0$, and the radius of the atom $a \approx a_0$. Therefore, $ka \ll 1$. For X-rays ΔE is larger by a factor Z^2 and a is smaller by a factor Z. Hence $k \sim Z/300$, and for large Z the result $ka \ll 1$ is no longer true. Replacing $e^{i\mathbf{k}\cdot\mathbf{r}}$ by 1, the relevant integral becomes

$$\begin{aligned} \int u_f^* \nabla_{\mathbf{A}} u_n \, d\tau &= \frac{i}{\hbar} \int u_f^* p_{\mathbf{A}} u_n \, d\tau \\ &= \frac{i}{\hbar} (p_{\mathbf{A}})_{fn} \\ &= \frac{mi}{\hbar} \frac{d}{dt} (r_{\mathbf{A}})_{fn} \\ &= -\frac{m}{\hbar} \omega_{fn} (r_{\mathbf{A}})_{fn} \end{aligned} \tag{12-23}$$

The subscript **A** indicates the component in the direction of **A**. The transition probability per unit time for absorption and induced emission is then

$$w = \frac{4\pi^2 e^2}{\hbar c} \omega_{fn} N(\omega_{fn}) \,|\, (r_A)_{fn} \,|^2 \tag{12-24}$$

If we write $|\mathbf{r}_{fn}|^2 = \mathbf{r}_{fn} \cdot \mathbf{r}^*_{fn}$, assume Θ is the angle between $\mathbf{r}$ and $\mathbf{A}$, and average over Θ, the above becomes

$$w_{av} = \frac{4\pi^2 e^2}{3\hbar c} \omega_{fn} N(\omega_{fn}) \,|\mathbf{r}_{fn}|^2 \tag{12-25}$$

This has obviously the correct dimension: $e^2/\hbar c$ is the fine-structure constant, $\omega N(\omega)$ is a number per cm^2 per sec, and $|\mathbf{r}|^2$ is an area.

Transitions for which the probability is accurately given by the above approximation are called electric dipole transitions, since $e\mathbf{r}$ is the operator representing the electric dipole of the atom. If the dipole matrix element $(\mathbf{r})_{fn}$ is zero the transition is said to be forbidden. If the unapproximated integral in (12-19) or (12-21) vanishes, the transition is said to be strictly forbidden. In neither instance is it to be concluded that no transition can occur. If the dipole transition is forbidden we must take further terms in the expansion of $e^{i\mathbf{k}\cdot\mathbf{r}}$. If the transition is strictly forbidden we must take higher orders of perturbation theory and must include the neglected term $e^2A^2/2mc^2$; this then leads to the simultaneous emission of two photons.

SPONTANEOUS EMISSION

A classical description of the spontaneous emission of radiation by a current density $\mathbf{J}$, oscillating with angular frequency ω, gives for the intensity of radiation in the radiation zone in the direction $\mathbf{k}$ the result

$$I = \frac{k^2}{2\pi r^2 c} \left| \int J_\perp(\mathbf{r}') e^{-i\mathbf{k}\cdot\mathbf{r}'} d\tau' \right|^2 \tag{12-26}$$

where $\mathbf{J}(\mathbf{r})$ is defined by assuming that the current density at $\mathbf{r}$ and t is given by

$$\mathbf{J}(\mathbf{r},t) = \mathbf{J}(\mathbf{r}) e^{-i\omega t}$$

(Panofsky and Phillips, p. 248). Here $J_\perp$ is the component of $\mathbf{J}$ perpendicular to $\mathbf{k}$. In the dipole approximation (12-26) reduces to

$$\frac{k^2}{2\pi r^2 c} \left| \int J_\perp(\mathbf{r}')\, d\tau' \right|^2 \tag{12-27}$$

Writing

$$\mathbf{J}_0 \equiv \int \mathbf{J}(\mathbf{r}')\, d\tau' \tag{12-28}$$

we conclude that the polarization is linear if $\mathbf{J}_0$ has only one component in the plane perpendicular to $\mathbf{k}$, circular if $\mathbf{J}_0$ has two equal perpendicular components in the plane perpendicular to $\mathbf{k}$ and 90° out of phase; and so forth. Equation (12-27) can be rewritten as

$$\frac{k^2}{2\pi r^2 c} \, |\mathbf{J}_0|^2 \, \sin^2 \theta \tag{12-29}$$

where $|\mathbf{J}_0|^2 = (\mathbf{J}_0 \cdot \mathbf{J}_0^*)$ and θ is the angle between $\mathbf{J}_0$ and $\mathbf{k}$. The total power radiated is the integral of (12-29) over a sphere of radius r. This gives

$$\frac{4k^2}{3c} \, |\mathbf{J}_0|^2 \tag{12-30}$$

To convert this treatment to quantum mechanics we require a quantum mechanical operator corresponding to $\mathbf{J}_0$, and we interpret the radiated power as $\hbar\omega$ times the transition probability per unit time. In view of the usual identification of charge density with $e\,|\psi|^2$, it is plausible to assume that the quantum mechanical operator corresponding to $\mathbf{J}$ is given by the current, familiar from the Schrödinger continuity equation:

$$\mathbf{J}(\mathbf{r}) = \frac{e\hbar}{2im} \left[u_n^* \nabla u_f - (\nabla u_n^*) u_f\right] \tag{12-31}$$

The probability of emission of a quantum per unit time in a transition from state f to n is then given by (12-26) multiplied by $r^2\, d\Omega$ and divided by $\hbar\omega$, with (12-30) substituted for J, i.e.,

$$w = \frac{\omega}{2\pi\hbar c^3} \left(\frac{e\hbar}{m}\right)^2 \left| \int u_n^*(\mathbf{r}')\, e^{-i\mathbf{k}\cdot\mathbf{r}'} \, \nabla_\perp u_f(r')\, d\tau' \right|^2 d\Omega \tag{12-32}$$

An integration by parts of the second term occurring in (12-31) was used to obtain the form (12-32). For this integration it is important that only the component of ∇ perpendicular to $\mathbf{k}$ occurs; this ensures that the derivative of $e^{-i\mathbf{k}\cdot\mathbf{r}'}$ does not appear in (12-32).

Unlike induced emission, conservation of energy is not automatically obtained as a consequence of the theory; we must make the additional postulate $\omega_{fn} = \omega$. The emission of radiation of definite polarization $\mathbf{A} \perp \mathbf{k}$ is obtained by substituting $\nabla_{\mathbf{A}}$ instead of $\nabla_\perp$ in (12-32). In the dipole approximation (12-32) becomes after integration over angles,

$$w_{av} = \frac{4e^2\omega_{fn}^3}{3\hbar c^3} \, |\mathbf{r}_{nf}|^2 \tag{12-33}$$

EINSTEIN TRANSITION PROBABILITIES

That the above transition from the classical description to the quantum mechanical description gives correct results is proved by an argument due to Einstein (1917). We consider the thermal equilibrium between atoms and a radiation field which is achieved by the absorption and emission of photons of frequency $\omega_{fn} = (E_f - E_n)/\hbar > 0$. Two of the three available processes for attaining equilibrium, viz., stimulated emission and absorption, were found to be proportional to $\rho(\omega_{fn})$, the energy density of the external radiation field per unit frequency.

$$\rho(\omega_{fn}) = \frac{I(\omega_{fn})}{c} = \frac{\hbar\omega N(\omega_{fn})}{c} \tag{12-34}$$

The third process, spontaneous emission, occurs even in the absence of external radiation, hence does not depend on $\rho(\omega_{fn})$. The rate at which atoms make transitions $n \rightarrow f$ (absorption) is

$$\frac{dN(n \rightarrow f)}{dt} = B_{nf} N(n) \rho(\omega_{fn}) \tag{12-35}$$

where $N(n)$ is the number of atoms in state n. The rate at which the transition $f \rightarrow n$ (emission) proceeds is

$$\frac{dN(f \rightarrow n)}{dt} = B_{fn} N(f) \rho(\omega_{fn}) + A_{fn} N(f) \tag{12-36}$$

A_{fn} and B_{fn} are called the Einstein spontaneous and induced transition probabilities, respectively. The requirement of equilibrium equates the two rates; the principle of detailed balance gives $B_{fn} = B_{nf}$. Thus

$$B_{fn} N(f) \rho(\omega_{fn}) + A_{fn} N(f) = B_{fn} N(n) \rho(\omega_{fn}) \tag{12-37}$$

$$\rho(\omega_{fn}) = \frac{A_{fn}/B_{fn}}{[N(n)/N(f)] - 1} \tag{12-38}$$

From statistical mechanics we have at thermal equilibrium at temperature T,

$$\frac{N(n)}{N(f)} = e^{\hbar\omega_{fn}/kT} \tag{12-39}$$

and

$$\rho(\omega_{fn}) = \frac{\hbar\omega_{fn}^3}{\pi^2 c^3} \frac{1}{e^{(\hbar\omega_{fn}/kT)} - 1} \tag{12-40}$$

which is the density of radiant energy per unit frequency at temperature T. Equation (12-40) is, of course, the well-known formula due to Planck. (In fact this discussion is the method Einstein used to derive Planck's radiation formula. At that time there was no way of evaluating A_{fn}/B_{fn}.) For (12-38) to agree with (12-40) we must have

$$A_{fn} = \frac{\hbar\omega_{fn}^3}{\pi^2 c^3} B_{fn} \tag{12-41}$$

Comparing (12-33) with (12-25) we see that (12-41) is satisfied for dipole radiation. For the general case, we must compare (12-32) with (12-21), and use the fact that (12-32) includes two directions of polarization, which gives a factor of 2, and that it should be integrated over $d\Omega$, which gives a factor 4π. If (12-21) is then averaged over the directions of **k** and **A**, and (12-34) is used, we again find (12-41) satisfied.

Thus we have justified (12-32) for the spontaneous emission, including the numerical factors, by invoking Einstein's argument on statistical equilibrium. The form (12-32) is also made plausible by noting that the integral has the same form as the induced emission (12-21). The most satisfactory way to derive (12-32) is from field theory, which will be done in Chapter 21. Once (12-32), and hence (12-41), is justified, we may of course use Einstein's argument for his original purpose, viz., to deduce the Planck distribution.

LINE BREADTH

Our discussion so far has led to the conclusion that spectral lines will be infinitely sharp, corresponding to the well-defined energies of the stationary states that are involved in the transition. This, of course, is an approximation, as observed spectral lines are known to have finite width, as owing to the spontaneous emission, the energy states are not in fact stable but decay. The probability of transition per unit time γ_n for this decay is given by (12-33) and is seen to be independent of time. It is well known from probability theory that such time-independent processes obey an exponential law of decay; i.e., the depletion of the occupation probability $|a_n|^2$ of a state n is given by $e^{-\gamma_n t}$, where $1/\gamma_n$ is called the lifetime. The amplitude a_n then decays as $e^{-1/2\gamma_n t}$. For optical transition $1/\gamma_n \approx 10^{-8}$ sec, and is very much larger than the characteristic period of electron motion (about 10^{-15} sec). Hence it is justified in first approximation to have considered the states stationary.

Weisskopf and Wigner (1930) analyzed the effects of this decay. They found, using the full quantum theory of the radiation field, that the spectrum of the emitted radiation is correctly given if we assume that the initial state n, as well as the final state m, have wave functions with the time-dependence

$$\Psi_n = e^{-iE_n t/\hbar - \frac{1}{2}\gamma_n t} u_n \tag{12-42}$$

Then the "current" $\Psi_m^* \nabla \Psi_n$ has the time-dependence

$$\mathbf{J}(\mathbf{r},t) \sim e^{-i\omega_{nm} t - \frac{1}{2}(\gamma_n + \gamma_m)t} \tag{12-43}$$

If we make a Fourier analysis of this current, to determine the radiation of frequency ω, we find that its intensity (absolute square of amplitude) is proportional to

$$R(\omega) = \frac{1}{(\omega - \omega_{nm})^2 + \frac{1}{4}(\gamma_n + \gamma_m)^2} \tag{12-44}$$

This then gives the natural shape of the line (excluding Doppler effect, collision broadening, etc.). In emission, the intensity is distributed according to (12-44); in absorption, the absorption coefficient has that dependence.

The occurrence of $\gamma_n + \gamma_m$ in the width is, however, contrary to classical ideas, according to which one might expect a dependence on the initial state only. Or we might expect the Lorentz width, which is $\Delta\lambda_L = (2/3)(e^2/mc^2)$ in wavelength, or perhaps $\Delta\lambda_L$ multiplied by the oscillator strength (see Chapter 13) of the line. Most physicists, before quantum mechanics, favored the latter idea, and thus expected weak spectral lines to be narrow. Equation (12-44), on the other hand, predicts lines to be broad if either the initial or the final state has a short lifetime, regardless of the strength of the line itself. Experiments have shown that the quantum prediction is correct. A simple example (although not experimentally directly verified) is the transition $3\,^1S - 2\,^1P$ of He: It is a weak transition because n and ℓ change in opposite directions (see Chapter 13), but the $2\,^1P$ state has a very short lifetime, owing to the strong transition $2\,^1P - 1\,^1S$; hence $3\,^1S - 2\,^1P$ should be broad.

It is clear that line width is connected with the uncertainty principle. The lifetime of a state, $1/\gamma$, measures the time a quantum system occupies that state. Hence the energy cannot be determined to greater accuracy than $\hbar\gamma$. If the energy is uncertain by that amount, the frequency will be broadened by γ.

Chapter 13

INTENSITY OF RADIATION

SUM RULES

The following sum rules are useful in estimating the intensity of radiation. All summations are over the complete set of energy eigenvalues; that is, a summation over the discrete set and an integration over the continuous set.

1. Dipole Moment

$$\sum_k |x_{kn}|^2 = \sum_k x_{nk} x_{kn} = (x^2)_{nn} = \int |u_n|^2 x^2 \, dx \qquad (13\text{-}1)$$

If the state n is isotropic,

$$\sum_k |x_{kn}|^2 = \tfrac{1}{3} (r^2)_{nn} \qquad (13\text{-}2)$$

If $|\mathbf{A}|^2$ is defined as $(\mathbf{A} \cdot \mathbf{A}^*)$,

$$\sum_k |\mathbf{r}_{kn}|^2 = (r^2)_{nn} \qquad (13\text{-}3)$$

2. Oscillator Strength

The oscillator strength f_{kn} is defined as

$$f^x_{kn} = \frac{2m\omega_{kn}}{\hbar} |x_{kn}|^2 \qquad (13\text{-}4)$$

$$f_{kn} = f^x_{kn} + f^y_{kn} + f^z_{kn} \qquad (13\text{-}5)$$

Recalling that

$$p^x_{kn} = im\omega_{kn} x_{kn} \tag{13-6}$$

$$f^x_{kn} = \frac{-i}{\hbar}\left(x_{nk} p^x_{kn} - p^x_{nk} x_{kn}\right)$$

$$\sum_k f^x_{kn} = \frac{-i}{\hbar}[x, p^x]_{nn} = \frac{-i}{\hbar} i\hbar = 1$$

Therefore,

$$\sum_k f^x_{kn} = \sum_k f^y_{kn} = \sum_k f^z_{kn} = 1 \tag{13-7}$$

$$\sum_k f_{kn} = 3 \tag{13-8}$$

(Thomas, Reiche, Kuhn, 1925).

3. Momentum

$$\sum_k |p^x_{kn}|^2 = ((p^x)^2)_{nn} = -\hbar^2 \int u_n^* \frac{\partial^2}{\partial x^2} u_n \, d\tau \tag{13-9}$$

From (13-6) this is equivalent to

$$m^2 \sum_k \omega^2_{kn} |x_{kn}|^2 = -\hbar^2 \int u_n^* \frac{\partial^2}{\partial x^2} u_n \, d\tau$$

If the state u_n is spherically symmetric,

$$\sum_k \omega^2_{kn} |x_{kn}|^2 = \frac{-\hbar^2}{3m^2} \int u_n^* \nabla^2 u_n \, d\tau = \frac{2}{3m}(E - V)_{nn} \tag{13-10}$$

Also,

$$\sum_k \omega^2_{kn} |\mathbf{r}_{kn}|^2 = \frac{2}{m}(E - V)_{nn} \tag{13-11}$$

4. Force Times Momentum

$$\frac{d}{dt} p^x_{kn} = i\omega_{kn} p^x_{kn} = -\left(\frac{\partial V}{\partial x}\right)_{kn}$$

$$\sum_k \omega_{kn} \,|\, p^x_{kn} \,|^2 = i \sum_k p^x_{nk} \left(\frac{\partial V}{\partial x}\right)_{kn}$$

$$= -i \sum \left(\frac{\partial V}{\partial x}\right)_{nk} p^x_{kn}$$

$$= \tfrac{1}{2} i \left[p^x, \frac{\partial V}{\partial x}\right]_{nn}$$

$$= \frac{\hbar}{2} \left(\frac{\partial^2 V}{\partial x^2}\right)_{nn} \tag{13-12}$$

Using (13-6) again,

$$\sum_k \omega^3_{kn} \,|\, x_{kn} \,|^2 = \frac{\hbar}{2m^2} \left(\frac{\partial^2 V}{\partial x^2}\right)_{nn} \tag{13-13}$$

If the state n is spherically symmetric,

$$\sum_k \omega^3_{kn} \,|\, x_{kn} \,|^2 = \frac{\hbar}{6m^2} (\nabla^2 V)_{nn} = \frac{2\pi}{3} \frac{\hbar e^2}{m^2} (\rho(\mathbf{r}))_{nn} \tag{13-14}$$

where $\rho(r)$ is the density of positive charge which generates the potential energy V. For a bare nucleus, $\rho(\mathbf{r}) = Z\,\delta(\mathbf{r})$, and

$$(\rho(\mathbf{r}))_{nn} = Z \,|\, u_n(0) \,|^2 \tag{13-15}$$

Also,

$$\sum_k \omega^3_{kn} \,|\, \mathbf{r}_{kn} \,|^2 = \frac{2\pi \hbar e^2}{m^2} (\rho(\mathbf{r}))_{nn} \tag{13-16}$$

5. Force Squared

$$\sum_k \left| \left(\frac{\partial V}{\partial x}\right)_{kn} \right|^2 = \left(\left(\frac{\partial V}{\partial x}\right)^2\right)_{nn}$$

$$= \sum_k \omega^2_{kn} \,|\, p^x_{kn} \,|^2$$

$$= m^2 \sum_k \omega^4_{kn} \,|\, x_{kn} \,|^2 \tag{13-17}$$

$$\sum_k \omega^4_{kn} \,|\, x_{kn} \,|^2 = \frac{1}{m^2} \left(\left(\frac{\partial V}{\partial x}\right)^2\right)_{nn}$$

If the state n is spherically symmetric,

$$\sum_k \omega_{kn}^4 \, | x_{kn} |^2 = \frac{1}{3m^2} ((\nabla V)^2)_{nn} \qquad \text{and} \tag{13-18}$$

$$\sum_k \omega_{kn}^4 \, | \mathbf{r}_{kn} |^2 = \frac{1}{m^2} ((\nabla V)^2)_{nn} \tag{13-19}$$

Summary

The above results for $\Sigma_k \, \omega_{kn}^p \, | x_{kn} |^2$ are summarized in Table 13-1. In the table it is assumed for all p, except p = 1, that the state n is spherically symmetric. The values of $\Sigma_k \, \omega_{kn}^p \, | \mathbf{r}_{kn} |^2$ can be obtained by multiplying the sums by 3. Clearly in this case no assumptions about spherical symmetry are made.

Table 13-1
Sum Rules

p	Sum
0	$\frac{1}{3} (r^2)_{nn}$
1	$\frac{\hbar}{2m}$
2	$\frac{2}{3m} (E - V)_{nn}$
3	$\frac{1}{6} \frac{\hbar}{m^2} (\nabla^2 V)_{nn}$
4	$\frac{1}{3m^2} ((\nabla V)^2)_{nn}$

Many Electrons

The above sum rules are for transitions of one electron. For Z electrons the relevant integral becomes

$$\int u_k^* \sum_{j=1}^{Z} e^{-i\mathbf{k} \cdot \mathbf{r}_j} \frac{\partial}{\partial x_j} u_n \, d\tau \tag{13-20}$$

which in the dipole approximation is

$$\int u_k^* \left(\sum_{j=1}^{Z} x_j \right) u_n \; d\tau = X_{kn} \tag{13-21}$$

Then

(1′) $$\sum_k |X_{kn}|^2 = X^2_{nn}$$

$$= \int |u_n|^2 \left(\sum_{j=1}^{Z} x_j^2 + 2 \sum_{i<j} x_i x_j \right) d\tau \tag{13-22}$$

(2′) $$\sum_k f^x_{kn} = \frac{-i}{\hbar} \sum_k \left\{ \left(\sum_i x_i \right)_{nk} \left(\sum_j p_j^x \right)_{nk} - \left(\sum_j p_j^x \right)_{nk} \left(\sum_i x_i \right)_{kn} \right\}$$

$$= \frac{-i}{\hbar} \left[\left(\sum_i x_i \right), \left(\sum_j p_j^x \right) \right]_{nn}$$

$$= \frac{-i}{\hbar} \sum_{ij} \left[x_i , p_j^x \right]_{nn}$$

$$= \frac{-i}{\hbar} \sum_{i=1}^{Z} \sum_{j=1}^{Z} \delta_{ij} \, i\hbar = Z \tag{13-23}$$

Hydrogen

As an example of the application of sum rules we give results for hydrogen, the electron in the lowest (isotropic) state (principal quantum number = 1).

$$\sum_k \omega^p_{k1} |\mathbf{r}_{k1}|^2 = 3 \sum_k \omega^p_{k1} |x_{k1}|^2 \qquad \text{for } \ell = 0$$

p	0	1	2	3
sum	$3a_0^2$	$3a_0^2$ Ry	$4a_0^2$ Ry^2	$16a_0^2$ Ry^3

where Ry = $e^2/2a_0\hbar$ is the Rydberg frequency. From this table, we

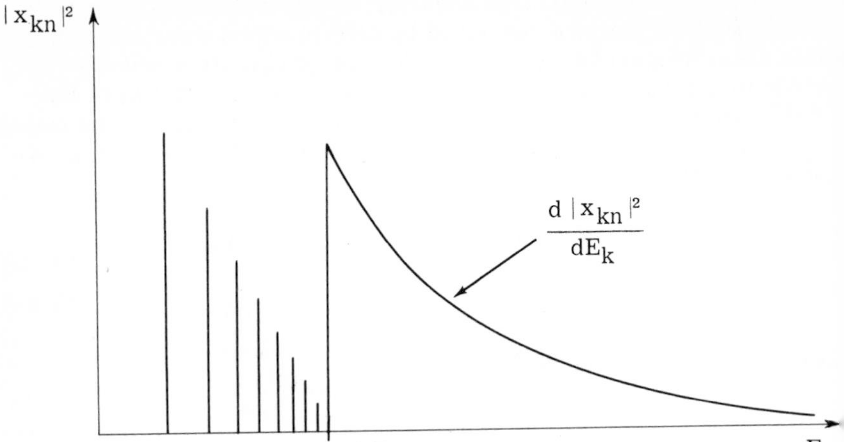

Figure 13-1

deduce that the average frequency of transitions from the ground state is just Ry, the root-mean-square frequency is $\sqrt{4/3}$ Ry = 1.14 Ry the cube root of the mean cube frequency is $(16/3)^{1/3}$ Ry = 1.75 Ry.

For the case $p = 3$, $(\rho(r))_{nn} \propto (\delta(r))_{nn} = |u_n(0)|^2$. Since $u_{n\ell} \sim r^\ell$ we have $\Sigma_k\, \omega_{kn}^3 |\mathbf{r}_{kn}|^2 = 0$ for $\ell \neq 0$. For $p = 4$, $(\nabla V)^2 \propto 1/r^4$, $((\nabla V)^2)_{nn} \propto \int |u_{n\ell}|^2 (1/r^2)\, d\tau$. For $\ell = 0$ this diverges, for $\ell \neq 0$ it is finite. From this we conclude that for $E_k \to \infty$, $|x_{kn}|^2 \propto c/\omega_{kn}^r$, where c is a constant and r a number. We know that $\int^\infty \omega_{kn}^{3-r}\, d\omega_{kn}$ converges and $\int^\infty \omega_{kn}^{4-r}\, d\omega_{kn}$ diverges. Hence $4 < r < 5$.

Figure 13-1 shows the general variation of $|x_{kn}|^2$ with energy E_k for fixed n in hydrogen. E_{kI} is the energy of ionization = 1 Ry for n = 1. It is most convenient for our present purpose to normalize the continuum wave functions per unit energy; this has been indicated by denoting the matrix elements by $d|x_{kn}|^2/dE_k$. The scale for this is not directly comparable to that for $|x_{kn}|^2$; hence the break in the figure at 1 Ry. Our previous sums can be written

$$\sum_{k=1}^{k=kI} \omega_{kn}^p\, |x_{kn}|^2 + \int_{E_{kI}}^{\infty} \left(\frac{E_k - E_n}{\hbar}\right)^p \frac{d\,|x_{kn}|^2}{dE_k}\, dE_k$$

SELECTION RULES AND MATRIX ELEMENTS

Since the operator $\mathbf{r} = \Sigma_i\, \mathbf{r}_i$ has odd parity it follows that $\mathbf{r}$ has no matrix elements between states of the same parity. Hence transitions between states of the same parity are forbidden. This is known as *Laporte's rule*.

Since $\mathbf{r}$ is a one-electron operator, it will have matrix elements between states that are described by determinantal wave functions that differ at most by one orbital. In view of Laporte's rule we conclude that $\mathbf{r}$ has matrix elements between determinantal wave functions that differ exactly by one orbital. According to (6-13) the matrix element reduces to $\langle i' | \mathbf{r}_1 | i \rangle$, where i is the different orbital. We want therefore

$$\langle n'\ell' m'_\ell m'_s | x_\mu | n\ell m_\ell m_s \rangle$$

$$= \delta(m'_s, m_s) \int R_{n'\ell'} R_{n\ell}\, x_\mu\, Y^*_{\ell' m'}\, Y_{\ell m}\, d\tau \qquad (13\text{-}24)$$

where the various x_μ are

$$z = r\cos\theta = \frac{a}{\sqrt{2}}\, rY_{10}$$

$$x + iy = r\sin\theta\, e^{i\varphi} = arY_{11}$$

$$x - iy = r\sin\theta\, e^{-i\varphi} = arY_{1-1}$$

$$a = \left(\frac{8\pi}{3}\right)^{1/2}$$

Equation (13-24) then reduces to

$$a \int \mathcal{R}_{n'\ell'} \mathcal{R}_{n\ell}\, r\, dr \int Y^*_{\ell' m'}\, Y_{\ell m}\, Y_{1t}\, d\Omega \qquad (13\text{-}25)$$

$t = 0, 1, -1$, and with $t = 0$, there is a factor $2^{-1/2}$ multiplying the whole matrix element. Considering the angular integration first we obtain, according to (6-49) and (6-50),

$$\left(\frac{3}{4\pi}\right)^{1/2} c^1(\ell' m', \ell m) \qquad t = m' - m$$

$$|\ell' - \ell| \le 1 \le \ell' + \ell = \text{odd integer} \qquad (13\text{-}26)$$

Assume $\ell' \ge \ell$, $\ell' = \ell + \Delta\ell$, $\Delta\ell \ge 0$. Equation (13-26) then implies $\Delta\ell \le 1$, $\Delta\ell$ odd; therefore $\Delta\ell = 1$. We conclude therefore that the only possible transitions are

$$z:\ m' = m$$

$$x + iy:\ m' = m + 1$$

$$x - iy:\ m' = m - 1$$

and, in any case,

$$\Delta \ell = \pm 1 \qquad m_s' = m_s \tag{13-27}$$

The selection rules for m (which become relevant for Zeeman splitting) are associated (in the classical limit) with the angular momentum carried away by the radiation. Emitted light propagating in the z direction and circularly polarized, $\mathbf{A} = A\mathbf{i} \pm iA\mathbf{j}$, carries off ± 1 unit of angular momentum about the z axis (see Panofsky and Phillips, p. 269). Hence $\Delta m = \pm 1$. The classical analogy is not easy to draw for $\Delta m = 0$, which leads to light polarized linearly in the z direction, and hence propagating in the xy plane. If we wanted to discuss its angular momentum, we would have to consider the angular momentum of the electron about the direction of propagation of the light; this cannot be done easily since we have chosen L_z as quantized, and L_z fails to commute with L_x and L_y. However, the total orbital angular momentum changes by ± 1 in quantum mechanics, thus allowing for the unit angular momentum of the emitted light.

If we are dealing with one-electron spectra such as hydrogen or the alkali atoms, the selection rules (13-27) entirely determine the spectrum. In an atom with many electrons, if the states are described by a single configuration, then because $\Sigma \mathbf{r}_i$ is a one-electron operator, the configuration change is restricted to just the $n\ell$ of one electron, the change in ℓ being ± 1. These are called one-electron jumps. Transitions are observed in which two $n\ell$'s appear to change (two-electron jumps). This is interpreted as a breakdown in the characterization of energy levels by configuration assignment.

The angular integrals in (13-25) can be evaluated and are found to be (we have suppressed m_s and replaced m_ℓ by m)

$$\langle n'\ell+1 \;\; m \,|\, z \,|\, n\ell m\rangle = \sqrt{\frac{(\ell+1)^2 - m^2}{(2\ell+3)(2\ell+1)}} \;\; \langle n'\ell+1 \,|\, r \,|\, n\ell\rangle$$

$$\langle n'\ell-1 \;\; m \,|\, z \,|\, n\ell m\rangle = \sqrt{\frac{\ell^2 - m^2}{(2\ell+1)(2\ell-1)}} \;\; \langle n'\ell-1 \,|\, r \,|\, n\ell\rangle$$

$$\langle n'\ell+1 \;\; m\pm 1 \,|\, x \pm iy \,|\, n\ell m\rangle = \pm\sqrt{\frac{(\ell \pm m+2)(\ell \pm m+1)}{(2\ell+3)(2\ell+1)}} \;\; \langle n'\ell+1 \,|\, r \,|\, n\ell\rangle$$

$$\langle n'\ell-1\ \ m\pm 1 \mid x \pm iy \mid n\ell m\rangle$$

$$= \mp \sqrt{\frac{(\ell \mp m)(\ell \mp m - 1)}{(2\ell + 1)(2\ell - 1)}}\ \langle n'\ell-1 \mid r \mid n\ell\rangle$$

$$\langle n\ell \mid r \mid n'\ell'\rangle$$

$$= \int_0^\infty r\, \mathcal{R}_{n\ell}\, \mathcal{R}_{n'\ell'}\ dr \tag{13-28}$$

When ± signs are given, the upper signs go together and so do the lower signs.

Equations (13-28) have the following consequences:

$$\sum_{m'} \mid\langle n'\ell+1\ \ m' \mid \mathbf{r} \mid n\ell m\rangle\mid^2$$

$$= \frac{\ell+1}{2\ell+1}\ \langle n'\ell+1 \mid r \mid n\ell\rangle^2$$

$$\sum_{m'} \mid\langle n'\ell-1\ \ m' \mid \mathbf{r} \mid n\ell m\rangle\mid^2 \tag{13-29}$$

$$= \frac{\ell}{2\ell+1}\ \langle n'\ell-1 \mid r \mid n\ell\rangle^2$$

We have added the intensities of transition regardless of polarization from a certain state $n\ell m$ to all levels m' of $n'\ell'$ and conclude that the lifetime of a state depends only on n, n', and ℓ.

$$\sum_{m} \mid\langle n'\ell-1\ \ m \mid z \mid n\ell m\rangle\mid^2 = \tfrac{1}{3}\ell\,\langle n'\ell-1 \mid r \mid n\ell\rangle^2$$

$$\sum_{m} \mid\langle n'\ell-1\ \ m+1 \mid x \mid n\ell m\rangle\mid^2 + \mid\langle n'\ell-1\ \ m-1 \mid x \mid n\ell m\rangle\mid^2$$

$$= \tfrac{1}{3}\ell\,\langle n'\ell-1 \mid r \mid n\ell\rangle^2 \tag{13-30}$$

In (13-30) we have summed the intensities of all the Zeeman components of a spectral line that have the same polarization and concluded that the total intensity is the same for each of the three components of a Lorentz triplet in the normal Zeeman effect. Both (13-29) and (13-30) are consequences of the isotropy of space.

The following two "partial oscillator strength sum rules" can now be proved (see Bethe and Salpeter, pp. 260–261).

$$\sum_{n'} \langle n'\ell+1 \mid f^x \mid n\ell\rangle = \frac{1}{3}\,\frac{(\ell+1)(2\ell+3)}{2\ell+1}$$

$$\sum_{n'} \langle n'\ell - 1 \mid f^x \mid n\ell \rangle = -\frac{1}{3}\,\frac{\ell(2\ell - 1)}{2\ell + 1}$$

$$\langle n'\ell' \mid f^x \mid n\ell \rangle = \frac{1}{2\ell + 1} \sum_{m'=-\ell'}^{\ell'} \sum_{m=-\ell}^{\ell} f^x_{n'\ell' m', n\ell m} \tag{13-31}$$

If the two sums in (13-31) are added, we obtain 1 as expected from (13-7). Since the first sum is positive we conclude that among the transitions $\ell \to \ell + 1$ absorption ($\omega_{n'\ell+1,n\ell} > 0$) predominates. Since the second sum is negative, in $\ell \to \ell - 1$ transitions, emission ($\omega_{n'\ell-1,n\ell} < 0$) predominates. Since energy increases with increasing principal quantum number, (13-31) shows that a change of principal and orbital quantum numbers in the same sense is more probable than a jump in the opposite sense. Similarly, the two last equations of (13-28) show that $|m|$ is likely to jump in the same direction as ℓ. Both results have classical analogues, derivable from a study of the motion of an electron in an ellipse.

SELECTION RULES FOR MANY ELECTRONS

Returning to the problem of determining the selection rules for a complex atom we first consider the LS coupling scheme. Since $\mathbf{r}$ commutes with $\mathbf{S}$, $\mathbf{r}$ cannot connect states with different S or M_S. Hence transitions between levels of different multiplicity are forbidden, and $\Delta M_S = 0$. $\Delta M_S = 0$ for one-electron spectra also.

Since $\mathbf{r}$ is a vector of type $\mathbf{A}$ with respect to $\mathbf{L}$ and $\mathbf{J}$, i.e., of the type considered in (10-17), we have $\Delta L = 0, \pm 1$; $\Delta J = 0, \pm 1$. As for the magnetic quantum number, the matrix element of z is nonvanishing only for $M_L' = M_L$; of $x \pm iy$ only for $M_L' = M_L \pm 1$. The polarization of the light follows the same rules as for one-electron spectra.

For any atom, $J = 0$ to $J = 0$ is strictly forbidden. For consider

$$\int u_f^* \sum_i e^{i\mathbf{k}\cdot\mathbf{r}_i} \frac{\partial}{\partial x_i} u_n \, d\tau$$

Since $J_f = J_n = 0$, the wave functions will not change if we rotate the system in any manner. If in particular we rotate about $\mathbf{k}$ as an axis, then $e^{i\mathbf{k}\cdot\mathbf{r}_i}$ also does not change. For instance, we can rotate the system about $\mathbf{k}$ through 180° for each i. Then $x_i \to -x_i$ and the integral changes sign, without a change in value. Hence it is 0.

We summarize the selection rules for LS coupling:

1. Parity changes.
2. Configuration must change by $\Delta \sum \ell_i = \pm 1$.

3. Multiplicity does not change, $\Delta S = 0$.
4. $\Delta M_S = 0$.
5. $\Delta L = 0, \pm 1$.
6. $\Delta M_L = 0, \pm 1$.
7. $\Delta J = 0, \pm 1$.
8. $J = 0 \rightarrow J = 0$ strictly forbidden.
9. $\Delta M = 0, \pm 1$.

It is seen that these are quite similar to those previously discussed for one-electron spectra. The first, seventh, eighth, and ninth rules hold for arbitrary coupling. The second holds as long as the configuration description is valid. The others hold for LS coupling only. Whenever the description is in terms of orbitals, we recall that parity is + (−) when $\Sigma_j \ell_j$ is even (odd). If the system cannot be approximated by orbitals, we still know the parity from the fact that the admixtures to the orbital eigenfunctions must be of the same parity, i.e., as far as parity is concerned, the orbitals are always a good approximation.

It is important to note that rule 5 permits $\Delta L = 0$, which is not permitted for one-electron spectra. This latter point is a consequence of the parity selection rule: for one electron, $L = \ell$ directly determines the parity, so $\Delta \ell = 0$ would mean no parity change. For a many-electron atom, on the other hand, L has no direct relation to the parity, but the sum of the ℓ's of the individual orbitals does. We have seen, e.g., that for two equivalent electrons of a given ℓ all triplet states have odd L, but of course all these states have even parity. Thus $\Delta L = 0$ is compatible with change of parity.

It should further be noticed that although rule 9 follows from 4 and 6, rule 7 does not follow from 3 and 5. For consider $J_1 = L + \frac{1}{2}$, $J_2 = L - \frac{1}{2}$; set $L' = L - 1$, then $J_1' = L - \frac{1}{2}$, $J_2' = L - \frac{3}{2}$. Rules 3 and 5 would allow all four transitions, however rule 7 prohibits $J_1 \rightarrow J_2'$. Rules 4, 6, and 9 are useful only when an external field has removed the magnetic degeneracy.

The following intensity sum rule can be proved for LS coupling. In a transition array going from one multiplet LS to another, L′S, the sum of the strengths of the lines having a given initial level J is proportional to $2J + 1$. The sum of the strengths having a given final J' is proportional to $2J' + 1$ (Condon and Shortley, p. 238).

In intermediate, or jj, coupling, only rules 1, 2, 7, 8, and 9 apply. The intensity sum rule is no longer valid as formulated above, but other sum rules exist (Condon and Shortley, pp. 278–281).

HIGHER MOMENTS

If a transition is forbidden, i.e., if the dipole matrix element is zero, higher terms in the expansion of $e^{i\mathbf{k}\cdot\mathbf{r}}$ must be taken. Taking the second term $\mathbf{k}\cdot\mathbf{r}$, assuming it equal to $k_z z$, we wish to discuss the physical significance of this expression. If the polarization is in the x direction, the operator appearing in the matrix element is proportional to $\Sigma_i z_i(\partial/\partial x_i)$, which we may conveniently write as

$$\sum_i \left[\left(z_i \frac{\partial}{\partial x_i} - x_i \frac{\partial}{\partial z_i}\right) + \left(x_i \frac{\partial}{\partial z_i} + z_i \frac{\partial}{\partial x_i}\right)\right] \tag{13-32}$$

The first half of this expression is proportional to the total orbital angular momentum operator. Angular momentum is in turn proportional to the magnetic (dipole) moment of the atom. If we make the usual extension to include spin angular momentum, we conclude that the second term in the multipole expansion leads to magnetic dipole radiation with the matrix elements proportional to

$$\langle f \mid \mathbf{L} + 2\mathbf{S} \mid i \rangle = \langle f \mid \mathbf{J} + \mathbf{S} \mid i \rangle \tag{13-33}$$

Since $[\mathbf{J},H] = 0$, (13-33) reduces to $\langle f \mid \mathbf{S} \mid i \rangle$, which would be zero for exact LS coupling. That is, if there were no spin-orbit interaction to break exact LS coupling, there would be no magnetic dipole radiation. Since the spin-orbit interaction breaks LS coupling by mixing states with different L,S but in general of the same configuration, magnetic dipole radiation occurs, but it is quite weak, since the energy difference of two such states belonging to the same configuration is rather small.

The selection rules for magnetic dipole radiation are

1. Parity must remain unchanged.
2. $\Delta J = 0, \pm 1$.
3. $\Delta M = 0, \pm 1$.
4. $J = 0 \rightarrow J = 0$ strictly forbidden.
5. $\Delta \ell_i = \Delta n_i = 0$ (i runs over all orbitals).

(For nuclei the magnetic dipole radiation is quite prominent. For one thing, nuclear coupling is jj rather than LS. However, even if it were LS, the relevant matrix element would be proportional to

$$\langle f \mid \mathbf{L}_p + \mu_p \mathbf{S}_p + \mu_n \mathbf{S}_n \mid i \rangle \tag{13-34}$$

where p and n refer to proton and neutron, respectively, and $\mu_p = 2.8$ $\mu_n = -1.9$. The quantity that is conserved is $\mathbf{L}_p + \mathbf{S}_p + \mathbf{S}_n$ and not $\mathbf{L}_p + \mu_p \mathbf{S}_p + \mu_n \mathbf{S}_n$, hence magnetic dipole transitions are strong.)

The remaining part of (13-32) when operating on u_n satisfies the following identity:

$$2\sum_i \left(x_i \frac{\partial}{\partial z_i} + z_i \frac{\partial}{\partial x_i}\right) u_n = \sum_i \nabla_i^2 (z_i x_i u_n) - z_i x_i \nabla_i^2 u_n \tag{13-35}$$

Therefore the matrix element of the left-hand side between states f and n is proportional to

$$\left[\left(\sum_i z_i x_i\right) H - H \left(\sum_i z_i x_i\right)\right]_{fn}$$

$$= \left[\left(\sum_i z_i x_i\right), H\right]_{fn} \propto \left(\frac{d}{dt} \sum_i z_i x_i\right)_{fn}$$

$$\propto \omega_{fn} \left(\sum_i z_i x_i\right)_{fn} \qquad (13\text{-}36)$$

We recognize this to be the electric quadrupole moment of the atom and therefore this term leads to electric quadrupole radiation.

The selection rules for quadrupole radiation of one-electron atoms can be obtained as follows. From matrix multiplication

$$(xy)_{fn} = \sum_{n'} x_{fn'} y_{n'n}$$

Applying the dipole selection rules to the matrix elements of x and y we obtain $\Delta \ell = 0, \pm 2$; $\Delta m_\ell = 0, \pm 1, \pm 2$; $\Delta S = 0$; $\Delta M_S = 0$; $\Delta J = 0, \pm 1, \pm 2$; $\ell: 0 \to 0$ forbidden, $J: 0 \to 0$ forbidden. It is also seen that parity must remain the same. For many-electron atoms the selection rules can be obtained by general arguments (Condon and Shortley, p. 93). With the substitution of L for ℓ and the modification $\Delta L = 0, \pm 1, \pm 2$, the results are the same as above. The transition $L: 0 \to 0$ is still forbidden in the LS coupling. It can also be shown that $L: 0 \to 1$ or $1 \to 0$, and $J: 0 \to 1$, $1 \to 0$, and $\frac{1}{2} \to \frac{1}{2}$ is forbidden.

We saw (p. 141) that in the expansion of $e^{i\mathbf{k}\cdot\mathbf{r}}$, the ratio of the successive integrals is $0(ka) \sim 1/300$ if a is taken to be a_0 and $\hbar\omega_{fn} \sim$ Ry. The quadrupole radiation is further reduced by the fact that the angular average of zx is small ($zx \propto \sin\theta \cos\theta \sin\varphi$). It is found that the ratio of transition probabilities of quadrupole to dipole radiation is usually less than 10^{-6}, making the lifetime of states which can decay *only* by quadrupole radiation greater than 10^{-2} seconds.

As an example we consider oxygen. It has a p^4 configuration leading to states ^3P, ^1D, ^1S. The ground state is the ^3P and the successive separation of the other two states is about 1 ev. Dipole transitions between these states are forbidden since the parity is the same for all of them, as the configuration does not change. The quadrupole transition $^1S \to {}^1D$ is allowed and has a long life. $^1D \to {}^3P$ is doubly forbidden since S changes. Since spin-orbit coupling breaks LS coupling, $^1D \to {}^3P_{2,1}$ can actually occur, via a magnetic dipole transition, but has a very long lifetime. In a discharge tube filled with oxygen under reasonable pressure, atoms in the ^1D state decay by collision. But under low pressure, e.g., in the ionosphere, the atom has time to radiate before making a collision. This is the origin of the famous red line of the aurora. The oxygen is excited by incoming protons and then decays. Forbidden transitions are also seen frequently in the sun's corona and in some nebulae. It was first thought that these lines corresponded to a new element, nebulium. Bowen (1928) finally showed them to be forbidden transitions in highly ionized familiar atoms.

ABSOLUTE TRANSITION PROBABILITIES

The total transition probability for spontaneous emission from state k to n is given by

$$A_{kn} = \frac{4}{3} \frac{e^2 \omega_{kn}^3}{\hbar c^3} \, |(\mathbf{r})_{kn}|^2 \tag{12-33}$$

In terms of the oscillator strength this becomes

$$A_{kn} = \frac{2}{3} \frac{e^2}{mc^3} \omega_{kn}^2 f_{kn} \tag{13-37}$$

If one sums (12-33) or (13-37) over all states n which have energy less than that of the initial state k, one arrives at the total probability per unit time that the state k is vacated through spontaneous emission.

$$\beta_k = \sum_{E_n < E_k} A_{kn} \tag{13-38}$$

The reciprocal of this quantity is called the lifetime of the state k.

$$T_k = \frac{1}{\beta_k} \tag{13-39}$$

Bethe and Salpeter (pp. 262-269) list the squares of the dipole moments, the oscillator strengths, and the transition probabilities for hydrogen for transition $n\ell \rightarrow n'\ell \pm 1$. We discuss the qualitative behavior of their results.

The oscillator strength decreases rapidly with increasing n'. To see this we recall that the oscillator strength involves the radial integral

$$\left| \int r \mathcal{R}_{n'\ell'} \mathcal{R}_{n\ell} \, dr \right|^2$$

Table 13-2

Initial state	Final state	Average oscillator strength
2p	3s	0.014
	3d	0.7
4f	5d	0.009
	5g	1.35

If $n \ll n'$ then $\mathcal{R}_{n\ell}$ is large only for small r. But for small r, we found that $\mathcal{R}_{n'\ell'} \propto n'^{-3/2}$; see (4-34). Therefore,

$$f_{n\ell, n'\ell'} \propto \frac{1}{n'^3} \tag{13-40}$$

for large n'.

We found from sum rules that if $n' > n$, ℓ' tends to be greater than ℓ. This rule is verified. For example, see Table 13-2.

For small orbital quantum numbers (eccentric orbits in Bohr theory) transitions into the continuum are more frequent than for large quantum numbers (circular orbits). For example, the oscillator strengths for transitions from $n\ell$ to the continuum are given in Table 13-3.

The emission probability is largest if the final state is the ground state. For example, the emission probabilities from the 6p state to various states are: 1s, $0.20 \times 10^{+8}$ sec^{-1}; 2s, $0.03 \times 10^{+8}$ sec^{-1}; 5s, $0.002 \times 10^{+8}$ sec^{-1}.

The lifetimes of highly excited states are longer than those of moderately excited states. For example, the lifetimes of various $n\ell$ states are given in Table 13-4.

For alkalis, where the valence electron is subject to a non-Coulombic potential, the first (so-called resonance) line, ns → np, has a

Table 13-3
Transitions from State $n\ell$ to Continuum

$n\ell$	Total oscillator strength
1s	0.43
4s	0.25
4f	0.056

Table 13-4
Lifetimes of Various States $n\ell$

$n\ell$	Lifetime
2p	0.16×10^{-8} sec
6p	4.1×10^{-8} sec
6h	61×10^{-8} sec

Table 13-5

	Na	H
3p	0.98	0
4p	0.014	0.48
6p	0.001	0.05

much larger oscillator strength than the lines from the ground state ns to higher states. As an example, we list in Table 13-5 the oscillator strengths for Na for transitions from the 3s level, and compare them with the corresponding ones in H.

Finally we observe that in hydrogen the transition $2s \rightarrow 2p_{1/2}$ has a lifetime $\sim$ 2 days for dipole radiation. A faster way for the 2s to decay is by emitting two quanta and going to the 1s level. The lifetime for this process is $\frac{1}{7}$ second. The energies of the individual quanta can be arbitrary as long as the sum equals the energy difference of the levels.

Chapter 14

PHOTOELECTRIC EFFECT

In Chapter 12 we found the differential cross section for the absorption of radiation of frequency ω by an atom and removal of an electron into the continuum. This is the experimental condition for the photo effect. We found

$$\sigma(\theta, \varphi) = \frac{e^2}{2\pi mc} \frac{k_f}{\omega} \left| \int u_f^* e^{i\mathbf{k}\cdot\mathbf{r}} \nabla_A u_n \, d\tau \right|^2 \tag{12-14}$$

where the subscript f indicates the final state. We now discuss three approaches to evaluating this integral assuming that the atom is hydrogen and the initial state is the ground state.

BORN APPROXIMATION

We replace the final state by $e^{i\mathbf{k}_f\cdot\mathbf{r}}$. This is reasonably good if $p_f \gg p_{1s}$, the momentum of the ground state. We have

$$\frac{\hbar^2 k_f^2}{2m} = \hbar\omega - \frac{e^2}{2a_0} > 0$$

and require

$$\hbar k_f \gg \sqrt{\frac{e^2 m}{a_0}} \qquad \text{or} \qquad a_0^2 k_f^2 \gg 1 \tag{14-1}$$

The integral becomes

$$\int e^{-i\mathbf{q}\cdot\mathbf{r}} \frac{\partial u_{10}}{\partial x} \, d\tau \tag{14-2}$$

with $\mathbf{q} = \mathbf{k}_f - \mathbf{k}$. We assumed that $\mathbf{A}$, the polarization vector, is along the x axis and thus **k** has no x component. We integrate by parts, substitute the ground-state wave function for hydrogen and obtain, with the aid of some algebra for the differential cross section,

$$\sigma(\theta, \varphi) = \frac{32e^2}{mc\,\omega} \frac{\cos^2\alpha\,(k_f a_0)^3}{(1 + q^2 a_0^2)^4}$$

$$\cos\alpha = \frac{\mathbf{k}_f \cdot \mathbf{x}}{k_f x} \tag{14-3}$$

Equation (14-3) depends on angle in two ways. First $\cos^2\alpha$ indicates that the electron preferentially comes out along the direction of the electric field of the incident light wave (polarization vector). If the initial state had not been an isotropic state, then an expression of the form $A + B\cos^2\alpha$ would replace the $\cos^2\alpha$ term.

The second dependence on angle arises from the q^2 dependence in the denominator.

$$q^2 = k_f^2\left(1 - 2\frac{k}{k_f}\cos\theta + \left(\frac{k}{k_f}\right)^2\right)$$

$$\cos\theta = \frac{\mathbf{k}\cdot\mathbf{k}_f}{kk_f} \tag{14-4}$$

From (14-1) we conclude that

$$\frac{k}{k_f} = \frac{\omega}{ck_f} \approx \frac{\hbar k_f}{2mc} = \frac{v}{2c} \tag{14-5}$$

where v is the velocity of the ejected electron. Since we are dealing with a nonrelativistic theory we can write

$$q^2 = k_f^2\left(1 - \frac{v}{c}\cos\theta\right) \tag{14-6}$$

Further $q^2 a_0^2 \sim k_f^2 a_0^2 \gg 1$. Therefore we can replace $1 + q^2 a_0^2$ by $k_f^2 a_0^2(1 - (v/c)\cos\theta)$.

$$\sigma(\theta, \varphi) = \frac{32e^2}{mc\omega\,(k_f a_0)^5} \frac{\sin^2\theta\cos^2\varphi}{\left(1 - \frac{v}{c}\cos\theta\right)^4} \tag{14-7}$$

since $\cos\alpha = \sin\theta\cos\varphi$.

The angular dependence of (14-7) is easily understood. If we neglect the term with v/c, which is reasonable in the nonrelativistic case, the angular dependence is as $\cos^2\alpha$, having a maximum in the direction of the electric field of the incident light wave. The result means that the electron goes from the initial s state into a final state, whose m = 0 with respect to the x axis (field direction). This corresponds to the selection rules derived in Chapter 13. With respect to the direction of propagation, the distribution has a maximum in the equatorial plane, $\theta = \pi/2$. If we now take the retardation term with v/c into account, this maximum is shifted forward to approximately

$$\theta_{max} \approx \frac{\pi}{2} - 4\frac{v}{c} \tag{14-8}$$

There is no special significance to the factor 4; it is different for other initial states.

If we integrate (14-7) over angles, neglecting terms of relative order $(v/c)^2$, we obtain

$$\sigma = 2^8 \frac{\pi}{3} \frac{e^2}{\hbar c} a_0^2 \left(\frac{Ry}{\hbar\omega}\right)^{7/2} \tag{14-9}$$

Had we performed the dipole approximation in (12-14) we would have obtained for σ the result

$$\frac{e^2}{\omega} \frac{k_f}{2\pi mc} \frac{1}{\hbar^2} \left| (p_x)_{fn} \right|^2$$

$$= \frac{e^2}{\omega} \frac{k_f m}{2\pi c} \frac{\omega_{fn}^2}{\hbar^2} \left| (x)_{fn} \right|^2 \propto \omega^{3/2} \left|(x)_{fn}\right|^2 \tag{14-10}$$

since $\omega_{fn} = \omega \propto k_f^{1/2}$. Comparing with (14-9) we find $|x_{fn}|^2 \propto \omega^{-5}$. This result applies to the case when u_f is normalized to unit amplitude, $e^{i\mathbf{k}_f\cdot\mathbf{r}}$. If instead we normalize per unit energy, we get an extra factor $\rho(k_f)$, the number of states near k_f per unit energy. We have $\rho(k_f) \propto k_f \propto \omega^{1/2}$, so that the dipole matrix element in the energy normalization behaves for large ω as

$$\left| x_{fn}^E \right|^2 \propto \omega^{-9/2} \tag{14-11}$$

This agrees with our previous conclusion from sum rules, p. 152.

DIPOLE APPROXIMATION

The second method of calculating the photoelectric effect is to ignore the retardation but use correct wave functions for the continuum. This calculation is described, e.g., in Bethe and Salpeter, pp. 303–304. The result is

$$\sigma = \frac{2^9 \pi^2}{3} a_0^2 \frac{e^2}{\hbar c} \left(\frac{Ry}{\hbar\omega}\right)^4 f(n')$$

$$f(n') = \frac{e^{-4n' \operatorname{arccot} n'}}{1 - e^{-2\pi n'}} \tag{14-12}$$

$$\hbar\omega = \left(1 + \frac{1}{n'^2}\right) Ry$$

For large $\hbar\omega$, n' becomes small, and

$$f(n') \approx \frac{1}{2\pi n'} \approx \frac{1}{2\pi}\left(\frac{\hbar\omega}{Ry}\right)^{1/2}$$

Then

$$\sigma = \frac{2^8 \pi}{3} a_0^2 \frac{e^2}{\hbar c}\left(\frac{Ry}{\hbar\omega}\right)^{7/2} \tag{14-9}$$

which is identical with the Born approximation. This is to be expected because for $\hbar\omega \gg Ry$ the Born approximation should be valid, and for $v \ll c$ the retardation is negligible, and has in fact been neglected in (14-9). Near threshold, $n' \to \infty$, thus

$$f(n') \approx e^{-4}\left(1 + \frac{4}{3n'^2}\right) \approx e^{-4}\left(1 + \frac{1}{n'^2}\right)^{4/3}$$
$$f(n') \approx e^{-4}\left(\frac{\hbar\omega}{Ry}\right)^{4/3} \tag{14-13}$$

Then

$$\sigma = \frac{2^9 \pi^2 e^{-4}}{3} a_0^2 \frac{e^2}{\hbar c}\left(\frac{Ry}{\hbar\omega}\right)^{8/3} \tag{14-14}$$

Since also $\hbar\omega \approx Ry$, this can be written

$$\sigma = 31 \frac{a_0^2 e^2}{\hbar c} \tag{14-15}$$

The factors a_0^2 and $e^2/\hbar c$ could have been expected from dimensional arguments; the numerical factor 31 can only be obtained from direct calculation. Since this factor is large, there is strong absorption of X-rays above threshold.

ROUGH ESTIMATE

The third method of calculating the photoelectric effect cross section is a very rough approximation and is useful when little is known, e.g., for calculations for atoms other than hydrogen. We use a normalization such that u_f is normalized per unit energy, i.e.,

$$\int d\tau \; u_f(\mathbf{r}) \left\{ \int_{E-\Delta E}^{E+\Delta E} dE' \; u_{f'}(\mathbf{r}) \right\} = 1 \qquad (14\text{-}16)$$

Accordingly, we call the oscillator strength calculated with this normalization, df/dE. Neglecting retardation,

$$\sigma = 2\pi^2 e^2 \frac{\hbar}{mc} \frac{df}{dE} \qquad (14\text{-}17)$$

For hydrogen we assume

$$\frac{df}{dE} = \frac{(Ry)^2}{(\hbar\omega)^3} \, 2 \times 0.43$$

This is chosen so that

$$\int_{Ry}^{\infty} d(\hbar\omega) \frac{df}{dE} = 0.43$$

which we know to be the total oscillator strength from the 1s state to the continuum. The dependence on ω is chosen in accord with empirical data on X-ray absorption, and is an average between the $\omega^{-7/2}$ of (14-9) and the $\omega^{-8/3}$ of (14-14). At $\hbar\omega = Ry$, (14-17) gives

$$\sigma = 34 a_0^2 \frac{e^2}{\hbar c} \qquad (14\text{-}18)$$

instead of (14-15), an error of 10 per cent.

Chapter 15

COLLISIONS BETWEEN ATOMS AND CHARGED PARTICLES

We shall study the collision of a particle of charge ze with an atom with atomic number Z. We shall assume the particle to be fast enough for the Born approximation to hold, but nevertheless nonrelativistic. (We shall nevertheless write many of the subsequent formulas in a fashion which makes them relativistically correct.) Thus we assume the initial particle velocity to be between $(Z/137)c$ and about $\frac{1}{2}c$.

The Hamiltonian for the entire problem is

$$H = H_a + H_p + H^1 \tag{15-1}$$

H_a is the Hamiltonian of the atom, H_p the free-particle Hamiltonian, and H^1 the interaction Hamiltonian representing the interaction of the incident particle with the electrons and nucleus of the atom. Using the methods of time-dependent perturbation theory we expand the eigenfunctions of H in terms of the complete set of eigenfunctions of $H_a + H_p$ and consider H^1 as the perturbing Hamiltonian,

$$i\hbar \frac{\partial\psi}{\partial t} = H\psi \tag{15-2a}$$

$$\psi = \sum_n c_n(\mathbf{k},t)\,\psi_n(\mathbf{r}_1, \ldots, \mathbf{r}_Z)\,e^{i\mathbf{k}\cdot\mathbf{r}_0}\,e^{-i(E_n+W)t/\hbar} \tag{15-2b}$$

$$H^1 = -ze^2\left[\sum_{j=1}^{Z} \frac{1}{r_{0j}} - \frac{Z}{r_0}\right] \tag{15-2c}$$

In (15-2b) c_n is the nth expansion coefficient depending on $\mathbf{k}$, the propagation vector of the incident particle, and on time. ψ_n is the eigenfunction of H_a describing the nth state of the atom with energy E_n. ψ_n depends on Z-position variables corresponding to the Z electrons in the atom. (We neglect all considerations of spin.) The expression $e^{i\mathbf{k}\cdot\mathbf{r}_0}$ is the free-particle eigenfunction, with $\mathbf{r}_0$ being the position vector and W the energy including the rest mass of the incident particle. In the interaction Hamiltonian, $\mathbf{r}_{0j}$ is the distance between the incident particle and the jth electron. The first term in the interaction Hamiltonian is the potential energy of the interaction of the particle with the electron configuration; the second term describes the nuclear interaction. It is clear that we are assuming the nucleus to be at rest at the origin of the coordinate system.

Equation (15-2a) is then equivalent to

$$i\hbar \frac{\partial c_n(\mathbf{k},t)}{\partial t} = \sum_{n'} c_{n'}(\mathbf{k}',t) \int \psi_n^*(\mathbf{r}_1 \cdots \mathbf{r}_Z)\, e^{-i\mathbf{k}\cdot\mathbf{r}_0} \times H^1 \psi_{n'}(\mathbf{r}_1 \cdots \mathbf{r}_Z)\, e^{i\mathbf{k}'\cdot\mathbf{r}_0} \times e^{i\omega_{nn'}t}\, d\tau_0\, d\tau \qquad [d\tau = d\tau_1 \cdots d\tau_Z] \tag{15-3a}$$

$$\omega_{nn'} = \frac{(E_n + W) - (E_{n'} + W')}{\hbar} \tag{15-3b}$$

Here n,**k**,W describe the initial state of the atom and incident particles, and n′,**k**′,W′ are the corresponding final-state quantities.

If in the zero-order approximation we consider

$$c_{n'}(\mathbf{k}',t) = \delta_{n'0} \tag{15-4}$$

(i.e., initially the atom was in the ground state ψ_0 and the incident particle parameters are $\mathbf{k}_0$ and W_0), we obtain for the first-order approximation to the transition probability amplitude,

$$i\hbar \frac{\partial c_n(\mathbf{k}',t)}{\partial t} = \int \psi_n^*(\mathbf{r}_1 \cdots \mathbf{r}_Z)\, e^{-i\mathbf{k}\cdot\mathbf{r}_0} \times H^1 \psi_0(\mathbf{r}_1 \cdots \mathbf{r}_Z)\, e^{i\mathbf{k}_0\cdot\mathbf{r}_0}\, d\tau_0\, d\tau \times e^{it(E_n + W - E_0 - W_0)/\hbar} \tag{15-5}$$

Thus the probability of transition from the initial state to the nth state is sizeable only if

$$E_n + W = E_0 + W_0 \tag{15-6}$$

which is the usual energy conservation law. The scattering cross section, which is the transition probability per unit time divided by the incident current (i.e., by v_0 the velocity of the incident particle) is

$$\sigma(\theta,\varphi) = (ze^2)^2 \frac{2\pi}{\hbar v_0}$$
$$\times \left| \int \psi_n^* \psi_0 e^{i\mathbf{q}\cdot\mathbf{r}_0} \left(\frac{Z}{r_0} - \sum_{j=1}^{Z} \frac{1}{r_{0j}} \right) d\tau_0 \, d\tau \right|^2$$
$$\times \delta(E_n + W - E_0 - W_0) \tag{15-7a}$$

where

$$\mathbf{q} = \mathbf{k}_0 - \mathbf{k} \tag{15-7b}$$

is the change of momentum in scattering, and $\theta\varphi$ define the direction of k. Since W lies in the continuum (i.e., the incident particle is assumed not to be captured) we integrate over a small energy interval about W and replace the delta function with $\rho(W)$, the density of states per unit energy, which equals $p^2 \, dp/(2\pi\hbar)^3 \, dW$. (The usual volume term has been absorbed in the normalization of the free-particle solutions.) With $dW/dp = v$, $p^2/v = (W/c^2)^2 v$, we obtain for the scattering cross section

$$\sigma(\theta,\varphi) = \left(\frac{Wze^2}{c^2 \, 2\pi\hbar^2} \right)^2 \frac{v}{v_0}$$
$$\times \left| \int \psi_n^* \psi_0 e^{i\mathbf{q}\cdot\mathbf{r}_0} \left(\frac{Z}{r_0} - \sum_{j=1}^{Z} \frac{1}{r_{0j}} \right) d\tau_0 \, d\tau \right|^2 \tag{15-8}$$

The integration over the coordinates of the incident particle can be readily carried out. The integral $\int f(\mathbf{r}_0) e^{i\mathbf{q}\cdot\mathbf{r}_0} \, d\tau_0$ can be evaluated by noting that $e^{i\mathbf{q}\cdot\mathbf{r}_0} = -(1/q^2) \nabla^2 e^{i\mathbf{q}\cdot\mathbf{r}_0}$ and

$$\int f(\mathbf{r}_0) e^{i\mathbf{q}\cdot\mathbf{r}_0} \, d\tau_0 = -\frac{1}{q^2} \int \left(\nabla^2 e^{i\mathbf{q}\cdot\mathbf{r}_0} \right) f(\mathbf{r}_0) \, d\tau_0$$
$$= -\frac{1}{q^2} \int e^{i\mathbf{q}\cdot\mathbf{r}_0} \nabla^2 f(\mathbf{r}_0) \, d\tau_0 \tag{15-9}$$

The last expression is obtained by a double partial integration with the surface terms neglected.

$$\int \left[\frac{Z}{r_0} - \sum_{j=1}^{Z} \frac{1}{r_{0j}} \right] e^{i\mathbf{q}\cdot\mathbf{r}_0} \, d\tau_0$$

$$= -\frac{1}{q^2} \int e^{i\mathbf{q}\cdot\mathbf{r}_0} \left[\nabla_0^2 \frac{Z}{r_0} - \sum_{j=1}^{Z} \nabla_0^2 \frac{1}{r_{0j}} \right] d\tau_0$$

$$= \frac{4\pi}{q^2} \int e^{i\mathbf{q}\cdot\mathbf{r}_0} \left[Z\,\delta(r_0) - \sum_{j=1}^{Z} \delta(r_{0j}) \right] d\tau_0$$

$$= \frac{4\pi}{q^2} \left[Z - \sum_{j=1}^{Z} e^{i\mathbf{q}\cdot\mathbf{r}_j} \right] \tag{15-10}$$

$$\sigma(\theta,\varphi) = \left(\frac{2ze^2 W}{\hbar^2 c^2 q^2} \right)^2 \frac{v}{v_0} \times \left| \int \psi_n^* \psi_0 \left(Z - \sum_{j=1}^{Z} e^{i\mathbf{q}\cdot\mathbf{r}_j} \right) d\tau \right|^2 \tag{15-11}$$

We note that $\sigma(\theta,\varphi) \sim 1/q^4$, just as in the Rutherford formula. This indicates that scattering which results in small momentum change is preferred.

ELASTIC SCATTERING

We first examine elastic scattering, i.e., $\psi_n = \psi_0$, $v = v_0$. The first term in the integral can be integrated to give Z. The second term,

$$\sum_{j=1}^{Z} \int |\psi_0|^2 e^{i\mathbf{q}\cdot\mathbf{r}_j} \, d\tau_1 \cdots d\tau_Z$$

can be written

$$\sum_{j=1}^{Z} \int \left\{ \int |\psi_0|^2 \prod_{i \neq j}^{Z} d\tau_i \right\} e^{i\mathbf{q}\cdot\mathbf{r}_j} \, d\tau_j \tag{15-12a}$$

The quantity in curly brackets is seen to be the probability density of the jth electron. We define

$$\rho(\mathbf{r}_j) = Z \int |\psi_0|^2 \prod_{i \neq j} d\tau_i \tag{15-12b}$$

Then (15-12a) can be rewritten

$$\sum_{j=1}^{Z} \frac{1}{Z} \int \rho(\mathbf{r}_j)\, e^{i\mathbf{q}\cdot\mathbf{r}_j}\, d\tau_j \tag{15-12c}$$

Observing that $\mathbf{r}_j$ is a dummy variable of integration, (15-12c) becomes

$$F(q) = \int \rho(\mathbf{r})\, e^{i\mathbf{q}\cdot\mathbf{r}}\, d\tau \tag{15-12d}$$

where $\rho(\mathbf{r})$ is the total electron density at $\mathbf{r}$. The quantity $F(q)$ is called the form factor. We observe that with the above definition of ρ

$$\int \rho(r)\, d\tau = Z \tag{15-12e}$$

If θ is the angle of deflection (angle between $\mathbf{k}_0$ and $\mathbf{k}$), then $\hbar q = 2p \sin(\theta/2)$ for elastic scattering. The formula for the differential cross section for elastic scattering in the direction θ, φ is

$$\sigma(\theta, \varphi) = \left(\frac{ze^2 W}{2p^2 c^2}\right) \frac{1}{\sin^4(\theta/2)} \,|Z - F(q)|^2$$

$$= \left(\frac{ze^2}{2pv}\right)^2 \frac{1}{\sin^4(\theta/2)} \,|Z - F(q)|^2 \tag{15-13}$$

Let us expand $Z - F(q)$ in powers of q. The zero-order term is 0 from (15-12e). The first-order term is proportional to $\int \rho(\mathbf{r})\mathbf{r}\, d\tau$, which is the mean value of the dipole moment of the atom, and hence vanishes identically. The first nonvanishing term is proportional to $q^2 \int \rho(\mathbf{r}) r^2\, d\tau$. The differential cross section is seen to be independent of angle for small-angle scattering and depends simply on the mean-square distance of the electrons from the nucleus. It is seen that the singularity at $q = 0$, which occurs in the Rutherford formula, disappears. When $qa \ll 1$, where a is a characteristic radius of the atom, $F(q) \ll Z$.

The entire velocity dependence is given by pv. In the nonrelativistic region this is equal to twice the kinetic energy. In the extreme relativistic case $v \to c$, $pv \approx W$. The dependence on pv is correct for all velocities.

The form factor for heavy atoms can be evaluated from the Thomas Fermi theory of the atom, or, for any atom and more accurately, from the Hartree-Fock theory.

INELASTIC SCATTERING

For inelastic scattering, $n \neq 0$, the general formula (15-11) for the differential cross section reduces to

$$\sigma(\theta,\varphi) = \left(\frac{2ze^2W}{c^2\hbar^2q^2}\right)^2 \frac{v}{v_0}$$

$$\times \left| \int \sum_{j=1}^{Z} \psi_n^* \psi_0 e^{i\mathbf{q}\cdot\mathbf{r}_j} \, d\tau_1 \cdots d\tau_Z \right|^2 \qquad (15\text{-}14)$$

The term in (15-11) proportional to Z is 0, owing to the orthogonality of ψ_0 and ψ_n. We recall that ψ_n, ψ_0 describe the electron configuration of the atom. In particular, if they are approximated by Slater determinants, the observation that $\Sigma_{j=1}^{Z} e^{i\mathbf{q}\cdot\mathbf{r}_j}$ is a one-electron operator leads to the conclusion that inelastic scattering occurs when only one orbital changes between the initial and final state.

We estimate qa:

$$q^2 = k_0^2 + k^2 - 2k_0k\cos\theta$$

$$q_{min} = k_0 - k = \frac{p_0 - p}{\hbar}$$

$$= \frac{\Delta p}{\hbar} \approx \frac{\Delta W}{\hbar v} \qquad \text{since } \frac{dW}{dp} = v \qquad (15\text{-}15)$$

$$q_{min} \approx \frac{E_n - E_0}{\hbar v} \neq 0$$

Assume $E_n - E_0 \approx Ry \approx e^2/a$; $e^2/\hbar = u_0$ is the velocity of the electron in the first Bohr orbit. Therefore,

$$q_{min} \approx \frac{u_0}{va} \qquad q_{min}a \sim \frac{u_0}{v} \ll 1 \qquad (15\text{-}16)$$

because the Born approximation is supposed to be valid.

$$q_{max} = k + k_0 \approx 2k_0 \qquad q_{max}a \gg 1 \qquad (15\text{-}17)$$

Hence as q ranges from $k - k_0$ to $k + k_0$, qa goes from much less than one to much greater than one.

For $qa \ll 1$ we expand the exponential. The zero-order term vanishes because of the orthogonality of the wave functions. The first nonvanishing term leads to the integral

$$\mathbf{iq} \cdot \int \psi_n^* \psi_0 \sum_j \mathbf{r}_j \, d\tau \tag{15-18}$$

which is the dipole moment for the transition $0 \rightarrow n$. Since we know that the cross section contains a factor q^{-4}, small q are most frequent, and for these we see that the collisions mostly cause transitions which are also optically allowed. The result (15-18) does not depend on any Hartree-Fock approximation. For $qa \approx 1$, transitions to any state n are possible, not only dipole transitions.

For $qa \gg 1$, the integral occurring in (15-14) will become quite small due to the rapid oscillation of the exponential unless ψ_n varies the same way. If we consider the determinantal approximation, then the integral reduces to

$$\int e^{i\mathbf{q} \cdot \mathbf{r}} \, u_n^*(r) u_0(r) \, d\tau \tag{15-19}$$

This can be large only if u_n varies as $e^{i\mathbf{q} \cdot \mathbf{r}}$, i.e., if the final state of the excited atomic electron has momentum $\approx q$. This leads to the conclusion that there is approximate conservation of momentum between incident particle and excited electron; i.e., the nucleus gets little momentum in the case $qa \gg 1$.

This result has an important influence on q_{max} because $\hbar q_{max}$ is now the maximum momentum which can be transferred by the incident particle (mass M) to an electron in a collision which conserves momentum and energy between these two particles. By elementary classical mechanics this is in the nonrelativistic case

$$\hbar q_{max} = \frac{2Mmv_0}{M + m} \tag{15-20a}$$

$$\hbar q_{max} \approx 2mv_0 \qquad \text{if } M \gg m \tag{15-20b}$$

$$\hbar q_{max} \approx mv_0 \qquad \text{if } M \approx m \tag{15-20c}$$

In the latter case (incident electron) it is customary to consider the slower of the two resulting electrons as that ejected from the atom which modifies (15-20c) to

$$\hbar q_{max} \approx \frac{mv_0}{\sqrt{2}} \tag{15-20d}$$

Moreover, there is in this case an exchange term between incident and atomic electron which reduces the cross section when q is of the order of q_{max}.

ENERGY LOSS OF INCIDENT PARTICLE

When a charged particle goes through matter, it makes many collisions, the cross section for each being given by (15-11). Inelastic collisions occur even at large atomic distances between particle and atom, the largest being given by $1/q_{min}$, which is about 100 atomic radii when $v \to c$. (In the relativistic region, this distance increases further, as p.) The particle loses its kinetic energy by such collisions and eventually is brought to a stop.

The energy loss per unit path is

$$-\frac{dW}{dx} = \sum_n N \int \sigma_n(\theta,\varphi)\, d\Omega\, (E_n - E_0) \tag{15-21}$$

N is the number of atoms per unit volume. $\int \sigma_n(\theta,\varphi)\, d\Omega$ is the total cross section for the inelastic collision leading to the final atomic state with energy E_n; and $E_n - E_0 = W_0 - W$ is the energy loss in this collision. The summation over n is over all atomic states, to give the total energy loss by the particle $-dW/dx$.

To evaluate this quantity we consider first

$$\frac{v}{v_0}\, d\Omega = 2\pi \frac{v}{v_0} \sin\theta\, d\theta \tag{15-22}$$

From (15-15),

$$q\, dq = kk_0 \sin\theta\, d\theta \tag{15-23}$$

In the nonrelativistic case we have

$$k = \frac{mv}{\hbar} \qquad k_0 = \frac{mv_0}{\hbar}$$
$$\frac{v}{v_0}\, d\Omega = 2\pi \frac{k}{k_0} \sin\theta\, d\theta = \frac{2\pi q\, dq}{k_0^2} \tag{15-24}$$

In the relativistic case, with very good approximation, $v = v_0$ and $k = k_0$; (15-24) is again valid. Then (15-14), (15-21), and (15-24) combine to give

$$-\frac{dW}{dx} = N \sum_n \int_{q_{min}}^{q_{max}} \frac{2\pi q\, dq}{k_0^2 q^4} \left(\frac{2ze^2 W_0}{\hbar^2 c^2}\right)^2 \times \left| \int \psi_n^* A \psi_0\, d\tau \right|^2 (E_n - E_0) \tag{15-25}$$

where $A = \Sigma_i e^{i\mathbf{q}\cdot\mathbf{r}_i}$. We have replaced W by W_0. Now $W_0/\hbar c^2 k_0 = 1/v_0$, both in the relativistic and nonrelativistic region. Hence

$$-\frac{dW}{dx} = 2\pi N\left(\frac{2ze^2}{\hbar v_0}\right)^2 \sum_n \int_{q_{min}}^{q_{max}} \frac{dq}{q^3}$$

$$\times \left| \int \psi_n^* A \psi_0 \, d\tau \right|^2 (E_n - E_0) \tag{15-26}$$

We now make the approximation that we can interchange the summation over n with the integration over q. This is an approximation, since q_{max} and q_{min} both depend on E_n. Thus we are led to rewrite (15-26) as

$$-\frac{dW}{dx} = 2\pi N\left(\frac{2ze^2}{\hbar v_0}\right)^2 \int_{\bar{q}_{min}}^{\bar{q}_{max}} \frac{dq}{q^3}$$

$$\times \sum_n \left| \int \psi_n^* A \psi_0 \, d\tau \right|^2 (E_n - E_0) \tag{15-27}$$

where the bar over the limits of the q integration indicates that they have been replaced by suitable average values which are independent of n.

The sum over n can be evaluated exactly. It first is written as

$$\sum_n |A_{no}|^2 (E_n - E_0)$$

$$= \sum_n (A_{no})^* A_{no} (E_n - E_0)$$

$$= \sum_n (A^*)_{on} [H,A]_{no} = (A^*[H,A])_{oo} \tag{15-28}$$

We evaluate this in the nonrelativistic case.

$$H = V + \sum_i \frac{p_i^2}{2m} \tag{15-29}$$

V clearly commutes with A. Hence

$$[H,A] = \sum_{j,i} -\frac{\hbar^2}{2m}\left[\nabla_j^2, e^{i\mathbf{q}\cdot\mathbf{r}_i}\right]$$

$$= \sum_{j,i} -\frac{\hbar^2}{2m}\left(-q^2 e^{i\mathbf{q}\cdot\mathbf{r}_i} + 2i\mathbf{q}\cdot e^{i\mathbf{q}\cdot\mathbf{r}_i}\,\boldsymbol{\nabla}_j\right)\delta_{ij}$$

$$= \frac{\hbar^2}{2m}\sum_j e^{i\mathbf{q}\cdot\mathbf{r}_j}\left(q^2 - 2i\mathbf{q}\cdot\boldsymbol{\nabla}_j\right) \tag{15-30}$$

$$(A^*[H,A])_{00}$$

$$= \frac{\hbar^2}{2m}\sum_{ij}\int \psi_0^* e^{-i\mathbf{q}\cdot\mathbf{r}_i}\, e^{i\mathbf{q}\cdot\mathbf{r}_j}$$

$$\times\left(q^2 - 2i\mathbf{q}\cdot\boldsymbol{\nabla}_j\right)\psi_0\, d\tau \tag{15-31}$$

Assume ψ_0 real (which we can always do); then we write (15-31) as

$$\frac{\hbar^2}{2m}\sum_{i\neq j}\int e^{i\mathbf{q}\cdot(\mathbf{r}_j-\mathbf{r}_i)}\left[q^2\psi_0^2 - i\mathbf{q}\cdot\boldsymbol{\nabla}_j\,\psi_0^2\right] d\tau$$

$$+ \frac{\hbar^2}{2m}\sum_i \int\left(q^2\psi_0^2 - i\mathbf{q}\cdot\boldsymbol{\nabla}_i\,\psi_0^2\right) d\tau \tag{15-32a}$$

The second term in the first integral can be integrated by parts, the surface term is dropped, and the integrated term just cancels the first term in the first integral. The second term in the second integral is zero, as can be seen by performing partial integration. Therefore (15-32a) becomes

$$\frac{\hbar^2}{2m}\sum_i \int q^2\psi_0^2\, d\tau = \frac{\hbar^2}{2m} Zq^2 \tag{15-32b}$$

This is a remarkable generalization of the f (oscillator strength) sum rule.

Returning to (15-27),

$$-\frac{dW}{dx} = \frac{4\pi z^2 e^4}{mv_0^2} NZ \log\frac{\bar{q}_{max}}{\bar{q}_{min}} \tag{15-33}$$

The quantity NZ is seen to be the total number of electrons per unit volume. For $\bar{q}_{max}$ we can use (15-20b), which is independent of energy, and for $\bar{q}_{min}$ we use an average of (15-15).

$$\frac{\bar{q}_{max}}{\bar{q}_{min}} = \frac{2mv_0^2}{I_{av}} \qquad I_{av} = (E_n - E_0)_{av} \tag{15-34}$$

This is the form commonly used for the stopping-power formula. One can, however, go further and obtain the dependence of I_{av} on Z from the Thomas-Fermi model. Bloch has done this and found that

$$I_{av} = CZ \tag{15-35}$$

where C is some constant. Experiment verifies this law and an empirical value of about 10 ev is found for C. The final stopping-power formula, for heavy, nonrelativistic particles, is then

$$-\frac{dW}{dx} = \frac{4\pi z^2 e^4}{mv_0^2} NZ \log \frac{2mv_0^2}{CZ} \tag{15-36}$$

This depends only on the velocity of the particle, not on its mass. For further evaluation see, e.g., Bethe and Ashkin, in Segrè's book "Experimental Nuclear Physics."

Part II

RELATIVISTIC THEORIES

Chapter 16

KLEIN-GORDON EQUATION

The nonrelativistic Schrödinger equation for a free particle can be obtained by replacing E by $i\hbar(\partial/\partial t)$ and $\mathbf{p}$ by $(\hbar/i)\nabla$ in the nonrelativistic equation

$$\frac{p^2}{2m} = E \tag{16-1}$$

If the same substitution is performed in the relativistic equation,

$$c^2 p^2 + m^2 c^4 = E^2 \tag{16-2}$$

the Klein-Gordon equation is obtained:

$$-\hbar^2 \frac{\partial^2}{\partial t^2} \psi = -\hbar^2 c^2 \nabla^2 \psi + m^2 c^4 \psi \tag{16-3}$$

This equation was also derived by Schrödinger.

We wish to obtain quantities ρ and $\mathbf{j}$, which satisfy the following criteria: ρ is real; $\int \rho \, d\tau$ is time-independent and transforms as a scalar under Lorentz transformations; and a continuity equation of the form

$$\nabla \cdot \mathbf{j} + \frac{\partial p}{\partial t} = 0 \tag{16-4}$$

is satisfied. To achieve this we define

$$\rho = \frac{i\hbar}{2mc^2}\left(\psi^* \frac{\partial \psi}{\partial t} - \psi \frac{\partial \psi^*}{\partial t}\right) = \frac{\hbar}{mc^2} \ \mathrm{Im}\, \psi \frac{\partial \psi^*}{\partial t} \tag{16-5a}$$

$$\mathbf{j} = \frac{\hbar}{2im} (\psi^* \nabla \psi - \psi \nabla \psi^*) \tag{16-5b}$$

It is clear that ρ is real; it can be verified that (16-4) is satisfied. Considering the four-vector $(c\rho, \mathbf{j})$ and requiring that ψ fall off sufficiently rapidly for large r, (16-4) implies that $\int \rho \, d\tau$ is Lorentz-invariant and time-independent.

Equation (16-3) has the solution

$$\psi = e^{i(\mathbf{k} \cdot \mathbf{r} - \omega t)} \tag{16-6}$$

where

$$\hbar^2 \omega^2 = (\hbar^2 c^2 k^2 + m^2 c^4) \tag{16-7}$$

To regain (16-2) we require

$$E = \hbar\omega \qquad \mathbf{p} = \hbar\mathbf{k} \tag{16-8}$$

Then

$$E = \pm c \sqrt{p^2 + m^2 c^2} \tag{16-9}$$

PHYSICAL INTERPRETATION OF THE KLEIN-GORDON EQUATION

The Klein-Gordon equation can be written in an invariant-looking form:

$$\Box^2 \psi = \frac{m^2 c^2}{\hbar^2} \psi$$

$$\Box^2 \equiv \nabla^2 - \frac{1}{c^2} \frac{\partial^2}{\partial t^2} \tag{16-10}$$

Since ψ has only one component, it must transform as a scalar under Lorentz transformation. This also implies that the particles (or as shall be seen later, quantized fields) described by ψ must have no degrees of freedom other than translations in space-time. In particular the Klein-Gordon equation (without the addition of subsidiary equations) can only describe particles of zero spin, such as π or K mesons

Replacing $i\hbar(\partial\psi/\partial t)$ by E in (16-5a) we obtain

$$\rho = \frac{E}{mc^2} \, |\psi|^2 \tag{16-11}$$

In the nonrelativistic limit, $E \approx mc^2$; ρ and $\mathbf{j}$ reduce to the nonrelativistic expression for position probability density and probability current. However ρ cannot be interpreted as a probability density nor can ψ be considered a position probability amplitude. This is because (16-5a) can be either positive or negative, while a probability density must be nonnegative. The indefinite sign of (16-5a) arises from the fact that ψ *and* $\partial\psi/\partial t$ can (and must) be specified arbitrarily at an initial time $t = 0$ in order to determine the solution $\psi(\mathbf{r},t)$, since the Klein-Gordon equation is of second order in t, rather than of first order as is the nonrelativistic Schrödinger equation. Thus if for some value of $\partial\psi/\partial t$ the expression (16-5a) is positive, then since the time derivative is arbitrary, $-\partial\psi/\partial t$ is also an acceptable value, and for this choice ρ becomes negative. Since (16-3) is second order in the time derivative, ρ must contain the first derivative in order to satisfy the continuity equation (16-4). From (16-11) it is seen that it is the existence of negative-energy solutions which permits ρ to become negative. A further consequence of these properties of the Klein-Gordon equation is that the quantum-mechanical postulate that ψ is determined by its initial value at one time is no longer true.

Owing to these difficulties, the Klein-Gordon equation was at first discarded. It was Pauli and Weisskopf (1934) who provided the valid interpretation of the Klein-Gordon equation by considering it as a classical field equation (analogous to the electromagnetic field equations) and then quantizing it, a program we shall discuss in Chapter 19. It then becomes reasonable to interpret ρ and $\mathbf{j}$ as the charge and current densities of the particles of this field.

For a free particle the negative energy solutions need not be considered, for if the free particle has energy greater than mc^2 it will always have this energy and never will undergo a transition to a state with energy less than $-mc^2$. In this case ρ remains positive definite, and it might be asked whether or not a probabilistic interpretation is possible. This problem has been investigated by Newton and Wigner (1949), who give an affirmative answer but find that the position operator no longer has as its eigenfunctions $\delta(x - x')$ but instead a fairly complicated function in which the particle is not localized at a point but is spread out over a region of order $\hbar/mc$.

In the presence of external fields, transitions to states of negative E can occur. Such states, according to the theory of Pauli and Weisskopf, should be interpreted as particles of negative charge (if positive E corresponds to positive charge) but of positive energy. Transitions from a state of positive to one of negative E are interpreted as the production (or annihilation) of a pair of particles of opposite charge. This will be discussed in more detail in Chapter 18 in connection with the Dirac equation.

INTERACTION WITH EXTERNAL ELECTROMAGNETIC FIELD

To include the effects of an electromagnetic field described by potentials $\mathbf{A}, \varphi$ we make the usual replacement

$$\begin{aligned} \mathbf{p} &\to \mathbf{p} - \frac{e}{c}\mathbf{A} \\ E &\to E - e\varphi \end{aligned} \tag{16-12}$$

and obtain

$$\left(i\hbar \frac{\partial}{\partial t} - e\varphi\right)^2 \psi = \left(\frac{c\hbar}{i} \nabla - e\mathbf{A}\right)^2 \psi + m^2 c^4 \psi \tag{16-13}$$

With the substitution

$$\psi(\mathbf{r},t) = \psi'(\mathbf{r},t)\, e^{-(imc^2 t/\hbar)} \tag{16-14}$$

equation (16-13) reduces to

$$-\hbar^2 \frac{\partial^2 \psi'}{\partial t^2} + 2i\hbar[mc^2 - e\varphi]\frac{\partial \psi'}{\partial t}$$

$$-e\varphi\left[2mc^2 - e\varphi + i\hbar \frac{\partial \log \varphi}{\partial t}\right]\psi'$$

$$= [-\hbar^2 c^2 \nabla^2 + 2ie\hbar c\mathbf{A}\cdot\nabla + ie\hbar c(\nabla\cdot\mathbf{A}) + e^2\mathbf{A}^2]\psi'$$

Assuming

$$\left| i\hbar \frac{\partial \psi'}{\partial t} \right| = O(e\varphi\psi')$$

and neglecting $e\varphi$ with comparison to mc^2 we obtain

$$i\hbar \frac{\partial \psi'}{\partial t} = \left[\frac{-\hbar^2}{2m}\nabla^2 + \frac{ie\hbar}{mc}\mathbf{A}\cdot\nabla + \frac{ie\hbar}{2mc}\nabla\cdot\mathbf{A} + \frac{e^2 A^2}{2mc^2} + e\varphi\right]\psi \tag{16-15}$$

which is the nonrelativistic electromagnetic Schrödinger equation. It can be shown that under gauge transformation ψ changes only by a phase factor $\exp(ie\chi/\hbar c)$, where χ is the gauge function. If further potentials are to be included, their Lorentz transformation properties must be studied. If they transform as four-vectors they are to be added to $(c\varphi, A)$. If they transform as relativistic scalars, they can be added to mc^2.

COULOMB FIELD

Setting

$$\mathbf{A} = 0 \qquad e\varphi(\mathbf{r}) = -\frac{Ze^2}{r} \qquad \psi(\mathbf{r},t) = R(r)\,Y_{\ell m}(\theta,\varphi)\,e^{-iEt/\hbar}$$

$$\rho = \alpha r \qquad \alpha^2 = \frac{4(m^2c^4 - E^2)}{\hbar^2 c^2} \qquad \lambda = \frac{2E\gamma}{\hbar c\alpha}$$

$$\gamma = \frac{Ze^2}{\hbar c} \qquad E = mc^2\left(1 + \frac{\gamma^2}{\lambda^2}\right)^{-1/2} \tag{16-16}$$

we obtain from (16-13)

$$\frac{1}{\rho^2}\frac{d}{d\rho}\left(\rho^2\frac{dR}{d\rho}\right) + \left(\frac{\lambda}{\rho} - \frac{1}{4} - \frac{\ell(\ell+1) - \gamma^2}{\rho^2}\right)R = 0 \tag{16-17}$$

This describes a spinless particle in a Coulomb field. It is not a description of the hydrogen atom, since electrons have spin $\frac{1}{2}$.

Equation (16-17) is like the Schrödinger equation for the hydrogen atom, except that the relativistic correction term γ^2 is subtracted from $\ell(\ell+1)$. We notice $\lim_{c\to\infty} \gamma^2 = 0$. However, λ is *not* small, because here γ is multiplied by the large factor E/c.

For small ρ, $R \propto \rho^s$, where

$$s_\pm = -\tfrac{1}{2} \pm \sqrt{(\ell + \tfrac{1}{2})^2 - \gamma^2} \tag{16-18}$$

In the nonrelativistic limit $s_+ = \ell$, $s_- = -\ell - 1$; hence we conclude that only s_+ should be considered. It is not obvious that this is correct, since for $\ell = 0$ and $\gamma \neq 0$, $s_+ = -\frac{1}{2} + \sqrt{\frac{1}{4} - \gamma^2} < 0$, and R diverges. We must therefore reexamine the finiteness requirements of the wave functions.

We see from the above that we cannot demand ψ to be finite everywhere. It is reasonable to require that the wave function be normalizable, i.e., that $\int\psi^2\, d\tau$ be finite. This implies $s > -\frac{3}{2}$. This is clearly satisfied for s_+. Unfortunately it is also satisfied for s_-, with $\ell = 0$ (also with higher ℓ for sufficiently large γ, but these large γ are unphysical, as we shall see below).

A sufficiently restrictive condition can be obtained by requiring that the matrix elements of the kinetic energy be finite. From (16-17) it is seen that this implies

$$\int\left(\frac{dR}{dr}\right)^2 r^2\, dr < \infty \tag{16-19}$$

i.e., $s > -\frac{1}{2}$. This is only satisfied by s_+. Condition (16-19) holds also in the nonrelativistic theory.

In this way, we have retained one and only one radial solution of (16-17) for each ℓ. This is the necessary and sufficient condition for the solutions R to form a complete, but not an over-complete, set.

Equation (16-18) further shows that s becomes complex for $\gamma > \frac{1}{2}$

and $\ell = 0$, viz., $s = -\frac{1}{2} + is_2$. Such complex s is not acceptable because then the wave function behaves at small r as

$$r^{s_1} e^{is_2 \log r} \qquad s = s_1 + is_2 \tag{16-20}$$

which means it has infinitely many oscillations. Also, (16-19) should read Re $s > -\frac{1}{2}$, which is not fulfilled. According to (16-16), $\gamma = Z/137$, so $\gamma > \frac{1}{2}$ for many existing nuclei. Further we know that the Klein-Gordon equation is supposed to hold for π mesons. The solution of the puzzle is that nuclei have finite size; in fact, the large nuclei with $Z > 137/2$ have radii several times the Compton wavelength of a π meson, $\hbar/m_\pi c = 1.4 \times 10^{-13}$ cm, and so the singularity (16-20) does not arise.

The subsequent analysis of the differential equation (16-17) proceeds by the usual series method. It is required that the series terminate, which can be achieved if and only if

$$\lambda = n' + \tfrac{1}{2} + [(\ell + \tfrac{1}{2})^2 - \gamma^2]^{1/2} \tag{16-21}$$

n' is a nonnegative integer. From (16-16) this means

$$E = \frac{mc^2}{\sqrt{1 + \dfrac{\gamma^2}{[n' + \frac{1}{2} + \sqrt{(\ell + \frac{1}{2})^2 - \gamma^2}\,]^2}}} \tag{16-22}$$

or setting $n = n' + \ell + 1$ and expanding in powers of γ^2,

$$E = mc^2 \left[1 - \frac{\gamma^2}{2n^2} - \frac{\gamma^4}{2n^4}\left(\frac{n}{\ell + \frac{1}{2}} - \frac{3}{4}\right)\right] + O(\gamma^6)$$

$$= mc^2 - \frac{Ry}{n^2} - \frac{Ry\,\gamma^2}{n^3}\left(\frac{1}{\ell + \frac{1}{2}} - \frac{3}{4n}\right) + O(Ry\ \gamma^4) \tag{16-23}$$

The first term is the rest energy, the second the nonrelativistic Rydberg formula for the energy. The third term is the relativistic correction and is seen to remove the ℓ degeneracy. The total spread of the fine-structure levels is from (16-23)

$$\frac{4\,Ry\,\gamma^2}{n^3}\left[\frac{n-1}{2n-1}\right] \tag{16-24}$$

The spread observed experimentally in the spectrum of hydrogen is only about half as large. The above should be valid for π-mesonic atoms (apart from the effect of the size of the nucleus), but no experimental verification has been obtained.

Chapter 17

DIRAC EQUATION, FORMAL THEORY

In what is undoubtedly one of the great papers in physics of this century, Dirac (1928) set up a relativistic wave equation which avoids the difficulties of negative probability densities of the Klein-Gordon equation. Until Pauli and Weisskopf reinterpreted the Klein-Gordon equation it was believed that this Dirac equation was the only valid relativistic equation. It is now recognized that the Dirac equation and the Klein-Gordon equation are equally valid; the Dirac equation represents particles of spin $\frac{1}{2}$, the Klein-Gordon equation those of spin zero. Between them they describe most of the known elementary particles (although the proper definition of "elementary particle" has recently been subject to question). Formally one can extend the ideas of the Dirac theory to particles with nonzero rest mass with higher spin (Bhabha, 1940), but these theories have not proved to be successful, in that their interaction with the electromagnetic field leads to uncorrectable divergences. We shall not discuss these extensions, nor shall we discuss the successful Weyl equations (1929), which describe relativistic massless particles of spin $\frac{1}{2}$ and 1. The former, which describes the neutrino, can be considered a natural simplification of the Dirac equation.

DERIVATION OF THE DIRAC EQUATION

To prevent the occurrence of negative probability densities, we must avoid time derivatives in the expression for ρ. Therefore we must admit time derivatives no higher than first order in the wave equation. Since in the theory of relativity x, y, z, and ct are treated symmetrically, the Dirac wave function ψ must satisfy a first-order differential equation in all four coordinates. Furthermore, the equation must be linear so that the superposition principle of quantum mechanics holds. The correspondence principle also requires that the Klein-Gordon equation be satisfied, since the latter merely implies that (16-2) is valid; i.e., that in the limit of large quantum numbers classical relativity holds.

A similar situation obtains in electrodynamics. Maxwell's equations are first order in both space and time. On the other hand, each field component satisfies a second-order wave equation similar to (16-3) with zero rest mass. These two requirements are reconciled by the fact that each of Maxwell's equations connects different field components. This structure may be used as the guiding principle to obtain the Dirac equation.

Assuming that ψ consists of N components ψ_ℓ, where the number N is yet unspecified, the most general equation which satisfies the above requirements is

$$\frac{1}{c}\frac{\partial\psi_\ell}{\partial t} + \sum_{k=1}^{3}\sum_{n=1}^{N}\alpha^k_{\ell n}\frac{\partial\psi_n}{\partial x^k} + \frac{imc}{\hbar}\sum_{n=1}^{N}\beta_{\ell n}\psi_n = 0$$

$$\ell = 1, 2, \ldots, N \qquad x^k = x, y, z \qquad \text{for } k = 1, 2, 3 \tag{17-1}$$

For a free particle, all points in space-time are equivalent (homogeneity of space-time). Hence the $\alpha^k_{\ell n}$ and $\beta_{\ell n}$ must be dimensionless constants independent of and commuting with $\mathbf{r}$ and $\mathbf{p}$.

The N equations (17-1) can be written more compactly by introducing the one-column matrix

$$\psi = \begin{pmatrix} \psi_1 \\ \psi_2 \\ \vdots \\ \psi_N \end{pmatrix}$$

and the $N \times N$ matrices α^k and β. Further, we may define the vector matrix

$$\boldsymbol{\alpha} = \alpha^1\mathbf{i} + \alpha^2\mathbf{j} + \alpha^3\mathbf{k}$$

Then (17-1) becomes

$$\frac{1}{c}\frac{\partial\psi}{\partial t} + \boldsymbol{\alpha}\cdot\nabla\psi + \frac{imc}{\hbar}\beta\psi = 0 \tag{17-2}$$

N components of ψ then must describe a new degree of freedom of the particle just as the components of the Maxwell field describe the polarization of the light quantum. We shall see below that this will be the spin of the particle.

We next seek an expression for probability density ρ and current $\mathbf{j}$ which satisfies the conditions given before (p. 181) together with the requirement that ρ be positive definite. We define

$$\rho = \psi^\dagger \psi \tag{17-3}$$

where $\psi^\dagger$ is the Hermitian adjoint of ψ_j, hence a one-row matrix with N columns, whose components are the complex conjugate of the corresponding components of ψ. Clearly, $\psi^\dagger$ satisfies

$$\frac{1}{c}\frac{\partial\psi^\dagger}{\partial t} + \nabla\psi^\dagger\cdot\boldsymbol{\alpha}^\dagger - \frac{imc}{\hbar}\psi^\dagger\beta^\dagger = 0 \tag{17-4}$$

where the interchange of ψ with $\boldsymbol{\alpha}$ and β is necessary, since $\psi^\dagger$ is a row matrix.

To arrive at $\mathbf{j}$ we write the continuity equation

$$\left(\psi^\dagger \frac{\partial\psi}{\partial t} + \frac{\partial\psi^\dagger}{\partial t}\psi\right) + \nabla\cdot\mathbf{j} = 0 \tag{17-5}$$

Multiplying (17-2) on the left by $\psi^\dagger$, (17-4) on the right by ψ, and adding, we obtain

$$\frac{1}{c}\frac{\partial}{\partial t}(\psi^\dagger\psi) + \nabla\psi^\dagger\cdot\boldsymbol{\alpha}^\dagger\psi + \psi^\dagger\boldsymbol{\alpha}\cdot\nabla\psi$$

$$+ \frac{imc}{\hbar}(\psi^\dagger\beta\psi - \psi^\dagger\beta^\dagger\psi) = 0 \tag{17-6}$$

To identify this with (17-5) we require

$$\begin{aligned}\beta^\dagger &= \beta\\ \alpha^\dagger &= \alpha\end{aligned} \tag{17-7}$$

$$\mathbf{j} = c\psi^\dagger\boldsymbol{\alpha}\psi \tag{17-8}$$

Equation (17-7) expresses the very reasonable condition that the Dirac matrices be Hermitian. That (17-7) is indeed necessary follows from the fact that (17-2) can be written

$$i\hbar\frac{\partial\psi}{\partial t} = H\psi \tag{17-9}$$

$$H = \left(c\boldsymbol{\alpha}\cdot\frac{\hbar}{i}\nabla + \beta mc^2\right) \tag{17-10}$$

It is clear that if H is to be Hermitian $\boldsymbol{\alpha}$ and β must also be. Equations (17-3) and (17-8) are the very simple expressions for probability density and current which satisfy the continuity equation.

DIRAC MATRICES I

To derive further properties of the Dirac matrices, we operate on (17-2) by

$$\frac{1}{c}\frac{\partial}{\partial t} - \boldsymbol{\alpha}\cdot\nabla - \frac{imc}{\hbar}\beta$$

and obtain

$$\frac{1}{c^2}\frac{\partial^2\psi}{\partial t^2} = \frac{1}{2}\sum_k\sum_\ell\left(\alpha^k\alpha^\ell + \alpha^\ell\alpha^k\right)\frac{\partial^2\psi}{\partial x^k\partial x^\ell}$$

$$- \frac{m^2c^2}{\hbar^2}\beta^2\psi + \frac{imc}{\hbar}\sum_k\left(\alpha^k\beta + \beta\alpha^k\right)\frac{\partial\psi}{\partial x^k} \qquad (17\text{-}11)$$

We have symmetrized the $\alpha^k\alpha^\ell$ term, which is permissible, since $\partial/\partial x^k$ and $\partial/\partial x^\ell$ commute. If (17-11) is to agree with the Klein-Gordon equation for each component, the Dirac matrices must satisfy

$$\tfrac{1}{2}\left(\alpha^k\alpha^\ell + \alpha^\ell\alpha^k\right) = \delta^{k\ell}\,I$$

$$\alpha^k\beta + \beta\alpha^k = 0 \qquad (17\text{-}12)$$

$$\left(\alpha^k\right)^2 = \beta^2 = I$$

where I is the unit matrix.

We now prove two important theorems about the Dirac matrices. From (17-12),

$$\beta\alpha^k = -\alpha^k\beta = (-I)\alpha^k\beta \qquad (17\text{-}13a)$$

Taking determinants,

$$(\det\beta)\left(\det\alpha^k\right) = (-1)^N\left(\det\alpha^k\right)(\det\beta) \qquad (17\text{-}13b)$$

Since (17-12) indicates that α^k and β have inverses, none of the determinants vanish, and

$$(-1)^N = 1 \qquad (17\text{-}13c)$$

Thus N, the dimension of the matrices, is even.

Since $\beta^2 = (\alpha^k)^2 = 1$, each matrix has an inverse, namely, itself. Therefore (17-13a) can be rewritten as

$$\left(\alpha^k\right)^{-1} \beta \alpha^k = -\beta \tag{17-14a}$$

Taking the trace of both sides we obtain

$$\mathrm{Tr}\left[\left(\alpha^k\right)^{-1} \beta \alpha^k\right] = \mathrm{Tr}\left[\alpha^k \left(\alpha^k\right)^{-1} \beta\right] = \mathrm{Tr}\,(\beta) = \mathrm{Tr}\,(-\beta) \tag{17-14b}$$

Therefore,

$$\mathrm{Tr}\,(\beta) = 0 \tag{17-14c}$$

The same holds for the other matrices:

$$\mathrm{Tr}\left(\alpha^k\right) = 0 \tag{17-14d}$$

COVARIANT FORM OF THE DIRAC EQUATION

To write the Dirac equation in covariant form we define

$$\begin{aligned} \beta &= \gamma^0 \\ \beta \boldsymbol{\alpha} &= \boldsymbol{\gamma} \\ \gamma^\mu &= (\gamma^0, \boldsymbol{\gamma}) \\ x^\mu &= (ct, \mathbf{r}) \end{aligned} \tag{17-15}$$

γ^0 is Hermitian, the other γ's are anti-Hermitian. These Hermiticity relations can be summarized compactly by

$$(\gamma^\mu)^\dagger = \gamma^0 \gamma^\mu \gamma^0 \tag{17-16}$$

The metric tensor that we shall use is $g_{\mu\nu}$:

$$g_{00} = 1 \qquad g_{kk} = -1,\ k = 1, 2, 3 \qquad g_{\mu\nu} = 0,\ \mu \neq \nu$$

We shall raise and lower indices on the γ's even though they are not components of a four-vector:

$$\gamma_\mu = g_{\mu\nu} \gamma^\nu \tag{17-17}$$

(summation over repeated Greek dummy indices implied). The commutation relations (17-12) can be summarized:

$$\begin{aligned} \gamma^\mu \gamma^\nu + \gamma^\nu \gamma^\mu &= 2g^{\mu\nu} \\ \gamma_\mu \gamma_\nu + \gamma_\nu \gamma_\mu &= 2g_{\mu\nu} \end{aligned} \tag{17-18}$$

Multiplying (17-2) by $i\hbar\beta$, one obtains

$$i\hbar\gamma^{\mu}\frac{\partial\psi}{\partial x^{\mu}} - mc\psi = 0 \tag{17-19}$$

Defining a (Dirac) adjoint function $\overline{\psi}$ by

$$\overline{\psi} = \psi^{\dagger}\gamma^{0} \tag{17-20a}$$

and multiplying (17-4) by $i\hbar\gamma^{0}\gamma^{0}$, one obtains

$$i\hbar\frac{\partial}{\partial x^{\mu}}\overline{\psi}\gamma^{\mu} + mc\overline{\psi} = 0 \tag{17-20b}$$

The four-current vector is defined

$$\frac{j^{\mu}}{c} = \overline{\psi}\gamma^{\mu}\psi = \left(\rho, \frac{\mathbf{j}}{c}\right) \tag{17-21}$$

If we operate on (17-19) with $i\hbar\gamma^{\mu}(\partial/\partial x^{\mu})$, we get

$$\begin{aligned} 0 &= -\hbar^{2}\gamma^{\mu}\gamma^{\nu}\frac{\partial^{2}}{\partial x^{\nu}\partial x^{\mu}}\psi - i\hbar mc\gamma^{\nu}\frac{\partial}{\partial x^{\nu}}\psi \\ &= \frac{-\hbar^{2}}{2}\left[\gamma^{\mu}\gamma^{\nu} + \gamma^{\nu}\gamma^{\mu}\right]\frac{\partial^{2}}{\partial x^{\nu}\partial x^{\mu}}\psi - m^{2}c^{2}\psi \\ &= -\hbar^{2}g^{\mu\nu}\frac{\partial^{2}}{\partial x^{\nu}\partial x^{\mu}}\psi - m^{2}c^{2}\psi \\ &= p^{\mu}p_{\mu}\psi - m^{2}c^{2}\psi \\ &= \left[\left(\frac{E^{2}}{c^{2}} - p^{2}\right) - m^{2}c^{2}\right]\psi \end{aligned} \tag{17-22}$$

We have introduced the four-momentum

$$p^{\mu} = i\hbar\frac{\partial}{\partial x_{\mu}} = \left(\frac{E}{c}, \mathbf{p}\right)$$

In symmetrizing $\gamma^{\mu}\gamma^{\nu}$ use has been made of the fact that the differentiation operators commute. Equation (17-22) shows that the relativistic relation between energy and momentum has been retained.

DIRAC MATRICES II

We now obtain several theorems about the Dirac matrices. To study these matrices it is not necessary to assume Hermiticity and we shall not do so. The fundamental relationship is of course (17-18). Any set of quantities satisfying $\gamma^\mu\gamma^\nu + \gamma^\nu\gamma^\mu = 2g^{\mu\nu}$ is called a Clifford algebra.

We may form new matrices from the four γ's by multiplying two or more together. Since the square of each γ equals $\pm I$ we need to consider only products whose factors are different. Order is immaterial, since the matrices commute or anticommute. This means there are $2^4 - 1$ different products of the four γ's. (The number of ways of making different combinations from n objects is $2^n - 1$.) If we also include I we can enumerate 16 different matrices.

$$\begin{array}{c} I \\ \gamma^0 \quad i\gamma^1 \quad i\gamma^2 \quad i\gamma^3 \\ \gamma^0\gamma^1 \quad \gamma^0\gamma^2 \quad \gamma^0\gamma^3 \quad i\gamma^2\gamma^3 \quad i\gamma^3\gamma^1 \quad i\gamma^1\gamma^2 \\ i\gamma^0\gamma^2\gamma^3 \quad i\gamma^0\gamma^3\gamma^1 \quad i\gamma^0\gamma^1\gamma^2 \quad \gamma^1\gamma^2\gamma^3 \\ i\gamma^0\gamma^1\gamma^2\gamma^3 \equiv i\gamma_5 \end{array} \tag{17-23}$$

Denoting elements in the above array by Γ_ℓ, $\ell = 1, 2, \ldots, 16$; the following properties can be verified (no summation over repeated Latin indices implied):

$$\Gamma_\ell\Gamma_m = a_{\ell m}\Gamma_n \qquad a_{\ell m} = \pm 1 \text{ or } \pm i \tag{17-24}$$

$$\Gamma_\ell\Gamma_m = I \qquad \text{if and only if } \ell = m \tag{17-25}$$

$$\Gamma_\ell\Gamma_m = \pm\Gamma_m\Gamma_\ell \tag{17-26}$$

If $\Gamma_\ell \neq I$, there always exists a Γ_k such that

$$\Gamma_k\Gamma_\ell\Gamma_k = -\Gamma_\ell \tag{17-27}$$

Theorem 1

$$\mathrm{Tr}(\Gamma_\ell) = 0 \qquad (\Gamma_\ell \neq I) \tag{17-28}$$

Proof

Choose a k such that by applying (17-25) and (17-27) we have

$$\mathrm{Tr}(\Gamma_k\Gamma_\ell\Gamma_k) = \mathrm{Tr}(\Gamma_\ell\Gamma_k\Gamma_k) = \mathrm{Tr}(\Gamma_\ell) = -\mathrm{Tr}(\Gamma_\ell)$$

Theorem 2

$$\sum_{k=1}^{16} x_k \Gamma_k = 0 \qquad \text{only if } x_k = 0;\ k = 1, 2, \ldots, 16 \qquad (17\text{-}29)$$

ie, Γ_k's are linearly independent & span the space of 4×4 matrices

Proof
Multiply (17-29) by Γ_m to get

$$x_m I + \sum_{k \neq m} x_k \Gamma_k \Gamma_m = x_m I + \sum_{k \neq m} x_k a_{km} \Gamma_n = 0$$

with $\Gamma_n \neq I$, since $k \neq m$. Taking the trace:

$$x_m \ \mathrm{Tr}\ I = -\sum_{k \neq m} x_k a_{km} \ \mathrm{Tr}(\Gamma_n) = 0 \qquad [\text{by } (17\text{-}28)]$$

$$x_m = 0$$

Theorem 2 gives us the first important result: The Γ_k's cannot be represented by matrices whose dimension is less than 4×4, since it is impossible to construct 16 linearly independent matrices from such matrices. Furthermore there exist precisely 16 linearly independent 4×4 matrices which we can use to represent the Γ_k's. We shall assume from now on that the γ's are in fact 4×4 matrices. It should be emphasized that the fact that the Dirac equation can be realized by 4×4 matrices is not a consequence of there being four components of space-time.

A corollary to Theorem 2 is that any 4×4 matrix X can be written uniquely as a linear combination of the Γ_k's.

$$X = \sum_{k=1}^{16} x_k \Gamma_k \qquad (17\text{-}30)$$

Multiplying by Γ_m and taking the trace,

$$\mathrm{Tr}(X\Gamma_m) = x_m \ \mathrm{Tr}(\Gamma_m \Gamma_m) + \sum_{k \neq m} x_k \ \mathrm{Tr}(\Gamma_k \Gamma_m)$$

$$= x_m \ \mathrm{Tr}(I) \qquad (17\text{-}31)$$

$$x_m = \tfrac{1}{4} \ \mathrm{Tr}(X\Gamma_m)$$

A further corollary to Theorem 2 is a stronger statement of (17-24). We can now say that $\Gamma_\ell \Gamma_m = a_{\ell m} \Gamma_n$, where Γ_n is a different Γ_n for each m, for fixed ℓ. For suppose

$$\Gamma_\ell \Gamma_m = a_{\ell m} \Gamma_n$$
$$\Gamma_\ell \Gamma_{m'} = a_{\ell m'} \Gamma_n \qquad \Gamma_m \neq \Gamma_{m'} \tag{17-32a}$$

Then

$$\Gamma_m = a_{\ell m} \Gamma_\ell \Gamma_n$$
$$\Gamma_{m'} = a_{\ell m'} \Gamma_\ell \Gamma_n \tag{17-32b}$$

and

$$\Gamma_m = \frac{a_{\ell m}}{a_{\ell m'}} \Gamma_{m'} \tag{17-32c}$$

which contradicts the fact that the Γ_k's are linearly independent.

Theorem 3

Any matrix X that commutes with γ^μ (for all μ) is a multiple of the identity.

Proof

Assume X is not a multiple of the identity. If X commutes with all the γ's, it commutes with all the Γ_i's: $X = \Gamma_i X \Gamma_i$. From (17-30) we can write

$$X = x_m \Gamma_m + \sum_{k \neq m} x_k \Gamma_k \qquad \Gamma_m \neq I \tag{17-33a}$$

From (17-27) there exists a Γ_i such that $\Gamma_i \Gamma_m \Gamma_i = -\Gamma_m$ and by hypothesis X commutes with this Γ_i. Therefore,

$$X = x_m \Gamma_m + \sum_{k \neq m} x_k \Gamma_k = \Gamma_i X \Gamma_i$$
$$= x_m \Gamma_i \Gamma_m \Gamma_i + \sum_{k \neq m} x_k \Gamma_i \Gamma_k \Gamma_i$$
$$= -x_m \Gamma_m + \sum_{k \neq m} x_k (\pm 1) \Gamma_k \tag{17-33b}$$

Since the expansion is unique, we have $x_m = -x_m = 0$. Since Γ_m was arbitrary except that $\Gamma_m \neq I$, we have proved

$$[X, \gamma^\mu] = 0 \text{ for all } \mu, \text{ implies } X = aI \tag{17-33c}$$

Theorem 4

The above results allow us to derive another important result, called Pauli's fundamental theorem, which states: Given two sets of 4×4 matrices γ^{μ} and γ'^{μ}, both of which satisfy (17-18), there exists a nonsingular matrix S such that

$$\gamma'^{\mu} = S\gamma^{\mu}S^{-1} \tag{17-34}$$

Proof

Set

$$S = \sum_{i=1}^{16} \Gamma'_i F \Gamma_i \tag{17-35}$$

where F is an arbitrary 4×4 matrix and the Γ'_i's are the set of 16 products formed from the γ'^{μ}'s just as the Γ_i's were constructed from the γ^{μ}'s. From (17-24) $\Gamma_i\Gamma_j = a_{ij}\Gamma_k$; then $\Gamma_i\Gamma_j\Gamma_i\Gamma_j = a_{ij}^2\Gamma_k^2$; therefore

$$\Gamma_j\Gamma_i = \left(\Gamma_i\Gamma_j\right)^{-1} = a_{ij}^2\Gamma_i\Gamma_j = a_{ij}^3\Gamma_k$$

$$\Gamma'_i\Gamma'_j = a_{ij}\Gamma'_k$$

since in the primed system the Γ'_i's are constructed in the same fashion as in the unprimed system. Then, for any i,

$$\Gamma'_i S \Gamma_i = \sum_j \Gamma'_i\Gamma'_j F \Gamma_j \Gamma_i = \sum_j a_{ij}^4 \Gamma'_k F \Gamma_k \tag{17-36}$$

Since $a_{ij}^4 = 1$ and since the sum over j ranges through all 16 elements it can be replaced by a sum over $k = k\ (j)$ to give, from (17-35),

$$\Gamma'_i S \Gamma_i = S \tag{17-37}$$

To show that S is nonsingular, we define a quantity S':

$$S' = \sum_{i=1}^{16} \Gamma_i G \Gamma'_i \tag{17-38}$$

where G is arbitrary. By symmetry

$$\Gamma_i S' \Gamma'_i = S' \tag{17-39a}$$

for any i. From (17-37),

$$S'S = \Gamma_i S' \Gamma'_i \Gamma'_i S \Gamma_i = \Gamma_i S' S \Gamma_i \tag{17-39b}$$

This by (17-33) implies that $S'S = aI$.

Now $a \neq 0$, since F and G occurring in (17-35) and (17-38) can be chosen arbitrarily. (It is easy to show by choosing for F and G matrices with only one nonzero element that $a = 0$ for all F and G would contradict the linear independence of the Γ_k's.) Hence S is nonsingular and

$$\gamma^{\mu'} = S\gamma^{\mu} S^{-1} \tag{17-34}$$

Furthermore S is unique up to a constant, for suppose $S_1\gamma^{\mu} S_1^{-1} = S_2\gamma^{\mu} S_2^{-1}$. Then $S_2^{-1}S_1\gamma^{\mu} = \gamma^{\mu} S_2^{-1}S_1$, which means that $S_2^{-1}S_1 = aI$ or $S_1 = aS_2$. Further, given four γ^{μ}'s that satisfy (17-18) and defining $\gamma^{\mu'} = S\gamma^{\mu}S^{-1}$, it is clear that the $\gamma^{\mu'}$ will also satisfy (17-18).

We conclude by noting that γ_5 defined in (17-23) anticommutes with γ^{μ} for any μ and $(\gamma_5)^2 = -I$. The subscript 5 cannot be raised.

EXPLICIT FORM OF THE DIRAC MATRICES

We now exhibit a nonunique matrix representation for the Dirac matrices. It should be clear that relations (17-7) and (17-12), or, alternatively, (17-16) and (17-18), do not specify the matrices uniquely. Thus it is usually best not to express the matrices explicitly when working problems.

We have seen that the Dirac matrices must have at least four rows and columns, and we shall restrict ourselves to 4×4 matrices. We have further seen that the trace of β and α^k must be zero. For most problems involving particles of moderate speed, including atomic problems, the term mc^2 in the Hamiltonian dominates; therefore it is convenient to represent β by a diagonal matrix. This, together with $\mathrm{Tr}\, \beta = 0$ and $\beta^2 = I$, leads to the choice

$$\beta = \begin{pmatrix} I & 0 \\ 0 & -I \end{pmatrix} \tag{17-40a}$$

where I is the 2×2 identity matrix.

The three α matrices, in order to anticommute with β and to be Hermitian, must have the form

$$\alpha^k = \begin{pmatrix} 0 & A^k \\ A^{k\dagger} & 0 \end{pmatrix} \tag{17-40b}$$

where A^k is a 2×2 matrix, not necessarily Hermitian. They must also anticommute with each other, and their squares must be unity. We remember here the Pauli spin matrices $\boldsymbol{\sigma}$, which have just this property. Clearly, all relations (17-12) are satisfied if we put

$$\alpha = \begin{pmatrix} 0 & \sigma \\ \sigma & 0 \end{pmatrix} \tag{17-40c}$$

together with (17-39c). Then (17-15) and (17-23) give

$$\gamma = \begin{pmatrix} 0 & \sigma \\ -\sigma & 0 \end{pmatrix} \qquad \gamma_5 = -i\begin{pmatrix} 0 & I \\ I & 0 \end{pmatrix} \tag{17-40d}$$

We shall find the choice (17-40a) and (17-40c) useful in discussion of spin. In the extreme relativistic case, it is usually more convenient to diagonalize γ_5. Of course all physical consequences must be independent of the representation.

RELATIVISTIC INVARIANCE OF THE DIRAC EQUATION

Before obtaining solutions and physical consequences from the Dirac equation we shall show that the physical results are independent of the Lorentz frame used to derive them. If the Dirac equation is solved in two different frames the solutions must describe the same physical state. This does not mean that the components of ψ are the same in the two Lorentz frames. This is analogous to the electromagnetic field tensor, where the components of $\mathcal{E}$ and $\mathcal{H}$ transform, but the form of the Maxwell equation remains invariant. So also here we shall see that ψ transforms but that the form of the Dirac equation remains the same.

The most general homogenous Lorentz transformation (i.e., omitting space-time translations) between two coordinate systems may be written

$$x'^{\mu} = a^{\mu}{}_{\nu}\, x^{\nu} \tag{17-41a}$$

with

$$a_{\mu}{}^{\nu}\, a^{\mu}{}_{\lambda} = a^{\nu\mu}\, a_{\lambda\mu} = \delta^{\nu}{}_{\lambda} \qquad a_{\mu}{}^{\nu} \text{ real} \tag{17-41b}$$

Equation (17-41b) follows from the requirement that the real quadratic form $x^{\mu} x_{\mu}$ is an invariant.

In the special case of the standard Lorentz transformation (motion of two coordinate systems along their mutual x axes with relative velocity v; origins coincident at t = 0),

$$a^{\mu}_{\ \nu} = \begin{array}{c} \nu \rightarrow \\ \mu \downarrow \end{array} \begin{pmatrix} \gamma & -\beta\gamma & 0 & 0 \\ -\beta\gamma & \gamma & 0 & 0 \\ 0 & 0 & 1 & 0 \\ 0 & 0 & 0 & 1 \end{pmatrix} \tag{17-41c}$$

$$\beta = v/c \qquad \gamma = (1 - \beta^2)^{-1/2}$$

Using

$$\frac{\partial}{\partial x^{\mu}} = a^{\lambda}_{\ \mu} \frac{\partial}{\partial x'^{\lambda}} \tag{17-42}$$

which follows from (17-41a), and the observation that $\partial/\partial x^{\mu}$ is a co-variant vector, we obtain from (17-19),

$$\frac{\hbar}{i} a^{\lambda}_{\ \mu} \gamma^{\mu} \frac{\partial\psi}{\partial x'^{\lambda}} + mc\psi = 0 \tag{17-43}$$

Defining $\gamma'^{\lambda} = a^{\lambda}_{\ \mu} \gamma^{\mu}$, we can verify with the help of (17-41b) that γ'^{λ} satisfies (17-18). Hence by Pauli's fundamental theorem, there exists a (unique up to multiplicative constant) S such that

$$a^{\lambda}_{\ \mu} \gamma^{\mu} = S^{-1} \gamma^{\lambda} S \tag{17-44}$$

Substituting this quantity in (17-43) and premultiplying by S gives

$$\frac{\hbar}{i} \gamma^{\mu} \frac{\partial S\psi}{\partial x'^{\mu}} + mcS\psi = 0 \tag{17-45}$$

Defining

$$\psi'(x') = S\psi(x) \tag{17-46}$$

(17-43) gives

$$\frac{\hbar}{i} \gamma^{\mu} \frac{\partial\psi'}{\partial x'^{\mu}} + mc\psi' = 0 \tag{17-47}$$

This is of the same form as (17-19). As we predicted above, the ψ transforms but the γ^{μ}'s remain the same. Thus if we can show that $S\psi = \psi'$ has the same physical significance in the primed system as

ψ has in the unprimed, we shall have demonstrated the covariance of the theory. To do this we derive some further properties of S.

From the Hermiticity relations (17-16), from (17-41b), and from (17-44) we have

$$a^{\lambda}{}_{\mu}\,\gamma^{\mu} = \gamma^0\left(a^{\lambda}{}_{\mu}\,\gamma^{\mu}\right)^{\dagger}\gamma^0 = \gamma^0\left(S^{-1}\gamma^{\lambda}S\right)^{\dagger}\gamma^0 \qquad (17\text{-}48a)$$

$$a^{\lambda}{}_{\mu}\,\gamma^{\mu} = (\gamma^0 S^{\dagger}\gamma^0)\,\gamma^{\lambda}\,(\gamma^0 S^{\dagger}\gamma^0)^{-1} \qquad (17\text{-}48b)$$

Substituting in (17-48b) $S^{-1}\gamma^{\lambda}S$ for $a^{\lambda}{}_{\mu}\,\gamma^{\mu}$, we obtain

$$(\gamma^0 S^{\dagger}\gamma^0)\,\gamma^{\lambda}\,(\gamma^0 S^{\dagger}\gamma^0)^{-1} = S^{-1}\gamma^{\lambda}S \qquad (17\text{-}49a)$$

$$(S\gamma^0 S^{\dagger}\gamma^0)\,\gamma^{\lambda} = \gamma^{\lambda}\,(S\gamma^0 S^{\dagger}\gamma^0) \qquad (17\text{-}49b)$$

From (17-33) this gives

$$(S\gamma^0 S^{\dagger}\gamma^0) = bI \qquad (17\text{-}50a)$$

$$S\gamma^0 S^{\dagger} = b\gamma^0 \qquad (17\text{-}50b)$$

Taking Hermitian conjugates of (17-50b) we find that b is real. Prescribing a normalization on S by $\det S = 1$, (17-50b) gives $b^4 = 1$, and since b is real,

$$b = \pm 1 \qquad (17\text{-}51)$$

To examine the physical significance of (17-51) we consider

$$S^{\dagger}S = S^{\dagger}\gamma^0\gamma^0 S = b\gamma^0 S^{-1}\gamma^0 S = b\gamma^0 a^0{}_{\nu}\,\gamma^{\nu}$$

$$= ba^0{}_0\, I - \sum_{k=1}^{3} ba^{0k}\,\gamma^0\gamma^k \qquad (17\text{-}52)$$

where (17-44) and (17-50) have been used. Since $S^{\dagger}S$ has positive definite eigenvalues, taking the trace of (17-52) we get

$$0 < \mathrm{Tr}\,(S^{\dagger}S) = 4ba^0{}_0 \qquad ba^0{}_0 > 0 \qquad (17\text{-}53)$$

i.e.,

$$a^0{}_0 < 0 \qquad b = -1 \qquad (17\text{-}54a)$$

$$a^0{}_0 > 0 \qquad b = 1 \qquad (17\text{-}54b)$$

The former case, $a^0{}_0 < 0$, corresponds to time reversal.

Next we consider the transformation properties of the adjoint function $\bar{\psi} = \psi^\dagger \gamma^0$.

$$\psi' = S\psi \tag{17-42}$$

$$(\psi')^\dagger = \psi^\dagger S^\dagger$$

$$\overline{\psi'} = (\psi')^\dagger \gamma^0 = \psi^\dagger S^\dagger \gamma^0$$

$$= b\psi^\dagger \gamma^0 S^{-1} = b\bar{\psi} S^{-1} \tag{17-55}$$

$$\bar{\psi}'(x') = b\bar{\psi}(x)S^{-1}$$

We are now ready to answer the question posed above; i.e., does ψ' describe the same physical situation in the primed system as ψ does in the unprimed? This will be so if $\bar{\psi}'\psi'$ gives the probability density in the primed system. Considering

$$\frac{j^\mu}{c} = \bar{\psi}\gamma^\mu \psi \tag{17-21}$$

$$\frac{j'^\mu}{c} = \bar{\psi}'\gamma^\mu \psi' = b\bar{\psi} S^{-1} \gamma^\mu S\psi = ba^\mu{}_\lambda \bar{\psi}\gamma^\lambda \psi$$

$$= ba^\mu{}_\lambda \frac{j^\lambda}{c} \tag{17-56}$$

Hence if we restrict ourselves to Lorentz transformations which do not include time reversal, j^μ/c transforms as a four-vector, which gives the proper transformation law for $\bar{\psi}\psi$. For a general Lorentz transformation we see that j^μ is a pseudovector.

EXPLICIT TRANSFORMATION MATRIX

Finally we exhibit the actual S corresponding to proper, continuous Lorentz transformations; $\det (a^\mu{}_\nu) = 1$, $a^0{}_0 > 0$. It is sufficient to deal only with infinitesimal transformations, since repeated applications of these will result in a finite transformation. For an infinitesimal transformation,

$$a^\mu{}_\nu = \delta^\mu{}_\nu + \lambda\epsilon^\mu{}_\nu \tag{17-57}$$

λ is the smallness parameter and in the following only terms linear in λ are kept.

From (17-41b) it follows that

$$\epsilon^{\mu\nu} = -\epsilon^{\nu\mu} \tag{17-58}$$

We write

$$\begin{aligned} S &= 1 + \lambda T \\ S^{-1} &= 1 - \lambda T \end{aligned} \tag{17-59}$$

$$\begin{aligned} a^{\mu}{}_{\nu}\,\gamma^{\nu} = S^{-1}\gamma^{\mu}S &= (1 - \lambda T)\gamma^{\mu}(1 + \lambda T) \\ &= \gamma^{\mu} + \lambda(\gamma^{\mu}T - T\gamma^{\mu}) \end{aligned} \tag{17-60a}$$

$$a^{\mu}{}_{\nu}\,\gamma^{\nu} = \gamma^{\mu} + \lambda\epsilon^{\mu}{}_{\nu}\,\gamma^{\nu} \tag{17-60b}$$

hence

$$\epsilon^{\mu}{}_{\nu}\,\gamma^{\nu} = \gamma^{\mu}T - T\gamma^{\mu} \tag{17-61}$$

T is uniquely defined up to the addition of a constant multiple of the identity. For if there were two such T's, from (17-61) their difference would commute with the γ^{μ}'s and would be a constant multiple of the identity. The normalization requirement removes this ambiguity, for

$$\begin{aligned} 1 = \det S &= \det(1 + \lambda T) \\ &= \det 1 + \lambda \operatorname{Tr} T \qquad \operatorname{Tr} T = 0 \end{aligned} \tag{17-62}$$

One readily establishes that

$$T = \tfrac{1}{8}\epsilon^{\mu\nu}\left(\gamma_{\mu}\gamma_{\nu} - \gamma_{\nu}\gamma_{\mu}\right) \tag{17-63}$$

satisfies (17-61) and (17-62). Therefore T is the required transformation and is seen to be antisymmetric.

Chapter 18

SOLUTIONS OF THE DIRAC EQUATION

FREE-PARTICLE SOLUTION

The Dirac equation possesses plane-wave solutions, i.e., solutions describing a single particle in the absence of interaction. We write

$$\psi(\mathbf{r},t) = u \exp\left\{\frac{-ip_\nu x^\nu}{\hbar}\right\} \tag{18-1}$$

where u is a four-component column matrix which satisfies, according to (17-19),

$$\left(\gamma^\mu p_\mu - mcI\right)u = 0 \tag{18-2}$$

This is a system of four simultaneous homogenous algebraic (not differential) equations for the four components of u. It has a nontrivial solution if and only if the matrix

$$\gamma^\mu p_\mu - mcI \tag{18-3}$$

has no inverse. Since the inverse of (18-3) is

$$\left(p_\mu p^\mu - m^2c^2\right)^{-1}\left(\gamma^\mu p_\mu + mcI\right) \tag{18-4}$$

(18-2) has a solution if and only if

$$p_\mu p^\mu - m^2c^2 = 0$$
$$E^2 = c^2p^2 + m^2c^4 \tag{18-5a}$$

For a given p, this yields two solutions:

$$E_+ = +\sqrt{c^2p^2 + m^2c^4}$$
$$E_- = -\sqrt{c^2p^2 + m^2c^4} \qquad (18\text{-}5b)$$

Thus we see that the Dirac equation leads to positive energy and negative energy solutions just as the Klein-Gordon equation did.

To obtain a specific expression for u we must represent the Dirac matrices in some definite fashion. It is convenient to choose the representation given by (17-40). Clearly there will be four linearly independent solutions, two belonging to E+ and two to E−. These can be shown to be

$$\text{(A)} \quad u_1 = 1 \quad u_2 = 0 \quad u_3 = \frac{cp_z}{E_+ + mc^2} \quad u_4 = \frac{c(p_x + ip_y)}{E_+ + mc^2} \qquad (18\text{-}6a)$$

$$\text{(B)} \quad u_1 = 0 \quad u_2 = 1 \quad u_3 = \frac{c(p_x - ip_y)}{E_+ + mc^2} \quad u_4 = \frac{-cp_z}{E_+ + mc^2} \qquad (18\text{-}6b)$$

for E_+; and

$$\text{(C)} \quad u_1 = \frac{-cp_z}{-E_- + mc^2} \quad u_2 = \frac{-c(p_x + ip_y)}{-E_- + mc^2} \quad u_3 = 1 \quad u_4 = 0 \qquad (18\text{-}7a)$$

$$\text{(D)} \quad u_1 = \frac{-c(p_x - ip_y)}{-E_- + mc^2} \quad u_2 = \frac{cp_z}{-E_- + mc^2} \quad u_3 = 0 \quad u_4 = 1 \qquad (18\text{-}7b)$$

for $E_- = -E_+$. Here u is taken to be

$$u = \begin{pmatrix} u_1 \\ u_2 \\ u_3 \\ u_4 \end{pmatrix}$$

These are unnormalized. To normalize u, i.e., to get $\Sigma_{n=1}^4 |u_n|^2 = 1$, each u_i must be multiplied by

$$\left\{1 + \frac{c^2p^2}{(E_+ + mc^2)^2}\right\}^{-1/2} = \left\{\frac{(E_+ + mc^2)}{2E_+}\right\}^{-1/2} \qquad (18\text{-}8)$$

We see that each solution has two components which, in the non-relativistic limit, $E_+ \approx mc^2$, are of the order v/c. These are called *small components* and the other two *large components*. For the positive energy solutions, u_1 and u_2 are the large components. In the non-relativistic limit we expect the large components to correspond to solutions of the Schrödinger free-particle equation. Examining (18-1) we see that this is indeed the case. Further insight can be obtained by defining the operator

$$\boldsymbol{\sigma}' = \begin{pmatrix} \boldsymbol{\sigma} & 0 \\ 0 & \boldsymbol{\sigma} \end{pmatrix} \tag{18-9}$$

In the limit when the small components can be neglected, (18-6a) and (18-7a) are eigenfunctions of σ_z' with eigenvalue +1; (18-6b) and (18-7b) are eigenfunctions of σ_z' with eigenvalue −1. We shall see below that $\frac{1}{2}\hbar\boldsymbol{\sigma}'$ is the spin angular momentum. Hence the four solutions of the free-particle Dirac equation correspond to positive energy, spin $\pm\frac{1}{2}$; negative energy, spin $\pm\frac{1}{2}$.

PHYSICAL INTERPRETATION OF DIRAC MATRICES

The matrix $\boldsymbol{\alpha}$ occurs in the expression for the probability current, $\psi^+ c\boldsymbol{\alpha}\psi$. We thus expect that $c\boldsymbol{\alpha}$ should be interpreted as velocity: $\dot{\mathbf{r}}$. That this is indeed so follows from the Heisenberg expression for the time derivative of an operator

$$\dot{A} = \frac{1}{i\hbar}[A,H] \tag{18-10}$$

which holds in the Dirac theory because of (17-9). Then

$$\begin{aligned} \dot{x} &= \frac{1}{i\hbar}[x,H] = c\alpha_x \\ \dot{\mathbf{r}} &= c\boldsymbol{\alpha} \end{aligned} \tag{18-11}$$

The meaning of (18-11) is, of course, that any matrix elements of the two sides are equal, i.e.,

$$\frac{d}{dt}\int \varphi^+ x\psi \; d\tau = c\int \varphi^+ \alpha_x \psi \; d\tau$$

The eigenvalues of α_k are ± 1, since $\alpha_k^2 = 1$. Thus the eigenvalues of velocity are $\pm c$. This is a very remarkable result, since we know in classical relativity theory that a particle of finite mass can never attain the velocity of light. Moreover, since the components of $\boldsymbol{\alpha}$ do not commute, when the velocity in any one direction is measured, the velocity in the other two directions is entirely undefined. This seems to deny the possibility of velocity measurements.

Because of these difficulties it has been suggested that the position operator should be redefined. One can go into a representation of the Dirac matrices which does not connect positive-energy states with negative ones. This is the so-called Foldy-Wouthuysen (1950) representation. The position operator x in this representation differs from that in the usual Dirac representation, which can be obtained from it by a unitary similarity transformation. The details of this theory can be found in Schweber, pp. 91–95. It is found that the x operator in the usual Dirac representation is identically the position operator for a spin $\frac{1}{2}$ particle derived by Newton and Wigner (1949) from general arguments.

A consequence of (18-11) is that the relativistic spin $\frac{1}{2}$ particle executes a complicated motion which is an average translation and a superimposed erratic motion called *Zitterbewegung* (Schrödinger, 1930). To see this we consider

$$\dot{\alpha}_x = \frac{1}{i\hbar}[\alpha_x, H] = \frac{2}{i\hbar}(\alpha_x H - cp_x)$$

$$= \frac{-2}{i\hbar}(H\alpha_x - cp_x) \tag{18-12}$$

because α_x anticommutes with all matrices in H except α_x itself. H and p_x are constants; therefore,

$$\ddot{\alpha}_x = \frac{2}{i\hbar}\dot{\alpha}_x H = \frac{-2}{i\hbar}H\dot{\alpha}_x \tag{18-13}$$

Integrating,

$$\dot{\alpha}_x = \dot{\alpha}_x^0 e^{-2iHt/\hbar} = e^{2iHt/\hbar}\dot{\alpha}_x^0 \tag{18-14}$$

where $\dot{\alpha}_x^0$ is the value of $\dot{\alpha}_x$ at $t = 0$.

From (18-12),

$$\alpha_x H = \frac{i\hbar}{2}\dot{\alpha}_x^0 e^{-2iHt/\hbar} + cp_x$$

$$\dot{x} = \frac{i\hbar c}{2}\dot{\alpha}_x^0 e^{-2iHt/\hbar} H^{-1} + c^2 p_x H^{-1} \tag{18-15}$$

Noting that $H^{-1} = H/E^2$,

$$\dot{x} = \frac{i\hbar c}{2}\dot{\alpha}^0_x e^{-2iHt/\hbar}\frac{H}{E^2} + \frac{c^2 p_x H}{E^2} \tag{18-16}$$

Thus we see that the *Zitterbewegung* is an oscillatory motion with frequency $2H/\hbar$, which is at least $2mc^2/\hbar$ and is thus very high. Of course, no practical experiment can observe this. Had we used the position operator which was discussed above in connection with the Foldy-Wouthuysen representation, no such *Zitterbewegung* would arise. For this reason, that operator is usually referred to as the *mean position* operator.

No physical interpretation is given to the β matrix but the following relations can be verified:

$$\frac{d}{dt}\left[\mathbf{r} + \frac{\hbar i}{2mc}\beta\boldsymbol{\alpha}\right] = \frac{\beta\mathbf{p}}{m}$$

$$\frac{d}{dt}\left[t + \frac{\hbar i}{2mc^2}\beta\right] = \frac{\beta}{mc^2}H \tag{18-17}$$

$$i\hbar\frac{d}{dt}\left[\alpha_x\alpha_y\alpha_z\right] = -2mc^2\beta\alpha_x\alpha_y\alpha_z$$

The significance of these results is not understood.

SPIN

We consider the angular momentum operator $\mathbf{L}$ and inquire about $[L_x, H]$

$$\frac{1}{i\hbar}[L_x, H] = \frac{1}{i\hbar}\left[\left(yp_z - zp_y\right), \left(c\boldsymbol{\alpha}\cdot\mathbf{p} + \beta mc^2\right)\right]$$

$$= c\left(\alpha_y p_z - \alpha_z p_y\right) \tag{18-18a}$$

or

$$\frac{d\mathbf{L}}{dt} = c\boldsymbol{\alpha}\times\mathbf{p} \tag{18-18b}$$

Hence the angular momentum is no longer a constant of the motion. On the other hand, the existence of two linearly independent solutions corresponding to a given value of the energy indicates that an operator that commutes with the Hamiltonian must exist. We shall show that this operator is

$$\mathbf{L} + \tfrac{1}{2}\hbar\boldsymbol{\sigma}' \tag{18-19}$$

where $\boldsymbol{\sigma}'$ is, in the special representation, (17-40a) and (17-40c),

$$\boldsymbol{\sigma}' = \begin{pmatrix} \boldsymbol{\sigma} & 0 \\ 0 & \boldsymbol{\sigma} \end{pmatrix} \tag{18-20}$$

Remembering the commutation relations of the Pauli matrices $\boldsymbol{\sigma}$, we find

$$\left[\sigma_x', \alpha_y\right] = 2i\alpha_z \qquad \left[\sigma_x', \alpha_z\right] = -2i\alpha_y \tag{18-21a}$$

and cyclic permutations. Then

$$\frac{1}{i\hbar}\,\frac{\hbar}{2}\,[\sigma_x', H] = c\left(\alpha_z p_y - \alpha_y p_z\right) \tag{18-21b}$$

and therefore

$$[\mathbf{L} + \tfrac{1}{2}\hbar\boldsymbol{\sigma}', H] = 0 \tag{18-22}$$

Thus (18-19) is indeed a constant of motion.

It is evident from (18-20) that the eigenvalues of σ_k' are ± 1. Thus (18-22) shows that there is a conserved angular momentum, which is the vector sum of the orbital momentum $\mathbf{L}$, and a second term, which has the eigenvalues $\pm \frac{1}{2}\hbar$. We have thus shown that a particle obeying the Dirac equation has a spin of $\frac{1}{2}$. All our previous results about the compounding of orbital and spin angular momentum can be used.

The correct total angular momentum operator has become $\mathbf{L} + (\hbar/2)\boldsymbol{\sigma}'$. This is an example of the fact that the elementary rules for constructing operators from classical dynamical variables [e.g., in the $\mathbf{r}$ representation, replacing $\mathbf{r}$ by the operator $\mathbf{r}$ and $\mathbf{p}$ by $(\hbar/i)\nabla$] are not general enough. Instead we must allow for the possibility of adding further terms which disappear in the limit $\hbar \to 0$. Thus, to obtain the proper angular momentum operator from $\mathbf{r} \times \mathbf{p}$ we were forced to add $\frac{1}{2}\hbar\boldsymbol{\sigma}'$, which vanishes as $\hbar \to 0$.

If we do not wish to specify the representation of the Dirac matrices we may put

$$\boldsymbol{\sigma}' = i\gamma_5\boldsymbol{\alpha} \tag{18-23}$$

Using the last expression (17-23) for γ_5, and noting that γ_5 commutes with any α_k, we obtain

$$\frac{1}{i\hbar}\,[\sigma_x', H] = \frac{-2c}{\hbar}\left(\alpha_y p_z - \alpha_z p_y\right) \tag{18-21b}$$

From the definition (18-23) we find

$$\sigma'_k = i\gamma^\ell \gamma^m \tag{18-23a}$$

where k, ℓ, m follow cyclically. Inserting γ_5 and $\boldsymbol{\alpha}$ for the special representation, viz., (17-40c) and (17-40d), we find (18-20).

DIRAC EQUATION IN EXTERNAL FIELD

As in the Klein-Gordon case, the inclusion of an electromagnetic field can be achieved by the gauge-invariant, Lorentz-covariant replacement

$$p_\mu \rightarrow p_\mu - \frac{e}{c} A_\mu \tag{18-24}$$

i.e.,

$$E \rightarrow E - e\varphi \qquad \mathbf{p} \rightarrow \mathbf{p} - \frac{e}{c}\mathbf{A}$$

This leads to the equation

$$\left\{(E - e\varphi) - \boldsymbol{\alpha}\cdot(c\mathbf{p} - e\mathbf{A}) - \beta mc^2\right\}\psi = 0 \tag{18-25a}$$

$$\left(\gamma^\mu\left(p_\mu - \frac{e}{c}A_\mu\right) - mc\right)\psi = 0 \tag{18-25b}$$

Other fields can be taken into account by including the corresponding potentials with mc^2 if the potentials are relativistic scalars, in A_μ if they are four-vectors.

The substitution (18-24) is not completely general; a possible additional term will be given in (18-32).

To obtain a second-order equation similar in form to the Klein-Gordon equation we premultiply (18-25b) by $\gamma^\nu(p_\nu - (e/c)A_\nu)$ and obtain

$$\gamma^\mu\gamma^\nu\left(p_\mu - \frac{e}{c}A_\mu\right)\left(p_\nu - \frac{e}{c}A_\nu\right)\psi = m^2c^2\psi \tag{18-26}$$

We define

$$\sigma^{\mu\nu} = \frac{i}{2}\left(\gamma^\mu\gamma^\nu - \gamma^\nu\gamma^\mu\right) = -\sigma^{\nu\mu} \tag{18-27}$$

Noting from (17-18) that

$$\gamma^\mu\gamma^\nu = g^{\mu\nu} - i\sigma^{\mu\nu}$$

the left-hand side of (18-27) becomes

$$\left(g^{\mu\nu} - i\sigma^{\mu\nu}\right)\left(p_\mu - \frac{e}{c}A_\mu\right)\left(p_\nu - \frac{e}{c}A_\nu\right)$$

$$= \left(p_\mu - \frac{e}{c}A_\mu\right)\left(p^\mu - \frac{e}{c}A^\mu\right)$$

$$- \frac{i}{2}\left(\sigma^{\mu\nu} - \sigma^{\nu\mu}\right)\left(p_\mu - \frac{e}{c}A_\mu\right)\left(p_\nu - \frac{e}{c}A_\nu\right)$$

$$= \left(p_\mu - \frac{e}{c}A_\mu\right)\left(p^\mu - \frac{e}{c}A^\mu\right)$$

$$- \frac{i}{2}\sigma^{\mu\nu}\left[\left(p_\mu - \frac{e}{c}A_\mu\right), \left(p_\nu - \frac{e}{c}A_\nu\right)\right] \qquad (18\text{-}28)$$

The commutator in the last line is easily evaluated by recalling that

$$\left[p_\mu, A_\nu\right] = i\hbar\,\frac{\partial A_\nu}{\partial x^\mu}$$

and yields

$$\frac{ie\hbar}{c}\left[\frac{\partial A_\nu}{\partial x^\mu} - \frac{\partial A_\mu}{\partial x^\nu}\right] = \frac{ie\hbar}{c}\,F_{\mu\nu} \qquad (18\text{-}29)$$

where $F_{\mu\nu}$ is the component of the electromagnetic field tensor. One finally obtains the equation

$$\left[\left(p_\mu - \frac{e}{c}A_\mu\right)\left(p^\mu - \frac{e}{c}A^\mu\right) + \frac{e\hbar}{2c}\sigma^{\mu\nu}F_{\mu\nu}\right]\psi$$

$$= (mc)^2\,\psi \qquad (18\text{-}30)$$

Using the definition of $\boldsymbol{\sigma}'$ (18-23) the above can be written

$$[(E - e\varphi)^2 - (c\mathbf{p} - e\mathbf{A})^2 + e\hbar c\,(\boldsymbol{\sigma}' \cdot \boldsymbol{\mathcal{H}} - i\boldsymbol{\alpha} \cdot \boldsymbol{\mathcal{E}})]\,\psi$$

$$= m^2c^4\,\psi \qquad (18\text{-}31)$$

The first two terms on the left-hand side occur in the Klein-Gordon equation. The other two terms arise only in the Dirac theory and are seen to vanish as $\hbar \to 0$.

The last term of (18-30) is by itself relativistically invariant. It is in principle possible to multiply this term by an arbitrary factor $1 + K$ i.e., to add to (18-30) a term

$$K \frac{e\hbar}{2c} \sigma^{\mu\nu} F_{\mu\nu} \psi \tag{18-32}$$

This is known as a Pauli moment term, and means of course a corresponding modification of the original Dirac equation. Such a modification is in principle permissible because it tends to zero as $\hbar \to 0$, but it would of course complicate the theory.

NONRELATIVISTIC LIMIT

There are essentially two different ways of considering the nonrelativistic limit. In the first method no attention is paid to the mixing between large and small components of ψ. This is valid if we neglect terms of order v^2/c^2. In the second case terms of order v^2/c^2 are kept and a reduction to large components of ψ is made.

To obtain the first approximation we set

$$(E - e\varphi)^2 - m^2c^4 \simeq 2mc^2(E' - e\varphi)$$

where

$$E' + mc^2 = E \qquad \text{and} \qquad e\varphi \ll mc^2,\ E' \ll mc^2$$

Then (18-31) becomes

$$E'\psi = \left[\frac{1}{2m}\left(\mathbf{p} - \frac{e}{c}\mathbf{A}\right)^2 + e\varphi - \frac{e\hbar}{2mc}\boldsymbol{\sigma}' \cdot \boldsymbol{\mathcal{H}} + \frac{ie\hbar}{2mc}\boldsymbol{\alpha} \cdot \boldsymbol{\mathcal{E}}\right]\psi \tag{18-33}$$

We now estimate the term in $\boldsymbol{\mathcal{E}}$. The expectation value of $\boldsymbol{\alpha}$ is v/c, as seen from (18-11). For an electron that is part of a system of dimension a, $e\varphi$ is of order $e\mathcal{E}a$ and $\hbar/a \sim p \sim mv$. Therefore,

$$\frac{(e\hbar/2mc)\,\boldsymbol{\alpha} \cdot \boldsymbol{\mathcal{E}}}{e\varphi} \sim \frac{1}{2}\frac{v^2}{c^2}$$

and the electric field term should be neglected. The term in $\boldsymbol{\mathcal{E}}$ is necessary to preserve Lorentz covariance, but in the nonrelativistic approximation this is not relevant. Thus

$$E'\psi = \left[\frac{1}{2m}\left(\mathbf{p} - \frac{e}{c}\mathbf{A}\right)^2 + e\varphi - \frac{e}{mc}\frac{\hbar}{2}\boldsymbol{\sigma}' \cdot \boldsymbol{\mathcal{H}}\right]\psi \tag{18-34}$$

The term in $\boldsymbol{\mathcal{H}}$ has the form of magnetic-dipole-interaction energy.

In the usual representation $\boldsymbol{\sigma}'$ is $\begin{pmatrix} \boldsymbol{\sigma} & 0 \\ 0 & \boldsymbol{\sigma} \end{pmatrix}$ and we conclude that the magnetic moment of the electron is $(e\hbar/2mc)\boldsymbol{\sigma}$, which of course verifies the Uhlenbeck-Goudsmit hypothesis, and gives the proper gyromagnetic ratio.

It is beyond the scope of the present discussion to treat the corrections that quantum electrodynamics requires. Suffice it to say that the interaction of a charged particle with its own field leads to a correction factor g to the magnetic moment which is calculated to be

$$1 + \frac{e^2}{2\pi\hbar c} + 0\left(\frac{e^2}{\hbar c}\right)^2 = 1.00116$$

This value of the magnetic moment has been verified exactly. Another observable consequence of the self-interaction of the electron is the Lamb shift.

The Dirac theory does not predict the correct value for the magnetic moment of the proton. One could obtain the required result by adding to the first-order Dirac equation the so-called Pauli term,

$$K(\boldsymbol{\sigma}' \cdot \boldsymbol{\mathcal{H}} + i\boldsymbol{\alpha} \cdot \boldsymbol{\mathcal{E}})$$

which would still lead to a relativistically invariant equation. The constant K is then adjusted to give the correct answer. The arbitrary nature of this device makes it rather unsatisfactory. Physically, it is believed that the proton's magnetic moment is due to interaction with a meson field, but attempts at a quantitative theory have not yet been successful.

The reduction to large components proceeds from the first-order equation (18-25a). We write in (18-25a)

$$\psi = \begin{pmatrix} \psi_A \\ \psi_B \end{pmatrix} \tag{18-35}$$

where ψ_A and ψ_B are still two-component functions. If we use the explicit form of the Dirac matrices, then (18-25a) reads

$$\left\{\begin{bmatrix} 0 & I \\ I & 0 \end{bmatrix} \boldsymbol{\sigma} \cdot (c\mathbf{p} - e\mathbf{A}) + \begin{bmatrix} I & 0 \\ 0 & -I \end{bmatrix} mc^2 \right\} \begin{pmatrix} \psi_A \\ \psi_B \end{pmatrix}$$
$$= (E - e\varphi) \begin{pmatrix} \psi_A \\ \psi_B \end{pmatrix} \tag{18-36}$$

This is equivalent to two coupled equations

$$\boldsymbol{\sigma} \cdot (c\mathbf{p} - e\mathbf{A})\psi_B + mc^2 \psi_A = (E - e\varphi)\psi_A \tag{18-37a}$$

$$\boldsymbol{\sigma} \cdot (c\mathbf{p} - e\mathbf{A})\psi_A - mc^2 \psi_B = (E - e\varphi)\psi_B \tag{18-37b}$$

Here $\boldsymbol{\sigma}$ is the 2×2 Pauli matrix and ψ_A, ψ_B each have two components. From (18-37b) we obtain

$$\psi_B = (E - e\varphi + mc^2)^{-1} \boldsymbol{\sigma} \cdot (c\mathbf{p} - e\mathbf{A})\psi_A \tag{18-38a}$$

Setting $E = E' + mc^2$,

$$\psi_B = (E' - e\varphi + 2mc^2)^{-1} \boldsymbol{\sigma} \cdot (c\mathbf{p} - e\mathbf{A})\psi_A \tag{18-38b}$$

The nonrelativistic limit is

$$E' \ll mc^2 \qquad e\varphi \ll mc^2 \qquad \mathbf{p} \approx m\mathbf{v}$$

Hence

$$\psi_B = |\boldsymbol{\sigma}|\ 0\left(\frac{v}{c}\right)\psi_A \tag{18-39}$$

i.e., the four-component solution ψ has two large components ψ_A and two small components ψ_B, just as was the case for the free-particle solution. Furthermore, substituting the exact expression (18-38b) into (18-37a) we obtain with a little rearrangement and with the assumption $\mathbf{A} = 0$ and $e\varphi = V$,

$$\left[\frac{\boldsymbol{\sigma} \cdot \mathbf{p}}{2m}\left[1 + \frac{E' - V}{2mc^2}\right]^{-1} \boldsymbol{\sigma} \cdot \mathbf{p} + V\right]\psi_A = E'\psi_A \tag{18-40}$$

We now approximate this by keeping only the lowest terms in an expansion in powers of $(E' - V)/2mc^2$. The following relations are then true:

$$\left[1 + \frac{E' - V}{2mc^2}\right]^{-1} \approx 1 - \frac{E' - V}{2mc^2}$$

$$\mathbf{p}V = V\mathbf{p} - i\hbar\nabla V$$

$$(\boldsymbol{\sigma} \cdot \nabla V)(\boldsymbol{\sigma} \cdot \mathbf{p}) = \nabla V \cdot \mathbf{p} + i\boldsymbol{\sigma} \cdot [\nabla V \times \mathbf{p}]$$

Assuming spherical symmetry of V we obtain from (18-40)

$$\left[\left(1 - \frac{E' - V}{2mc^2}\right)\frac{p^2}{2m} + V\right]\psi_A - \frac{\hbar^2}{4m^2c^2}\frac{dV}{dr}\frac{\partial\psi_A}{\partial r} + \frac{1}{2m^2c^2}\frac{1}{r}\frac{dV}{dr}\mathbf{S}\cdot\mathbf{L}\,\psi_A = E'\psi_A \qquad (18\text{-}41a)$$

with

$$\mathbf{S} = \tfrac{1}{2}\hbar\boldsymbol{\sigma} \qquad \mathbf{L} = \mathbf{r}\times\mathbf{p}$$

Finally, setting in the correction term $E' - V \approx p^2/2m$, we obtain

$$E'\psi_A = \left[\frac{p^2}{2m} + V - \frac{p^4}{8m^3c^2} - \frac{\hbar^2}{4m^2c^2}\frac{dV}{dr}\frac{\partial}{\partial r} + \frac{1}{2m^2c^2}\frac{1}{r}\frac{dV}{dr}\mathbf{S}\cdot\mathbf{L}\right]\psi_A \qquad (18\text{-}41b)$$

The first two terms on the right side of (18-41b) are the usual terms in the nonrelativistic Schrödinger equation. The third term is the second term in the expansion of E' in terms of p^2, i.e.,

$$E' = E - mc^2 = mc^2\left(1 + \frac{p^2}{m^2c^2}\right)^{1/2} - mc^2 \approx \frac{p^2}{2m} - \frac{p^4}{8m^3c^2}$$

The next term has no classical analogue. Finally the last term is the spin-orbit coupling energy including the Thomas factor of $\frac{1}{2}$ (see p. 112).

The procedure of solution is to solve the nonrelativistic Schrödinger equation for the two components of ψ_A; then to form linear combinations such that J, M_J, L, S are quantized; and then to consider

$$\frac{-p^4}{8m^3c^2} - \left(\frac{\hbar}{2mc}\right)^2\frac{dV}{dr}\frac{\partial}{\partial r}$$

and the spin-orbit interaction as a perturbation.

EXACT SOLUTION OF DIRAC EQUATION FOR COULOMB POTENTIAL

We solve the Dirac differential equation for a Coulomb field. We use the explicit Dirac representation; i.e., we solve the four equations, (18-37a) and (18-37b) with $e\varphi = -Ze^2/r$, $\mathbf{A} = 0$. Also writing

$$\psi_A = \begin{pmatrix} u_1 \\ u_2 \end{pmatrix} \qquad \psi_B = \begin{pmatrix} u_3 \\ u_4 \end{pmatrix}$$

we get

$$
\begin{aligned}
-\frac{i}{\hbar c}\left[E + \frac{Ze^2}{r} - mc^2\right]u_1 + \frac{\partial u_4}{\partial x} - i\frac{\partial u_4}{\partial y} + \frac{\partial u_3}{\partial z} &= 0 \\
-\frac{i}{\hbar c}\left[E + \frac{Ze^2}{r} - mc^2\right]u_2 + \frac{\partial u_3}{\partial x} + i\frac{\partial u_3}{\partial y} - \frac{\partial u_4}{\partial z} &= 0 \\
-\frac{i}{\hbar c}\left[E + \frac{Ze^2}{r} + mc^2\right]u_3 + \frac{\partial u_2}{\partial x} - i\frac{\partial u_2}{\partial y} + \frac{\partial u_1}{\partial z} &= 0 \\
-\frac{i}{\hbar c}\left[E + \frac{Ze^2}{r} + mc^2\right]u_4 + \frac{\partial u_1}{\partial x} + i\frac{\partial u_1}{\partial y} - \frac{\partial u_2}{\partial z} &= 0
\end{aligned}
\tag{18-42}
$$

To find a solution we now make use of the fact that if we consider only large components, i.e., set the small components equal to zero, then $[\boldsymbol{\ell}, H]$, which is proportional to $\boldsymbol{\alpha} \times \mathbf{p}$, will be 0, since $\boldsymbol{\alpha}$ connects the large and small components. Thus ψ_A will be an eigenfunction of $\boldsymbol{\ell}$. Furthermore it must contain one component with spin up and another with spin down. Of course $\mathbf{j}$ and j_z are constants of the motion. Hence for $j = \ell + \frac{1}{2}$ we set

$$
\begin{aligned}
u_1 &= g(r)\sqrt{\frac{\ell + m + \frac{1}{2}}{2\ell + 1}}\; Y_{\ell, m-\frac{1}{2}}(\Omega) \\
u_2 &= -g(r)\sqrt{\frac{\ell - m + \frac{1}{2}}{2\ell + 1}}\; Y_{\ell, m+\frac{1}{2}}(\Omega)
\end{aligned}
\tag{18-43}
$$

This differs from the Pauli nonrelativistic treatment in that $g(r)$ is an as-yet arbitrary radial function and not the solution of the radial nonrelativistic Schrödinger equation.

To obtain the small components, we note that the small components are given by

$$
\psi_B = (2mc^2 + E' - V)^{-1}\, c\boldsymbol{\sigma}\cdot\mathbf{p}\psi_A \tag{18-38a}
$$

The operator which gives the small component from the large component has odd parity ($\mathbf{p}$ is odd, everything else is even) and commutes with $\mathbf{j}$. Hence ψ_B must belong to the same j value as ψ_A but must have a different ℓ. Corresponding to $j = \ell + \frac{1}{2}$ the only other possible value of the orbital momentum is $\ell' = \ell + 1$. Hence we set, remembering the Clebsch-Gordan coefficients,

$$
\begin{aligned}
u_3 &= -if(r)\sqrt{\frac{\ell - m + \frac{3}{2}}{2\ell + 3}}\; Y_{\ell+1, m-\frac{1}{2}}(\Omega) \\
u_4 &= -if(r)\sqrt{\frac{\ell + m + \frac{3}{2}}{2\ell + 3}}\; Y_{\ell+1, m+\frac{1}{2}}(\Omega)
\end{aligned}
\tag{18-44}
$$

where f(r) is some radial function. Inserting (18-43) and (18-44) in (18-42) we find that for $j = \ell + \frac{1}{2}$ the connection between f and g is given by

$$\frac{1}{\hbar c}\left(E + \frac{Ze^2}{r} + mc^2\right) f = \frac{dg}{dr} - \ell\,\frac{g}{r}$$
$$\frac{1}{\hbar c}\left(E + \frac{Ze^2}{r} - mc^2\right) g = -\frac{df}{dr} - (\ell + 2)\,\frac{f}{r} \qquad (18\text{-}45)$$

Arguing completely analogously one finds that for $j = \ell - \frac{1}{2}$

$$u_1 = g(r)\sqrt{\frac{\ell - m + \frac{1}{2}}{2\ell + 1}}\; Y_{\ell, m-\frac{1}{2}}(\Omega)$$
$$u_2 = g(r)\sqrt{\frac{\ell + m + \frac{1}{2}}{2\ell + 1}}\; Y_{\ell, m+\frac{1}{2}}(\Omega)$$
$$u_3 = -if(r)\sqrt{\frac{\ell + m - \frac{1}{2}}{2\ell - 1}}\; Y_{\ell-1, m-\frac{1}{2}}(\Omega) \qquad (18\text{-}46)$$
$$u_4 = if(r)\sqrt{\frac{\ell - m - \frac{1}{2}}{2\ell - 1}}\; Y_{\ell-1, m+\frac{1}{2}}(\Omega)$$

and

$$\frac{1}{\hbar c}\left(E + \frac{Ze^2}{r} + mc^2\right) f = \frac{dg}{dr} + (\ell + 1)\,\frac{g}{r}$$
$$\frac{1}{\hbar c}\left(E + \frac{Ze^2}{r} - mc^2\right) g = -\frac{df}{dr} + (\ell - 1)\,\frac{f}{r} \qquad (18\text{-}47)$$

We define

$$k = -(\ell + 1) \qquad \text{if } j = \ell + \tfrac{1}{2}$$
$$k = \ell \qquad \text{if } j = \ell - \tfrac{1}{2}$$

i.e., (18-48)

$$k = 1, 2, \ldots \qquad \text{for } j = \ell - \tfrac{1}{2}$$
$$k = -1, -2, \ldots \qquad \text{for } j = \ell + \tfrac{1}{2}$$

Equations (18-45) and (18-47) can be combined as

$$\frac{1}{\hbar c}\left(E + \frac{Ze^2}{r} + mc^2\right)f - \left(\frac{dg}{dr} + (1+k)\frac{g}{r}\right) = 0$$
$$\frac{1}{\hbar c}\left(E + \frac{Ze^2}{r} - mc^2\right)g + \left(\frac{df}{dr} + (1-k)\frac{f}{r}\right) = 0 \qquad (18\text{-}49)$$

Setting

$$F = rf \qquad G = rg$$
$$\alpha_1 = \frac{mc^2 + E}{\hbar c} \qquad \alpha_2 = \frac{mc^2 - E}{\hbar c} \qquad (18\text{-}50a)$$
$$\alpha = (\alpha_1\alpha_2)^{1/2} \qquad \gamma = \frac{Ze^2}{\hbar c} \qquad \rho = \alpha r$$

we obtain

$$\left(\frac{d}{d\rho} + \frac{k}{\rho}\right)G - \left(\frac{\alpha_1}{\alpha} + \frac{\gamma}{\rho}\right)F = 0$$
$$\left(\frac{d}{d\rho} - \frac{k}{\rho}\right)F - \left(\frac{\alpha_2}{\alpha} - \frac{\gamma}{\rho}\right)G = 0 \qquad (18\text{-}50b)$$

We use the time-honored series method. First we substitute

$$F = \varphi(\rho)e^{-\rho} \qquad G = \chi(\rho)e^{-\rho} \qquad (18\text{-}51)$$

and obtain

$$\chi' - \chi + \frac{k\chi}{\rho} - \left(\frac{\alpha_1}{\alpha} + \frac{\gamma}{\rho}\right)\varphi = 0$$
$$\varphi' - \varphi - \frac{k\varphi}{\rho} - \left(\frac{\alpha_2}{\alpha} - \frac{\gamma}{\rho}\right)\chi = 0 \qquad (18\text{-}52)$$

We then substitute the power series

$$\varphi = \rho^s \sum_{m=0}^{\infty} a_m \rho^m \qquad a_0 \neq 0$$
$$\chi = \rho^s \sum_{m=0}^{\infty} b_m \rho^m \qquad b_0 \neq 0 \qquad (18\text{-}53)$$

The requirement that f, g be everywhere finite will be seen to be impossible to satisfy. We therefore require that the integrated probability density be finite, i.e., that

$$\int_0^\infty \{|F(\rho)|^2 + |G(\rho)|^2\}\, d\rho < \infty \tag{18-54}$$

This assures us that $s \neq -\infty$. Substituting the series into (18-52) and equating coefficients of the same power of ρ gives

$$\begin{aligned} (s + v + k) b_v - b_{v-1} - \gamma a_v - \frac{\alpha_1}{\alpha} a_{v-1} &= 0 \\ (s + v - k) a_v - a_{v-1} + \gamma b_v - \frac{\alpha_2}{\alpha} b_{v-1} &= 0 \end{aligned} \tag{18-55}$$

For $v = 0$ we get

$$\begin{aligned} (s + k) b_0 - \gamma a_0 &= 0 \\ (s - k) a_0 + \gamma b_0 &= 0 \end{aligned} \tag{18-56}$$

This will have a nontrivial solution if and only if

$$s = \pm(k^2 - \gamma^2)^{1/2} \tag{18-57a}$$

We first examine the negative root. For small ρ the integrand of (18-54) is $\sim\rho^{2s}$ and we must have $2s > -1$, $(k^2 - \gamma^2)^{1/2} < \frac{1}{2}$. The minimum s occurs for $k^2 = 1$; this would mean $Z \geq 109$. For $k^2 > 1$, no value of Z will permit the negative root. Restricting ourselves to $Z < 109$, we choose the positive root

$$s = (k^2 - \gamma^2)^{1/2} \tag{18-57b}$$

For $k = 1$, $s < 1$, and f,g diverge; however (18-54) converges.

The recursion relations (18-55) can easily be seen to lead to functions of the order $e^{2\rho}$; hence we must require the series to terminate for (18-54) to hold. Suppose this happens for $v = n'$, i.e., $a_{n'+1} = b_{n'+1} = 0$. Then from (18-54) we get

$$\alpha_1 a_{n'} = -\alpha b_{n'} \qquad n' = 0, 1, \ldots \tag{18-58}$$

Multiplying the first of (18-54) by α, the second by α_1, and subtracting

$$b_v[\alpha(s + v + k) - \alpha_1 \gamma] = a_v[\alpha_1(s + v - k) + \alpha\gamma] \tag{18-59}$$

Inserting $v = n'$ and using (18-58),

$$2\alpha(s + n') = \gamma(\alpha_1 - \alpha_2) = \frac{2E\gamma}{\hbar c}$$

which leads to

$$E = mc^2 \left[1 + \frac{\gamma^2}{(s + n')^2}\right]^{-1/2} \tag{18-60a}$$

$$E = mc^2 \left[1 + \frac{\gamma^2}{(n' + \sqrt{k^2 - \gamma^2})^2}\right]^{-1/2} \tag{18-60b}$$

Noting that $|k| = j + \frac{1}{2}$,

$$E = mc^2 \left[1 + \frac{\gamma^2}{(n' + \sqrt{(j + \frac{1}{2})^2 - \gamma^2})^2}\right]^{-1/2} \tag{18-60c}$$

$$n' = 0, 1, \ldots; \qquad j + \tfrac{1}{2} = 1, 2, \ldots$$

From (18-60b) it is seen that negative values of $k = -1, -2, -3, \ldots$ are also acceptable. However, for $n' = 0$ (18-56) and (18-58) give

$$\frac{b_0}{a_0} = \frac{\gamma}{s + k} = -\frac{\alpha_1}{\alpha} \tag{18-61}$$

Since $s < |k|$, the first expression for b_0/a_0 will be positive or negative, depending on whether k is positive or negative. The second will always be negative. Hence for $n' = 0$, k can only be negative, i.e., $j = \ell + \frac{1}{2}$. Equation (18-60c) can be expanded in powers of γ^2:

$$E = mc^2 \left[1 - \frac{\gamma^2}{2n^2} - \frac{\gamma^4}{2n^3}\left(\frac{1}{|k|} - \frac{3}{4n}\right)\right] \tag{18-62}$$

where $n = n' + |k|$.

It is seen that the Dirac theory leads to accidental degeneracy in ℓ; i.e., states with the same j but different ℓ have the same energy. This degeneracy is removed by the Lamb shift, which is due to the interaction of the electron with its own field. For $j = \frac{1}{2}$, this effect is one order of magnitude smaller than the fine-structure splitting; for $j \geq \frac{3}{2}$, two orders of magnitude. For example, the Dirac theory predicts, for $n = 2$, two states with the same energy $s_{1/2}$, $p_{1/2}$ and a fine-structure splitting of $\sim 0.36\ \text{cm}^{-1}$ between these and the $p_{3/2}$ state. The Lamb shift raises the $s_{1/2}$ state by about $0.035\ \text{cm}^{-1}$ above the $p_{1/2}$. The binding energy is $27{,}000\ \text{cm}^{-1}$, so we are really dealing with a "fine" structure.

NEGATIVE ENERGY SOLUTIONS

We have seen that both the Klein-Gordon and the Dirac theories lead to positive energy states $\gtrsim mc^2$ and negative energy states $\lesssim -mc^2$. In classical theory negative energy solutions exist also, but they can be excluded by physical continuity: it is impossible for a classical particle to pass from positive energy states to negative energy without going through energy states in between. Hence the removal of the negative energy states is equivalent to the boundary condition that "in the beginning" all particles had positive energy.

A completely free single quantum mechanical particle also will not make transitions. However, no particle is completely free and transitions can always occur, by radiation if by no other means; e.g., for an electron bound in a hydrogen atom, one can calculate that the transition to the negative energy states by radiation will take place in about 10^{-10} sec. Once an electron has made the transition it would quickly "fall" toward negative infinite energy. This is clearly contrary to observation.

Dirac proposed that the negative energy states be regarded as full. Then the Pauli exclusion principle will prevent transitions into such occupied states. It is assumed that there are no gravitational or electromagnetic effects of the electrons occupying the negative states. That is to say, according to Dirac the vacuum is the condition when all the negative energy states are filled. Occasionally one or more of the negative energy states can become empty. The absence of a negative energy electron would manifest itself as the presence of a positively charged electron, i.e., of a positron. When Pauli in 1932 considered (in his article in the "Handbuch der Physik") this interpretation of the negative energy states, he rejected it because at the time there was no experimental evidence for the existence of such positrons. However by the time the article had appeared in print in 1933, the theory was vindicated by Anderson's (1932) discovery of the positron.

Using the concept of the "sea of negative energy electrons" one can calculate the probability of pair production in the electric field of a nucleus by considering the probability of raising an electron from a negative to a positive energy state.

The apparent asymmetry between the treatment of positive and negative electrons can be removed, and this has been done by Heisenberg (1934) and Kramers (1937).

It should be pointed out that similar techniques cannot be applied to the Klein-Gordon equation, because particles of zero spin do not obey an exclusion principle. Pauli and Weisskopf (1934) have shown that the quantized field energy is always positive. The parameter E in the wave equation is positive for positively charged particles and negative for negatively charged particles, and so is the charge density

PERTURBATION THEORY

It is clear from the general structure of the Dirac theory that time independent and time-dependent perturbation theory is formally the same as for the nonrelativistic Schrödinger theory, except that the matrix elements are now calculated between spinors and not just between one-component (scalar) wave functions. We shall examine the results for scattering of free particles by a constant potential V.

The transition probability per unit time is given by Fermi's golden rule

$$\omega = \frac{2\pi}{\hbar} \left| V_{fi} \right|^2 \rho(E) \tag{18-63}$$

$$\rho(E) = \frac{d\Omega \, p^2}{(2\pi\hbar)^3} \frac{dp}{dE} = \frac{d\Omega \, p^2}{(2\pi\hbar)^3 v} \tag{18-64}$$

For free particles the initial wave function is

$$\psi_i = u_i e^{i\mathbf{k}_i \cdot \mathbf{r}} \tag{18-65}$$

where u_i is a four-spinor independent of $\mathbf{r}$. The final states are

$$\psi_f = u_f e^{i\mathbf{k}_f \cdot \mathbf{r}} \tag{18-66}$$

where u_f is again independent of $\mathbf{r}$.

$$V_{fi} = \int V e^{i\mathbf{q}\cdot\mathbf{r}} \, d\tau \left(u_f^\dagger u_i\right)$$

$$\mathbf{q} = \mathbf{k}_i - \mathbf{k}_f \tag{18-67}$$

This is exactly the same as the nonrelativistic Born approximation result except for the new factor $(u_f^\dagger u_i)$.

We consider the quantity $|(u_f^\dagger u_i)|^2$. Usually we are not interested in the specific final spin, hence we must sum this over all final spin states. Furthermore we may wish to take one-half of the sum over initial spin states, which amounts to averaging over the initial spins —a necessary procedure if the initial states were unpolarized.

A simple method for evaluating such sums is in terms of *Casimir projection operators*. It should be noted that dealing with elastic scattering we cannot use closure, since sums do not extend over all possible energy states. Specifically, both initially and finally energy must be positive.

We define

$$P = \frac{1}{2}\left[\frac{|E| + \boldsymbol{\alpha}\cdot\mathbf{p} + \beta m}{|E|}\right]$$

$$\hbar = c = 1 \tag{18-68}$$

We note that

$$Pu = \frac{1}{2}\left[u + \frac{(\boldsymbol{\alpha}\cdot\mathbf{p} + \beta m)u}{|E|}\right]$$

$$= \tfrac{1}{2}[u \pm u] = u \text{ or } 0 \qquad (18\text{-}69)$$

depending on whether u is a positive energy state or a negative energy state. We rewrite

$$P = \tfrac{1}{2}(1 + \boldsymbol{\alpha}\cdot\mathbf{v} + \beta\mu)$$
$$\mu = \frac{m}{|E|} = \left(1 - \frac{v^2}{c^2}\right)^{1/2} \qquad (18\text{-}70)$$

Therefore,

$$\tfrac{1}{2}\sum_{\substack{i \\ E>0}}\sum_{f}\left(u_i^\dagger u_f\right)\left(u_f^\dagger u_i\right)$$
$$= \tfrac{1}{2}\sum_{\substack{i \\ \text{all } E}}\sum_{f}\left(u_i^\dagger P_f u_f\right)\left(u_f^\dagger P_i u_i\right) \qquad (18\text{-}71)$$

The two sums are the same since the projection operators annihilate the states with negative energy. We further note that

$$P_f = \tfrac{1}{2}(1 + \boldsymbol{\alpha}\cdot\mathbf{v}_f + \beta\mu)$$
$$P_i = \tfrac{1}{2}(1 + \boldsymbol{\alpha}\cdot\mathbf{v}_i + \beta\mu) \qquad (18\text{-}72)$$

The μ's in the two operators are the same because the scattering is elastic. Using closure in the sum over the final states we get

$$\tfrac{1}{8}\sum_i u_i^\dagger(1 + \boldsymbol{\alpha}\cdot\mathbf{v}_f + \beta\mu)(1 + \boldsymbol{\alpha}\cdot\mathbf{v}_i + \beta\mu)u_i \qquad (18\text{-}73)$$

Since the summation is over a complete set of spinors u_i we can just as well sum over any other complete set. Specifically choosing the set to be

$$\begin{pmatrix}1\\0\\0\\0\end{pmatrix} \quad \begin{pmatrix}0\\1\\0\\0\end{pmatrix} \quad \begin{pmatrix}0\\0\\1\\0\end{pmatrix} \quad \begin{pmatrix}0\\0\\0\\1\end{pmatrix}$$

we get

$$\tfrac{1}{8}\,\mathrm{Tr}\,(1 + \boldsymbol{\alpha}\cdot\mathbf{v}_f + \beta\mu)(1 + \boldsymbol{\alpha}\cdot\mathbf{v}_i + \beta\mu) \tag{18-74}$$

Expanding the product and making use of the results that

$$\mathrm{Tr}\ \alpha = \mathrm{Tr}\ \beta = \mathrm{Tr}\ \alpha\beta = 0$$

we finally get

$$\tfrac{1}{2}(1 + \mathbf{v}_i\cdot\mathbf{v}_f + \mu^2) = \tfrac{1}{2}(2 - v^2 + v^2 \cos\theta) \tag{18-75}$$

where

$$\frac{\mathbf{v}_i\cdot\mathbf{v}_f}{v^2} = \cos\theta$$

We conclude that the scattering cross section of Dirac particles is the same as the nonrelativistic result times a factor

$$1 - v^2 \sin^2(\tfrac{1}{2}\theta) \tag{18-76}$$

Part III

INTRODUCTION TO FIELD THEORY

Chapter 19

FIELD QUANTIZATION

In previous chapters we have repeatedly stated that the correct quantum mechanical description of the interaction of electromagnetic fields and particles requires the quantization of the electromagnetic field, i.e., quantum field theory. The reason for this is that if mechanical parameters (coordinates and momenta) are to be quantized then the fields coupled to them must also be quantized. Otherwise, as pointed out by Bohr and Rosenfeld (1933), it would be possible to violate Heisenberg's uncertainty principle by setting up a *Gedanken* experiment which would simultaneously measure the position and momentum of a particle by observing the fields generated by the particle.

Having accepted the need to quantize classical fields such as the electromagnetic field, we may also regard the one-particle Schrödinger, Klein-Gordon, or Dirac equation as a classical field equation for the particle or charge density of the system, and quantize it according to the same program as is used for the electromagnetic field. This procedure is usually called second quantization of matter fields. The main reason for quantizing such a particle field is to take into account the possibility that the number of particles changes. We know from the discussion of the Dirac theory of the positron that pairs of particles can be produced so that the number of particles can indeed change. Now with the usual Schrödinger theory, a 3n-dimensional space is used to describe n particles. When n changes (by creation or annihilation of particles) it is much more convenient to use a formalism which explicitly permits a change in the number of particles than to change the dimensionality of the space. The ordinary Schrödinger theory is contained in this formalism. Indeed, Jordan and Wigner (1928) showed that a field theory with a fixed number of particles is identical to the usual many-particle theory. Since the quantization of the electromagnetic field poses several special problems we shall first discuss the quantization of matter fields (second quantization) and postpone the treatment of quantum electrodynamics to Chapter 21.

ANALYTICAL MECHANICS OF FIELDS; LAGRANGIAN FORMALISM

The program of quantization of fields follows precisely the general procedure for quantizing the equations of motion of any classical system. A classical Lagrangian is set up for the system; the momenta canonically conjugate to the coordinates are defined and a Hamiltonian function is obtained. The quantum equations of motion are given by the substitution of commutator brackets for Poisson brackets.

We consider a field described by a single field variable (amplitude) ψ which is a function of x, y, z, and t. Although we shall be concerned at first with the nonrelativistic Schrödinger equation, it is convenient to use the concise notation of space-time variables, which is also quite natural, since much of the formalism of the analytic mechanics of fields treats space and time coordinates symmetrically. Hence we say ψ is a function of the space-time variable x_μ. The Lagrangian for the field L is the space integral of a Lagrangian field density $\mathcal{L}$ and the equations of motion of the field are obtained from Hamilton's principle, which requires that the action S (time integral of the Lagrangian) be an extremum. That is, we define the Lagrangian density

$$\mathcal{L} = \mathcal{L}(\psi, \psi_\mu) \tag{19-1}$$

$$\psi_\mu = \frac{\partial \psi}{\partial x_\mu} \tag{19-2}$$

and the action

$$S = \int_\Omega \mathcal{L}(\psi, \psi_\mu)\ d^4x \tag{19-3}$$

Hamilton's principle states

$$\delta S = 0 \tag{19-4}$$

with the restriction that

$$\delta\psi(\mathbf{r}, t_1) = \delta\psi(\mathbf{r}, t_2) = 0 \tag{19-5}$$

where t_1 and t_2 are the time limits of integration (19-1). (*Note:* This is less restrictive than requiring that the variations vanish on the "surface" Σ bounding the "volume" Ω.)

Carrying out the variation on (19-3),

$$\delta S = \int_\Omega d^4x \left[\delta\psi \frac{\partial \mathcal{L}}{\partial \psi} + \delta\psi_\mu \frac{\partial \mathcal{L}}{\partial \psi_\mu}\right] = 0 \tag{19-6}$$

(summation over repeated Greek indices is implied).

Remembering that

$$\delta(\psi_\mu) = (\delta\psi)_\mu \tag{19-7}$$

(19-6) becomes

$$\delta S = \int_\Omega d^4x \left[\frac{\partial \mathcal{L}}{\partial \psi} - \frac{\partial}{\partial x^\mu}\left(\frac{\partial \mathcal{L}}{\partial \psi_\mu}\right)\right]\delta\psi + \int_\Omega d^4x \, \frac{\partial}{\partial x^\mu}\left(\frac{\partial \mathcal{L}}{\partial \psi_\mu}\,\delta\psi\right) \tag{19-8}$$

The second term in (19-8) can be transformed into a "surface" integral by the four-dimensional Gauss' theorem

$$\int_\Omega d^4x \, \frac{\partial}{\partial x^\mu}\left(\frac{\partial \mathcal{L}}{\partial \psi_\mu}\,\delta\psi\right) = \int_\Sigma d\Sigma_\mu \, \frac{\partial \mathcal{L}}{\partial \psi_\mu}\,\delta\psi \tag{19-9}$$

where Σ is the three-dimensional "surface" of the four-dimensional volume Ω and $d\Sigma_\mu$ is the projection of an element of this "surface" normal to the direction x_μ. One of the four integrals implied in (19-9) is carried out at the extremes of the time variation and vanishes because of (19-5). The other three are over two-dimensional space surfaces and vanish, since we always consider our fields to tend to zero at large spatial distances. Hence from (19-8)

$$\int_\Omega d^4x \left[\frac{\partial \mathcal{L}}{\partial \psi} - \frac{\partial}{\partial x^\mu}\left(\frac{\partial \mathcal{L}}{\partial \psi_\mu}\right)\right]\delta\psi = 0 \tag{19-10}$$

Since $\delta\psi$ is arbitrary inside Ω the integrand must vanish identically, and we obtain the Euler-Lagrange equations of motion:

$$\frac{\partial \mathcal{L}}{\partial \psi} - \frac{\partial}{\partial x^\mu}\left(\frac{\partial \mathcal{L}}{\partial \psi_\mu}\right) = 0 \tag{19-11}$$

Given a Lagrangian density, it is said to be the Lagrangian density for the field, if the Euler-Lagrange equation (19-11) gives the correct field equations. It is clear that the Lagrangian density is not unique. In particular, the addition of any term of the form $(\partial/\partial x^\mu)[C^\mu(\psi)]$, where $C^\mu(\psi)$ is an arbitrary function of ψ, to the Lagrangian density will not affect the equations of motion, inasmuch as the variation of such a term vanishes. If the field is to be described by a field function that is not a scalar, i.e., if the field has more than one component, the Lagrangian density will depend on all these components ψ^α and on their gradients ψ^α_μ. Varying each component independently we obtain a Euler-Lagrange equation for each component. In (19-1) we have assumed that $\mathcal{L}$ depends only on ψ and the gradient of ψ. In principle one could allow dependence on higher derivatives of ψ. This would lead to equations of motion of degree higher than the second. This does not seem to arise in problems of physical interest. Finally we note that if we require that the action, S, be a Lorentz scalar or pseudoscalar, $\mathcal{L}$ must be a Lorentz pseudoscalar or scalar, since d^4x is a pseudoscalar

HAMILTONIAN FORMALISM

It has been possible to define an action and a Lagrangian density in a covariant fashion. This has led to the Euler-Lagrange equations of motions, which are also covariant. To introduce a Hamiltonian, it is necessary to single out the time. This is a result of the fact that we are dealing with a system of nondenumerably infinite number of degrees of freedom, corresponding to the nondenumerable infinity of values of $\psi(x_\mu)$, i.e., that we must speak of densities which are components of a second-rank tensor, rather than scalars.

To overcome the difficulty of infinite degrees of freedom, let us divide the three-dimensional space into small cells, δx^s at a fixed instant of time t. Each δx^s is considered so small that no important physical quantity varies appreciably inside this cell. The average value of ψ over δx^s, ψ_s can be adopted as a coordinate Q_s. We then further identify $\dot{\psi}_s$ with $\dot{Q}_s$, where the dot indicates time differentiation.

The spatial derivatives $(\partial\psi_s/\partial x^k)$ are replaced by the difference $(Q_{s+1} - Q_s)/\delta x^{sk}$, if we use $\delta x^s = \delta x^{s_1}\,\delta x^{s_2}\,\delta x^{s_3}$. The Lagrangian L is considered a function only of Q_s and $\dot{Q}_s$ and can be written

$$L = \sum_s \mathcal{L}_s\,\delta x^s \tag{19-12}$$

(no summation over repeated Latin indices is implied). $\mathcal{L}_s$ corresponds to the average of the Lagrangian density in cell δx^s and is a function of Q_s, Q_{s+1}, and $\dot{Q}_s$. In the limit $\delta x^s \to 0$ we regain

$$L = \int \mathcal{L}\,d\tau \tag{19-13}$$

We proceed as in classical mechanics and obtain the canonically conjugate momenta

$$P_s = \frac{\partial L}{\partial \dot{Q}_s} = \frac{\partial \mathcal{L}_s}{\partial \dot{Q}_s}\,\delta x^s \tag{19-14}$$

since only $\mathcal{L}_s$ depends on $\dot{Q}_s$. We define a momentum density

$$\pi_s = \frac{P_s}{\delta x^s} = \frac{\partial \mathcal{L}_s}{\partial \dot{Q}_s} \tag{19-15}$$

which in the continuous limit becomes

$$\pi = \frac{\partial \mathcal{L}}{\partial \dot{\psi}} \tag{19-16}$$

We form the Hamiltonian

$$H = \sum_s P_s \dot{Q}_s - L$$

$$= \sum_s \delta x^s (\pi_s \dot{Q}_s - \mathcal{L}_s) \tag{19-17}$$

which again in the limit becomes

$$H = \int (\pi\dot{\psi} - \mathcal{L})\, d\tau \tag{19-18}$$

Equation (19-18) indicates that we can define a Hamiltonian density

$$\mathcal{H} = \pi\dot{\psi} - \mathcal{L} \tag{19-19}$$

It is useful to define a functional derivative of a quantity $F = \int \mathfrak{F}\, d\tau$,

$$\frac{\delta F}{\delta \dot{\psi}} = \frac{\partial \mathfrak{F}}{\partial \dot{\psi}} - \sum_{i=1}^{3} \frac{\partial}{\partial x_i} \frac{\partial \mathfrak{F}}{\partial(\partial\dot{\psi}/\partial x_i)} \tag{19-20a}$$

$$\frac{\delta F}{\delta \psi} = \frac{\partial \mathfrak{F}}{\partial \psi} - \sum_{i=1}^{3} \frac{\partial}{\partial x_i} \frac{\partial \mathfrak{F}}{\partial(\partial\psi/\partial x_i)} \tag{19-20b}$$

$$\frac{\delta F}{\delta \pi} = \frac{\partial \mathfrak{F}}{\partial \pi} - \sum_{i=1}^{3} \frac{\partial}{\partial x_i} \frac{\partial \mathfrak{F}}{\partial(\partial\pi/\partial x_i)} \tag{19-20c}$$

In terms of the functional derivative, the Euler-Lagrange equations of motion can be written

$$\frac{\delta L}{\delta \psi} - \frac{d}{dt}\left(\frac{\delta L}{\delta \dot{\psi}}\right) = 0 \tag{19-21}$$

and the momentum density

$$\pi = \frac{\delta L}{\delta \dot{\psi}} \tag{19-22}$$

The functional derivative notation allows one to write the equations obeyed by the Lagrangian density in a way analogous to those obeyed by the usual particle Lagrangian. It is to be noted, however, that this notation treats the time coordinate differently from the space coordinates, as is indeed necessary in order to obtain a Hamiltonian formulation.

In order to obtain the canonical equations of motion we note that H is a functional of π, ψ, $\partial\psi/\partial x_i$, $\partial\pi/\partial x_i$, and (in general) t. Hence

$$dH = \int \left[\frac{\partial \mathcal{H}}{\partial \psi} d\psi + \sum_{i=1}^{3} \frac{\partial \mathcal{H}}{\partial(\partial\psi/\partial x_i)} d\left(\frac{\partial \psi}{\partial x_i}\right) + \frac{\partial \mathcal{H}}{\partial \pi} d\pi \right.$$

$$\left. + \sum_{i=1}^{3} \frac{\partial \mathcal{H}}{\partial(\partial\pi/\partial x_i)} d\left(\frac{\partial \pi}{\partial x_i}\right) + \frac{\partial \mathcal{H}}{\partial t} dt \right] d\tau \qquad (19\text{-}23a)$$

In the second and fourth terms, interchanging the differential and the derivative, integrating by parts and dropping the surface term by assuming sufficiently rapid convergence at large distances, (19-23a) can be rewritten in functional derivative notation as

$$dH = \int \left[\left(\frac{\delta H}{\delta \psi} d\psi + \frac{\delta H}{\delta \pi} d\pi \right) + \frac{\partial \mathcal{H}}{\partial t} dt \right] d\tau \qquad (19\text{-}23b)$$

Indeed the differential of any quantity whose density depends on π, ψ, $(\partial\psi/\partial x_i)$, $(\partial\pi/\partial x_i)$, and t can be expressed in the form (19-23).

Expressing the differential of H also by using the definition (19-18) we obtain

$$dH = \int \left[\left(\pi\, d\dot{\psi} + \dot{\psi}\, d\pi - \frac{\delta L}{\delta \psi} d\psi - \frac{\delta L}{\delta \dot{\psi}} d\dot{\psi} \right) \right.$$

$$\left. - \frac{\partial \mathcal{L}}{\partial t} dt \right] d\tau \qquad (19\text{-}24)$$

From (19-21) and (19-22) we have

$$\pi = \frac{\delta L}{\delta \dot{\psi}} \qquad (19\text{-}22)$$

$$\dot{\pi} = \frac{\delta L}{\delta \psi} \qquad (19\text{-}25)$$

Equating (19-24) with (19-23b) we obtain

$$\frac{\delta H}{\delta \psi} = -\dot{\pi} = \frac{\partial \mathcal{H}}{\partial \psi} - \sum_i \frac{\partial}{\partial x_i} \frac{\partial \mathcal{H}}{\partial(\partial\psi/\partial x_i)}$$

$$\frac{\delta H}{\delta \pi} = \dot{\psi} = \frac{\partial \mathcal{H}}{\partial \pi} - \sum_i \frac{\partial}{\partial x_i} \frac{\partial \mathcal{H}}{\partial(\partial\pi/\partial x_i)} \qquad (19\text{-}26)$$

$$\frac{\partial \mathcal{H}}{\partial t} = -\frac{\partial \mathcal{L}}{\partial t} \tag{19-27}$$

Equations (19-26) are the canonical equations of motion; (19-27) is a trivial identity.

For the total time derivative of F, a functional of ψ, π, $\partial\psi/\partial x_i$, and t, we have

$$\begin{aligned} \frac{dF}{dt} &= \int \left[\frac{\delta F}{\delta \psi} \dot{\psi} + \frac{\partial F}{\partial \pi} \dot{\pi} + \frac{\partial \mathcal{F}}{\partial t} \right] d\tau \\ &= \int \left[\frac{\delta F}{\delta \psi} \frac{\delta H}{\delta \pi} - \frac{\delta F}{\delta \pi} \frac{\delta H}{\delta \psi} \right] d\tau + \frac{\partial F}{\partial t} \\ &= \{F, H\} + \frac{\partial F}{\partial t} \end{aligned} \tag{19-28}$$

Equation (19-28) defines the Poisson brackets for functionals of field variables. It is clear that if H does not depend explicitly on time it is a constant of the motion.

FIELD QUANTIZATION

The Hamiltonian formalism enables us to quantize the system by replacing the Poisson brackets by $1/i\hbar$ times the commutators, thus making the field parameters (amplitude and conjugate momentum) into operators which in general are noncommuting. We return to the cellular model, where we identified Q_s with ψ_s and P_s with $\pi_s \, \delta x^s$. The commutation rules become

$$[Q_s(t), Q_r(t)] = [P_s(t), P_r(t)] = 0 \tag{19-29a}$$

$$[Q_s(t), P_r(t)] = i\hbar\delta_{sr} \tag{19-29b}$$

These then can be rewritten as

$$[\psi_s(t), \psi_r(t)] = [\pi_s(t), \pi_r(t)] = 0 \tag{19-30a}$$

$$[\psi_s(t), \pi_r(t)] = \frac{i\hbar\delta_{sr}}{\delta x^r} \tag{19-30b}$$

The continuous limit is obtained by summing (19-30) over all the cells and converting to integrals over all space:

$$\sum_s \delta x^s [\psi_s(t), \psi_r(t)] \to \int [\psi(\mathbf{r},t), \psi(\mathbf{r}',t)]\, d\tau = 0$$

$$\sum_s \delta x^s [\pi_s(t), \pi_r(t)] \to \int [\pi(\mathbf{r},t), \pi(\mathbf{r}',t)]\, d\tau = 0 \qquad (19\text{-}31a)$$

$$\sum_r \delta x^r [\psi_s(t), \pi_r(t)] \to \int [\psi(\mathbf{r}',t), \pi(\mathbf{r},t)]\, d\tau = i\hbar \qquad (19\text{-}31b)$$

from which it follows that

$$[\psi(\mathbf{r},t), \psi(\mathbf{r}',t)] = [\pi(\mathbf{r}',t), \pi(\mathbf{r},t)] = 0 \qquad (19\text{-}32a)$$

$$[\psi(\mathbf{r}',t), \pi(\mathbf{r},t)] = i\hbar\delta(\mathbf{r} - \mathbf{r}') \qquad (19\text{-}32b)$$

For fields with more than one component the commutation rules become

$$[\psi^\alpha(\mathbf{r},t), \psi^\beta(\mathbf{r}',t)] = [\pi^\alpha(\mathbf{r},t), \pi^\beta(\mathbf{r}',t)] = 0 \qquad (19\text{-}33a)$$

$$[\psi^\alpha(\mathbf{r},t), \pi^\beta(\mathbf{r}',t)] = i\hbar\delta_{\alpha\beta}\,\delta(\mathbf{r} - \mathbf{r}') \qquad (19\text{-}33b)$$

The equations (19-33) are the fundamental quantum conditions for the field system. The field variables become operators which may be noncommuting. The rules (19-33a) explicitly show that two π's or two ψ's at different points but at the same time refer to different degrees of freedom.

The equation of motion for any operator F is

$$\dot{F} = \frac{1}{i\hbar}[F,H] \qquad (19\text{-}34)$$

which can be evaluated with the aid of (19-33) when an explicit expression of F and H is given in terms of ψ and π.

As an example of a two-component field we shall consider a complex field, for which

$$\psi = 2^{-1/2}(\psi_1 + i\psi_2) \qquad (19\text{-}35a)$$

$$\psi^\dagger = 2^{-1/2}(\psi_1 - i\psi_2) \qquad (19\text{-}35b)$$

ψ_1 and ψ_2 are real. In (19-35b) $\psi^\dagger$ is written instead of the usual ψ^* for complex conjugation since we consider ψ as an operator. The Euler-Lagrange equations are obtained by independent variation of ψ_1 and ψ_2, or equivalently of ψ and $\psi^\dagger$. Then

$$\pi = \frac{\delta L}{\delta \dot{\psi}} = \frac{\partial \mathcal{L}}{\partial \dot{\psi}_1}\frac{\partial \dot{\psi}_1}{\partial \dot{\psi}} + \frac{\partial \mathcal{L}}{\partial \dot{\psi}_2}\frac{\partial \dot{\psi}_2}{\partial \dot{\psi}} = 2^{-1/2}(\pi_1 - i\pi_2) \qquad (19\text{-}36a)$$

$$\pi^\dagger = \frac{\partial L}{\delta \dot{\psi}^\dagger} = \frac{\partial \mathcal{L}}{\partial \dot{\psi}_1}\frac{\partial \dot{\psi}_1}{\partial \dot{\psi}^\dagger} + \frac{\partial \mathcal{L}}{\partial \dot{\psi}_2}\frac{\partial \dot{\psi}_2}{\partial \dot{\psi}^\dagger} = 2^{-1/2}(\pi_1 + i\pi_2) \qquad (19\text{-}36b)$$

It is clear that $\pi^\dagger$ is not necessarily the complex conjugate of π. π and $\pi^\dagger$ will be actually complex conjugates of each other if $\mathcal{L}$ is real (Hermitian). The commutation relations (19-33) for ψ_1 and ψ_2 clearly give

$$[\psi(\mathbf{r},t), \pi(\mathbf{r}',t)] = i\hbar\,\delta(\mathbf{r} - \mathbf{r}') \qquad (19\text{-}37a)$$

$$[\psi^\dagger(\mathbf{r},t), \pi^\dagger(\mathbf{r}',t)] = i\hbar\,\delta(\mathbf{r} - \mathbf{r}') \qquad (19\text{-}37b)$$

All other commutators are 0.

Chapter 20

SECOND QUANTIZATION OF SEVERAL MATTER FIELDS

QUANTIZATION OF THE NONRELATIVISTIC SCHRÖDINGER EQUATION

It can be verified that the Lagrangian density which leads to the Schrödinger equation can be taken to be

$$\mathcal{L} = i\hbar \psi^\dagger \dot{\psi} - \frac{\hbar^2}{2m} (\nabla \psi^\dagger) \cdot (\nabla \psi) - V(r,t) \psi^\dagger \psi \tag{20-1}$$

$\mathcal{L}$ is not Hermitian. The Euler-Lagrange equation for ψ gives

$$-i\hbar \dot{\psi}^\dagger = -\frac{\hbar^2}{2m} \nabla^2 \psi^\dagger + V(\mathbf{r},t) \psi^\dagger \tag{20-2a}$$

and, for $\psi^\dagger$,

$$i\hbar \dot{\psi} = -\frac{\hbar^2}{2m} \nabla^2 \psi + V(\mathbf{r},t) \psi \tag{20-2b}$$

which are seen to be the correct Schrödinger equations for ψ and for its complex conjugate. The momentum canonically conjugate to ψ is

$$\pi = \frac{\delta L}{\delta \dot{\psi}} = \frac{\partial \mathcal{L}}{\partial \dot{\psi}} = i\hbar \psi^\dagger \tag{20-3}$$

Since $\dot{\psi}^\dagger$ does not occur in (20-1), $\psi^\dagger$ has no conjugate momentum.

The Hamiltonian density is

$$\mathcal{H} = \pi \dot{\psi} - \mathcal{L} = \frac{-i\hbar}{2m} (\nabla \pi) \cdot (\nabla \psi) - \frac{i}{\hbar} V \pi \psi \tag{20-4}$$

The canonical equations of motion are

$$\dot{\psi} = \frac{\delta H}{\delta \pi} = \frac{\partial \mathcal{H}}{\partial \pi} - \sum_i \frac{\partial}{\partial x_i} \frac{\partial \mathcal{H}}{\partial(\partial \pi/\partial x_i)}$$

$$= -\frac{i}{\hbar} V\psi + \frac{i\hbar}{2m} \nabla^2 \psi \tag{20-5a}$$

$$\dot{\pi} = -\frac{\delta H}{\delta \psi} = -\frac{\partial \mathcal{H}}{\partial \psi} + \sum_i \frac{\partial}{\partial x_i} \frac{\partial \mathcal{H}}{\partial(\partial \psi/\partial x_i)}$$

$$= \frac{i}{\hbar} V\pi - \frac{i\hbar}{2m} \nabla^2 \pi \tag{20-5b}$$

Equations (20-5a) and (20-5b), together with (20-3), are easily seen to be equivalent to (20-2a) and (20-2b).

The fact that $\psi^\dagger$ has no conjugate momentum did not cause particular difficulty, since π could be identified with $\psi^\dagger$ and the Hamiltonian formalism could go through. This identification of $\psi^\dagger$ with π is related to the fact that the field equation is first order in time, hence $\dot{\psi}$ can be expressed in terms of ψ and $\nabla\psi$. Had the equation been second order in time, like the Klein-Gordon equation, then both ψ, π and $\psi^\dagger, \pi^\dagger$ would be pairs of canonically conjugate variables. Furthermore, if the Lagrangian is such that a particular conjugate momentum is undefined *and* if the coordinate conjugate to this momentum cannot be expressed in terms of the other coordinates and momenta, then the entire Hamiltonian formalism breaks down. We shall meet this situation when we quantize the electromagnetic field.

From (20-4) and (20-3) the Hamiltonian can be written

$$H = \int \left(\frac{\hbar^2}{2m} \nabla\psi^\dagger \cdot \nabla\psi + V\psi^\dagger \psi \right) d\tau \tag{20-6}$$

This is seen to be Hermitian once it is noticed that V is a real numerical function (not an operator) and that operators satisfy $(AB)^\dagger = B^\dagger A^\dagger$. By integrating by parts and neglecting the surface term we can write

$$H = \int \psi^\dagger \left(\frac{-\hbar^2}{2m} \nabla^2 + V \right) \psi \, d\tau \tag{20-7}$$

If V is time-independent, H is a constant of the motion.

So far, we have treated ψ as a classical field and $\mathcal{H}$ as its Hamiltonian density. To go over to quantum theory, we introduce the commutation relations. Because of (20-3), these are

$$[\psi(\mathbf{r}), \psi(\mathbf{r}')] = [\psi^\dagger(\mathbf{r}), \psi^\dagger(\mathbf{r}')] = 0 \tag{20-8a}$$

$$[\psi(\mathbf{r}), \psi^\dagger(\mathbf{r}')] = \delta(\mathbf{r} - \mathbf{r}') \tag{20-8b}$$

The omission of t in the above equations implies that both field operators are evaluated at the same time—an assumption we have been making throughout.

We shall now evaluate the time derivative of the quantum mechanical operator ψ.

$$\begin{aligned} i\hbar\dot{\psi} &= [\psi, H] \\ &= \left[\psi, \int \frac{\hbar^2}{2m} \nabla'\psi^\dagger(\mathbf{r}')\cdot\nabla'\psi(\mathbf{r}')\ d\tau'\right] \\ &\quad + [\psi, \int V(\mathbf{r}')\psi^\dagger(\mathbf{r}')\psi(\mathbf{r}')\ d\tau'] \end{aligned} \tag{20-9}$$

The first commutator is evaluated by using integration by parts, as in (20-7), and gives

$$\begin{aligned} -[\psi(\mathbf{r}), \int \psi^\dagger(\mathbf{r}')\nabla'^2\psi(\mathbf{r}')\ d\tau'] &= -\int [\psi(\mathbf{r}), \psi^\dagger(\mathbf{r}')]\nabla'^2\psi(\mathbf{r}')\ d\tau' \\ &= -\int \nabla'^2\psi(\mathbf{r}')\delta(\mathbf{r} - \mathbf{r}')\ d\tau' = -\nabla^2\psi(\mathbf{r}) \end{aligned}$$

where the second equation follows from the first, since $\nabla'^2\psi(\mathbf{r}')$ and $\psi(\mathbf{r})$ commute. That this is so follows from the fact that if

$$[f(x), g(x')] = h(x,x') \tag{20-10a}$$

then

$$\left[\frac{d}{dx}f(x), g(x')\right] = \frac{\partial}{\partial x}h(x,x') \tag{20-10b}$$

To prove (20-10b) we expand the derivative

$$\begin{aligned} \left[\frac{d}{dx}f(x), g(x')\right] &= \lim_{\epsilon\to 0}\frac{1}{\epsilon}\{[f(x+\epsilon), g(x')] - [f(x), g(x')]\} \\ &= \lim_{\epsilon\to 0}\frac{1}{\epsilon}\{h(x+\epsilon, x') - h(x,x')\} \\ &= \frac{\partial h(x,x')}{\partial x} \end{aligned} \tag{20-10c}$$

The second commutator gives

$$\int V(\mathbf{r}')\{\psi(\mathbf{r})\psi^\dagger(\mathbf{r}')\psi(\mathbf{r}') - \psi^\dagger(\mathbf{r}')\psi(\mathbf{r}')\psi(\mathbf{r})\}\, d\tau'$$

$$= \int V(\mathbf{r}')\{\psi(\mathbf{r})\psi^\dagger(\mathbf{r}') - \psi^\dagger(\mathbf{r}')\psi(\mathbf{r})\}\psi(\mathbf{r}')\, d\tau'$$

$$= \int V(\mathbf{r}')\psi(\mathbf{r}')\delta(\mathbf{r} - \mathbf{r}')\, d\tau' = V\psi$$

where the second line follows from the first since $\psi(\mathbf{r}')$ and $\psi(\mathbf{r})$ commute. Hence

$$i\hbar\dot{\psi} = -\frac{\hbar^2}{2m}\nabla^2\psi + V\psi \tag{20-11a}$$

Similarly,

$$-i\hbar\dot{\psi}^\dagger = -\frac{\hbar^2}{2m}\nabla^2\psi^\dagger + V\psi^\dagger \tag{20-11b}$$

We see that the equations obtained from classical and quantum mechanics are formally the same; as indeed must be so if we identify Poisson brackets with commutators.

The following statements can be verified by operating with Poisson brackets. The commutators given in (20-8) are constants of the motion. The operator N, defined as

$$N = \int \psi^\dagger\psi\, d\tau \tag{20-12}$$

is a constant of the motion. We also note that N is Hermitian.

THE N OR MANY-PARTICLE REPRESENTATION FOR THE SCHRÖDINGER FIELD

We consider the N operator in detail. N is Hermitian, thus its eigenvalues are real. We expand the ψ's in terms of a complete orthonormal set of functions

$$\psi(\mathbf{r},t) = \sum_k a_k(t)\, u_k(\mathbf{r}) \tag{20-13a}$$

$$\psi^\dagger(\mathbf{r},t) = \sum_k u_k^*(\mathbf{r})\, a_k^\dagger(t) \tag{20-13b}$$

The a's are considered to be operators depending on time and the u's ordinary functions. (Hence we use the dagger on $a_k^\dagger$ and the asterisk on u_k^*.) Using the orthonormality of the u_k's we can solve for the a_k's:

$$a_k(t) = \int \psi(\mathbf{r},t)\, u_k^*(\mathbf{r})\, d\tau \tag{20-14a}$$

$$a_k^\dagger(t) = \int u_k(\mathbf{r})\, \psi^\dagger(\mathbf{r},t)\, d\tau \tag{20-14b}$$

We evaluate

$$\begin{aligned}\left[a_k(t), a_\ell^\dagger(t)\right] &= \iint \left[u_k^*(\mathbf{r})\,\psi(\mathbf{r},t), u_\ell(\mathbf{r}')\,\psi^\dagger(\mathbf{r}',t)\right] d\tau\, d\tau' \\ &= \iint u_k^*(\mathbf{r})\, u_\ell(\mathbf{r}')\, \delta(\mathbf{r}-\mathbf{r}')\, d\tau\, d\tau' \\ &= \int u_k^*(\mathbf{r})\, u_\ell(\mathbf{r})\, d\tau = \delta_{k\ell}\end{aligned} \tag{20-15a}$$

$$[a_k(t), a_\ell(t)] = \left[a_k^\dagger(t), a_\ell^\dagger(t)\right] = 0 \tag{20-15b}$$

Furthermore,

$$N = \sum_{kk'} a_{k'}^\dagger a_k \int u_{k'}^* u_k\, d\tau = \sum_k a_k^\dagger a_k \tag{20-16}$$

$$N = \sum N_k \qquad N_k = a_k^\dagger a_k \tag{20-17}$$

From (20-15) it follows that the N_k's commute with each other and can be diagonalized simultaneously.

$$\begin{aligned}[N_k, N_\ell] &= \left[a_k^\dagger a_k, a_\ell^\dagger a_\ell\right] \\ &= a_k^\dagger \left[a_k, a_\ell^\dagger\right] a_\ell + a_\ell^\dagger \left[a_k^\dagger, a_\ell\right] a_k \\ &= \left(a_k^\dagger a_\ell - a_\ell^\dagger a_k\right)\delta_{k\ell} = 0\end{aligned} \tag{20-18}$$

Also

$$[a_k, N_k] = \left[a_k, a_k^\dagger a_k\right] = a_k \tag{20-19a}$$

$$\left[a_k^\dagger, N_k\right] = -a_k^\dagger \tag{20-19b}$$

We have as yet not indicated what these field amplitude operators operate on. They do not affect ordinary functions; as we saw they commute with $V(\mathbf{r})$ and the u_k's. However, they do operate on the state vectors describing the entire quantum mechanical system under consideration. From (20-17) and (20-18) it follows that we can select an orthonormal system of vectors such that N and all the N_k's are diagonal. A typical such vector can be represented as

$$|N\rangle = |N_1', N_2', \ldots, N_k', \ldots\rangle \tag{20-20}$$

where the presence of N_k''s in the ket indicates that (20-20) is an eigenket of each N_k, with N_k' the eigenvalue of N_k. When no ambiguity can arise, we shall simply write $|N_k'\rangle$ to denote the eigenvector of N_k with eigenvalue N_k'.

We shall now prove some formal results about the N_k's and a_k's which will help us in obtaining an interpretation for them. We have by definition

$$N_k |N_k'\rangle = N_k' |N_k'\rangle \tag{20-21a}$$

Therefore, using (20-19b),

$$\begin{aligned} N_k a_k^\dagger |N_k'\rangle &= \left(a_k^\dagger N_k + a_k^\dagger\right)|N_k'\rangle \\ &= \left(N_k' + 1\right) a_k^\dagger |N_k'\rangle \end{aligned} \tag{20-21b}$$

Similarly, using (20–19a),

$$N_k a_k |N_k'\rangle = \left(N_k' - 1\right) a_k |N_k'\rangle \tag{20-21c}$$

Equation (20-21b) indicates that $a_k^\dagger |N_k'\rangle$ is an eigenket of N_k with eigenvalue $N_k' + 1$. Similarly, a_k operating on an eigenket of N_k with eigenvalue N_k' results in an eigenket of N_k with eigenvalue $N_k' - 1$. If we assume the eigenkets to be normalized we have

$$a_k^\dagger |N_k'\rangle = c_1 |N_k' + 1\rangle \tag{20-22a}$$

$$a_k |N_k'\rangle = c_2 |N_k' - 1\rangle \tag{20-22b}$$

The constants can be determined:

$$\begin{aligned} &\langle N_k' a_k | a_k N_k'\rangle \\ &\quad = |c_2|^2 = \langle N_k' | a_k^\dagger a_k | N_k'\rangle = \langle N_k' | N_k | N_k'\rangle = N_k' \end{aligned} \tag{20-23a}$$

$$c_2 = \sqrt{N_k'}$$

$$\langle N'_k a_k^\dagger \mid a_k^\dagger N'_k \rangle = |c_1|^2$$

$$= \langle N'_k \mid a_k a_k^\dagger \mid N'_k \rangle = \langle N'_k \mid N_k + 1 \mid N'_k \rangle = N'_k + 1$$

$$c_1 = \sqrt{N'_k + 1} \tag{20-23b}$$

Thus

$$a_k^\dagger \mid N'_k \rangle = \sqrt{N'_k + 1} \mid N'_k + 1 \rangle \tag{20-24a}$$

$$a_k \mid N'_k \rangle = \sqrt{N'_k} \mid N'_k - 1 \rangle \tag{20-24b}$$

The operators $a_k^\dagger$ and a_k are called the *creation* and *annihilation* operators, respectively. We have chosen the phase of the constants to be zero, so that repeated application of the a's satisfies (20-15). (But this would also be satisfied by more general choices of the phase.)

We now show that the eigenvalues of N_k are nonnegative integers:

$$N'_k = \langle N'_k \mid N_k \mid N'_k \rangle = \langle N'_k a_k \mid a_k N'_k \rangle$$

$$= \| N_k a_k \|^2 \geq 0 \tag{20-25}$$

Hence the eigenvalues are nonnegative. From (20-24b) we see that if there existed a nonintegral eigenvalue, we could generate by repeated application of a_k an eigenket belonging to a negative eigenvalue. This is impossible. When only integral eigenvalues exist, then (20-24b) causes no difficulty, since repeated operation by a_k eventually terminates in an eigenket with 0 eigenvalue, and $a_k \mid 0 \rangle = 0$.

We investigate the time dependence of the N_k.

$$i\hbar \dot{N}_k = \left[a_k^\dagger a_k, H \right]$$

$$= \sum_{j\ell} \left[a_k^\dagger a_k, a_j^\dagger a_\ell \right] \int u_j^* h u_\ell \, d\tau$$

$$= \sum_{j\ell} \left(a_k^\dagger a_\ell \delta_{kj} h_{j\ell} - a_j^\dagger a_k \delta_{k\ell} h_{j\ell} \right)$$

$$= \sum_{i} \left(a_k^\dagger a_i h_{ki} - a_i^\dagger a_k h_{ik} \right) \tag{20-26}$$

$$h \equiv -\frac{\hbar^2}{2m} \nabla^2 + V$$

This vanishes if and only if $h_{ki} = 0$ for $i \neq k$. Hence the N_k's are constants of the motion if and only if the off-diagonal matrix elements of h are 0; i.e., if the u_k are Schrödinger eigenfunctions of the operator h. Of course $N = \Sigma_k N_k$ is always a constant, as can be seen by taking the sum over all k of the third line in (20-26).

We now examine the Hamiltonian (total energy) operator as given by (20-7). Substituting for $\psi, \psi^\dagger$ from (20-13) we obtain

$$H = \sum_{ij} a_i^\dagger a_j \int u_i^* \left(-\frac{\hbar^2}{2m} \nabla^2 + V \right) u_j \, d\tau \tag{20-27}$$

If we choose the u's to be solutions of the single-particle Schrödinger equation we obtain

$$H = \sum_i N_i E_i \tag{20-28a}$$

In our representation the N_i are assumed diagonal; hence

$$H = \sum_i N_i' E_i \tag{20-28b}$$

In this case the N_k are constants of the motion since h is diagonal.

We can obtain another suggestive relationship analogous to (20-28b) for the total field momentum operator (not to be confused with conjugate momentum). To obtain this we first notice that the energy density (19-19) is the (0,0) component of the covariant energy-momentum second-rank tensor

$$\frac{\partial \mathcal{L}}{\partial \psi^\mu} \psi^\nu - \mathcal{L} g^{\mu\nu} \tag{20-29}$$

The (0,k), k = x,y,z component of this is the momentum density, and the space integral of that is the momentum contained in the field.

$$\mathbf{P} = \int \frac{\partial \mathcal{L}}{\partial \dot{\psi}} \psi^k \, d^3x = - \int \pi \nabla \psi \, d^3x \tag{20-30a}$$

$$\begin{aligned} \mathbf{P} &= -i\hbar \int \psi^\dagger \nabla \psi \, d^3x \\ &= \sum_{k\ell} a_k^\dagger a_\ell (-i\hbar) \int u_k^* \nabla u_\ell \, d^3x \\ &= \sum_{k\ell} a_k^\dagger a_\ell \int u_k^* \mathbf{p} u_\ell \, d^3x \end{aligned} \tag{20-30b}$$

where $\mathbf{p} = -i\hbar\nabla$ is the single-particle momentum operator. If we choose the u's to be eigenfunctions of the single-particle momentum, instead of the energy, we obtain for the total field momentum operator

$$\mathbf{P} = \sum_{k} N'_k \mathbf{p}_k \tag{20-31}$$

If $V = 0$, the u's can be eigenfunctions of both energy and momentum.

Guided by the above results, we are now in a position to set up the Hilbert space on which the field operators operate, and to give a physical interpretation of our formal results. We construct a set of basis vectors which diagonalizes N and each N_k as follows. We start with the vector $|0\rangle$, called the *vacuum state*, such that

$$N_k |0\rangle = 0 \qquad \text{all } k \tag{20-32}$$

The existence of this state we demonstrated above. The physical interpretation of the vacuum state is that it describes a situation where no particles are present. We next construct vectors of the form

$$\frac{1}{\sqrt{1!}} a_k^\dagger |0\rangle \tag{20-33a}$$

The normalization factor is chosen with the help of (20-24). We have from (20-21b) that

$$N a_k^\dagger |0\rangle = a_k^\dagger |0\rangle \tag{20-33b}$$

We interpret this vector as a single-particle state, i.e., a physical situation in which one particle is present. However, this physical situation can also be described by ordinary quantum mechanics instead of field theory. To obtain a connection between these two descriptions, we *postulate* that the state $a_k^\dagger |0\rangle$ describes a particle which is in an ordinary quantum mechanical state $u_k(\mathbf{r})$ [see (20-14b)]. A convenient notation for single-particle states is

$$|1;k\rangle = a_k^\dagger |0\rangle \tag{20-33c}$$

Proceeding, we construct two-particle states

$$|2;k,\ell\rangle = \frac{1}{\sqrt{1!\,1!}} a_k^\dagger a_\ell^\dagger |0\rangle \qquad k \neq \ell \tag{20-34a}$$

$$|2;k,k\rangle = \frac{1}{\sqrt{2!}} a_k^\dagger a_k^\dagger |0\rangle \tag{20-34b}$$

We have

$$N |2;k,\ell\rangle = 2 |2;k,\ell\rangle \tag{20-34c}$$

Equation (20-34a) corresponds to two particles, one in state k and one in state ℓ; equation (20-34b), to two particles, both in state k. The normalization is again obtained from (20-24). The notation employed in the left-hand side of (20-34a,b) exhibits both the number of particles present and the states occupied. We note that this theory sets no limit on the number of particles that can occupy a state, hence we are dealing with bosons. Fermions are discussed below. The connection with ordinary quantum mechanics is given in a fashion which takes the symmetry of the wave function into account. The state $|2; k, \ell\rangle$ corresponds to $2^{-1/2}(u_k(\mathbf{r}_1)u_\ell(\mathbf{r}_2) + u_k(\mathbf{r}_2)u_\ell(\mathbf{r}_1))$ $(k \neq \ell)$, and the state $|2;k,k\rangle$ corresponds to $2^{-1/2}2^{-1/2}(u_k(\mathbf{r}_1)u_k(\mathbf{r}_2) + u_k(\mathbf{r}_2)u_k(\mathbf{r}_1)) = u_k(\mathbf{r}_1)u_k(\mathbf{r}_2)$. By repeated application of creation operators to the vacuum state, we can construct all the basis vectors of the theory:

$$|N'_k; \underbrace{k, k, \ldots, k}_{N'_k \text{ entries}}\rangle = \frac{1}{\sqrt{(N'_k + 1)!}} \left(a_k^\dagger\right)^{N'_k} |0\rangle \tag{20-35a}$$

which describes N'_k particles, all in the state k; and

$$\left| \sum_{k=1}^{n} N'_k;\ \underbrace{1, 1, \ldots, 1}_{N'_1 \text{ entries}},\ \underbrace{2, 2, \ldots, 2}_{N'_2 \text{ entries}},\ \ldots,\ \underbrace{n, n, \ldots, n}_{N'_n \text{ entries}} \right\rangle$$

$$= \prod_{k=1}^{n} \frac{1}{\sqrt{(N'_k + 1)!}} \left(a_k^\dagger\right)^{N'_k} |0\rangle \tag{20-35b}$$

which describes $\Sigma_{k=1}^{n} N'_k$ particles; N'_1 in the state 1, N'_2 in the state 2, and so forth.

With the above physical interpretation and correspondence to ordinary quantum mechanics, we conclude that N is the operator whose eigenvalue is the number of particles present. Recalling the definition of this operator (20-12), we see that if we consider $e\psi^*\psi$ as a classical charge density, then the field theoretic result obtained is that the total charge of a system of particles must be an integral multiple of e. N_k is the operator for the number of particles in state k. Similarly H and **P** eigenvalues give the total energy and momentum of the system.

If the u_k's are solutions of the single-particle Schrödinger equation, the field theory obtains stationary solutions for which the number of particles in the kth state is N'_k and the total energy is $\Sigma_k N'_k E_k$. If the system is free, **P** is diagonal also, and the total momentum is $\Sigma_k N'_k \mathbf{p}_k$.

In the usual parlance of field theory, $a_k^\dagger$ operating on the vacuum state is said to create a particle in state k inasmuch as it creates a particle described by $u_k(\mathbf{r})$. Also the operator $\psi^\dagger(\mathbf{r})$ operating on the vacuum state creates a particle at the point $\mathbf{r}$. To see this we write

$$\psi^\dagger(\mathbf{r})\,|\,0\rangle = \sum_k u_k^*(\mathbf{r})\,a_k^\dagger\,|\,0\rangle \tag{20-36}$$

Each $a_k^\dagger\,|\,0\rangle$ corresponds to a particle in a state $u_k(\mathbf{r}')$. (The position variable is primed because it corresponds to a dummy variable and must be distinguished from the argument of $\psi^\dagger$.) Hence $\psi^\dagger(\mathbf{r})\,|\,0\rangle$ corresponds to $\Sigma_k\, u_k^*(\mathbf{r})\,u_k(\mathbf{r}') = \delta(\mathbf{r} - \mathbf{r}')$, which is the wavefunction for a particle localized at $\mathbf{r}$.

We repeat that everything has been done at one particular instant of time t. To obtain the time dependence of the theory, one usually stays in the Heisenberg picture. The state vectors remain time-independent and the operators have a time dependence which is determined by H. It should be noted that to obtain a representation of the operators it was necessary to require that some operator be diagonal; that is, commutation relations are not sufficient to determine a representation; thus we chose to diagonalize N_k and thus N.

Field theory has led us to the Schrödinger theory for many-boson particles. However, we have implicitly assumed that the particles are noninteracting; i.e., no self-energy terms are present in the Hamiltonian; the only interaction is with an external potential. Jordan and Wigner (1928) have shown that the two theories—many-particle Schrödinger theory for bosons and second-quantized field theory—are completely equivalent, even when interaction are taken into account.

Finally we split a_k into two Hermitian operators,

$$\begin{aligned} a_k &= 2^{-1/2}\left(q_k + ip_k\right) \\ a_k^\dagger &= 2^{-1/2}\left(q_k - ip_k\right) \\ q_k^\dagger &= q_k \qquad p_k^\dagger = p_k \end{aligned} \tag{20-37}$$

Then

$$\begin{aligned} [q_k, q_\ell] &= [p_k, p_\ell] = 0 \\ [q_k, p_\ell] &= i\,\delta_{k\ell} \\ N_k + \tfrac{1}{2} &= \tfrac{1}{2}(p_k^2 + q_k^2) \end{aligned} \tag{20-38}$$

We see that the equation (20-38) is formally the same as that for a harmonic oscillator with the obvious identification of parameters. This observation could have been used for an alternative method of obtaining the above results (see Schiff, pp. 352–354).

FERMIONS AND ANTICOMMUTATION RELATIONS

The quantization of the Schrödinger field according to the usual commutator–Poisson bracket identification was seen to lead to a many-particle boson theory. Reviewing the above it is seen that the result that N_k can be any nonnegative integer stems essentially from the commutator relations (20-8), (20-15), or (20-38). Jordan and Wigner (1928) found that by replacing commutators by anticommutators results in a many-particle fermion theory. Pauli (1940) further showed that if the following physical conditions are to be satisfied by the quantized field theory, then fermions must indeed be quantized by anticommutators and bosons by commutators. The requirements postulated by Pauli are: (1) The commutator of two observables pertaining to space-time points separated by a space-like distance must be zero. Otherwise they could not be measured simultaneously with arbitrary accuracy, which would imply that the measurement perturbation was propagated across a space-like distance with speed faster than light. (2) Energy must be nonnegative.

To carry out this program for the nonrelativistic Schrödinger equation we replace (20-8) and (20-15) by

$$[\psi(\mathbf{r}), \psi(\mathbf{r}')]_+ = [\psi^\dagger(\mathbf{r}), \psi^\dagger(\mathbf{r}')]_+ = 0 \tag{20-39a}$$

$$[\psi(\mathbf{r}), \psi^\dagger(\mathbf{r}')]_+ = \delta(\mathbf{r} - \mathbf{r}') \tag{20-39b}$$

$$[a_k, a_\ell]_+ = \left[a_k^\dagger, a_\ell^\dagger\right]_+ = 0 \tag{20-40a}$$

$$\left[a_k, a_\ell^\dagger\right]_+ = \delta_{k\ell} \tag{20-40b}$$

where

$$[A,B]_+ = AB + BA \tag{20-40c}$$

Defining N_k as before, it can be verified that the N_k's commute, and hence can be diagonalized simultaneously. Using (20-40b),

$$N_k^2 = a_k^\dagger a_k a_k^\dagger a_k = a_k^\dagger\left(1 - a_k^\dagger a_k\right)a_k$$

$$= a_k^\dagger a_k - a_k^\dagger a_k^\dagger a_k a_k = a_k^\dagger a_k = N_k \tag{20-41}$$

since $a_k a_k = a_k^\dagger a_k^\dagger = 0$ by (20-40a). Hence the eigenvalues of N_k are 0 or 1, corresponding to the exclusion principle.

The a_k's cannot be diagonalized, for if a_k is diagonal, we have from (20-40a) that its eigenvalues are zero; then $a_k^\dagger a_k$ would also be zero, which contradicts (20-40b). The eigenvalues of $N = \Sigma_k N_k$ are nonnegative integers. It is seen that the previous results for the total energy and momentum remain unchanged.

We retain the Heisenberg expression for the time development of an operator. In this case it can be verified that the equations of motion, (20-9), remain the same. It is easy to verify that a_k and $a_k^\dagger$ are again annihilation and creation operators, respectively. A satisfactor choice is

$$a_k \,|\, N_k' \rangle = \theta_k N_k' \,|\, 1 - N_k' \rangle$$

$$a_k^\dagger \,|\, N_k' \rangle = \theta_k (1 - N_k') \,|\, 1 - N_k' \rangle \qquad (20\text{-}42a)$$

$$\theta_k = (-1)^{\nu_k} \qquad \nu_k = \sum_{j=1}^{k-1} N_j'$$

Then it is easily seen that

$$a_k^2 \,|\, N_k' \rangle = a_k^{\dagger 2} \,|\, N_k' \rangle = N_k'(1 - N_k') \,|\, N_k' \rangle = 0 \qquad (20\text{-}42b)$$

$$\left(a_k a_k^\dagger + a_k^\dagger a_k\right) |\, N_k' \rangle$$

$$= (1 - 2N_k' + 2N_k'^2) \,|\, N_k' \rangle = |\, N_k' \rangle \qquad (20\text{-}42c)$$

because of (20-41). This proves (20-40) is satisfied for $k = \ell$. The choice of phase in θ_k is necessary and sufficient to ensure that (20-40) is also fulfilled for $k \neq \ell$: If $k > \ell$, then the application of a_ℓ changes the sign of θ_k, because it changes N_ℓ' to $1 - N_\ell'$, but the application of a_k leaves θ_ℓ unchanged. This is just enough to make $a_k a_\ell + a_\ell a_k = 0$.

QUANTIZATION OF THE DIRAC EQUATION

The Lagrangian density for the Dirac equation can be taken to be

$$\mathfrak{L} = \bar{\psi} c \left(i\hbar \gamma^\mu \frac{\partial \psi}{\partial x^\mu} - mc\psi \right) \qquad (20\text{-}43)$$

Varying each component of ψ gives four Euler-Lagrange equations, which can be summarized as

$$c\left(i\hbar \frac{\partial\overline{\psi}}{\partial x^\mu} \gamma^\mu + mc\overline{\psi}\right) = 0 \tag{20-44a}$$

Similarly, varying the four components of $\overline{\psi}$ gives

$$c\left(-i\hbar\gamma^\mu \frac{\partial\psi}{\partial x^\mu} + mc\psi\right) = 0 \tag{20-44b}$$

These agree with (17-19) and (17-20b), which are the equations of motion for the Dirac field. The momentum conjugate to ψ is

$$\pi = \frac{1}{c}\frac{\partial\mathcal{L}}{\partial\psi_0} = i\hbar\overline{\psi}\gamma^0 = i\hbar\psi^\dagger \tag{20-45a}$$

It is to be remembered that ψ and π are four-component spinors; hence equation (20-45a) is a compact notation for four equations,

$$\pi_s = i\hbar(\psi^\dagger)_s \qquad s = 1,2,3,4 \tag{20-45b}$$

It is seen that $\overline{\psi}$ has no conjugate momentum.

The Hamiltonian density is

$$ci\hbar\psi^\dagger \frac{\partial\psi}{\partial x^0} - \mathcal{L}$$

$$= ci\hbar\left\{\psi^\dagger \frac{\partial\psi}{\partial x^0} - \psi^\dagger\frac{\partial\psi}{\partial x^0} - \sum_{k=1}^{3} \overline{\psi}\gamma^k \frac{\partial\psi}{\partial x^k}\right\} + mc^2\overline{\psi}\psi$$

$$\mathcal{H} = -i\hbar c\,\psi^\dagger \boldsymbol{\alpha}\cdot\nabla\psi + mc^2\psi^\dagger\beta\psi \tag{20-46a}$$

The Hamiltonian is

$$H = c\int\{-i\hbar\psi^\dagger\boldsymbol{\alpha}\cdot\nabla\psi + mc\psi^\dagger\beta\psi\}\,d\tau \tag{20-46b}$$

To show that H is Hermitian, we perform an integration by parts on half the first term and neglect the surface term:

$$H = c\int\{\tfrac{1}{2}i\hbar(-\psi^\dagger\boldsymbol{\alpha}\cdot\nabla\psi + \nabla\psi^\dagger\cdot\boldsymbol{\alpha}\psi) + mc\psi^\dagger\beta\psi\}\,d\tau \tag{20-46c}$$

We quantize the field by anticommutation relations since we wish to describe fermions. Using (20-45b) the quantization conditions become

$$[\psi_s(\mathbf{r}), \psi_\ell(\mathbf{r}')]_+ = \left[\psi_s^\dagger(\mathbf{r}), \psi_\ell^\dagger(\mathbf{r}')\right]_+ = 0 \tag{20-47a}$$

$$\left[\psi_s(\mathbf{r}), \psi_\ell^\dagger(\mathbf{r}')\right]_+ = \delta_{s\ell}\,\delta(\mathbf{r} - \mathbf{r}') \qquad s, \ell = 1, 2, 3, 4 \tag{20-47b}$$

The notation $\psi^\dagger$ is somewhat ambiguous. ψ is a column matrix with four entries ψ_ℓ that are operators. $\psi^\dagger$ is a row matrix with four operator entries $\psi_\ell^\dagger$.

The equation of motion of ψ_s is

$$i\hbar\dot{\psi}_s = [\psi_s, H] \tag{20-48a}$$

Writing out explicitly the relevant part of the first term in the commutator,

$$\left[\psi_s(\mathbf{r}), \int \sum_{k\ell} \psi_k^\dagger(\mathbf{r}')\,\boldsymbol{\alpha}_{k\ell}\cdot\nabla'\psi_\ell(\mathbf{r}')\;d\tau'\right]$$

$$= \int \sum_{k\ell} \Big(\psi_s(\mathbf{r})\,\psi_k^\dagger(\mathbf{r}')\,\boldsymbol{\alpha}_{k\ell}\cdot\nabla'\psi_\ell(\mathbf{r}')$$

$$- \psi_k^\dagger(\mathbf{r}')\,\boldsymbol{\alpha}_{k\ell}\cdot\nabla'\psi_\ell(\mathbf{r}')\,\psi_s(\mathbf{r})\Big)\;d\tau'$$

$$= \int \sum_{k\ell} \Big(\psi_s(\mathbf{r})\,\psi_k^\dagger(\mathbf{r}')$$

$$+ \psi_k^\dagger(\mathbf{r}')\,\psi_s(\mathbf{r})\Big)\,\boldsymbol{\alpha}_{k\ell}\cdot\nabla'\psi_\ell(\mathbf{r}')\;d\tau'$$

$$= \int \sum_{k\ell} \delta_{sk}\,\delta(\mathbf{r} - \mathbf{r}')\,\boldsymbol{\alpha}_{k\ell}\cdot\nabla'\psi_\ell(\mathbf{r}')\;d\tau'$$

$$= \sum_{\ell} \boldsymbol{\alpha}_{s\ell}\cdot\nabla\psi_\ell(\mathbf{r}) \tag{20-48b}$$

For the second term

$$\left[\psi_s(\mathbf{r}), \int \sum_{k\ell} \psi_k^\dagger(\mathbf{r}')\beta_{k\ell}\psi_\ell(\mathbf{r}')\ d\tau'\right]$$

$$= \int \sum_{k\ell} \Big(\psi_s(\mathbf{r})\psi_k^\dagger(\mathbf{r}')\beta_{k\ell}\psi_\ell(\mathbf{r}')$$

$$- \psi_k^\dagger(\mathbf{r}')\beta_{k\ell}\psi_\ell(\mathbf{r}')\psi_s(\mathbf{r})\Big)\ d\tau'$$

$$= \int \sum_{k\ell} \Big(\psi_s(\mathbf{r})\psi_k^\dagger(\mathbf{r}')$$

$$+ \psi_k^\dagger(\mathbf{r}')\psi_s(\mathbf{r})\Big)\psi_\ell(\mathbf{r}')\beta_{k\ell}\ d\tau'$$

$$= \int \sum_{k\ell} \delta_{sk}\,\delta(\mathbf{r} - \mathbf{r}')\psi_\ell(\mathbf{r}')\beta_{k\ell}\ d\tau'$$

$$= \sum_\ell \beta_{s\ell}\psi_\ell(\mathbf{r}) \tag{20-48c}$$

Summarizing these relations we obtain

$$\dot{\psi} = \frac{1}{i\hbar}[\psi, H] = -c\boldsymbol{\alpha}\cdot\nabla\psi - \frac{imc^2}{\hbar}\beta\psi \tag{20-48d}$$

which is the Dirac field equation. It can be verified that $\psi^\dagger$ also satisfies the appropriate field equation.

The number operator N is defined as before, $N = \int \psi^\dagger\psi\ d\tau$, and it can be verified that it is a constant of the motion.

THE N REPRESENTATION FOR THE DIRAC FIELD

It is convenient to expand the Dirac wave amplitudes ψ_ℓ in plane wave solutions, $\ell = 1, 2, 3, 4$. Since there are four linearly independent solutions for each value of the momentum $\mathbf{k}$, we shall use the index $i = 1, 2, 3, 4$ to distinguish among them. We then have

$$v_\ell(\mathbf{k}, r; i) = L^{-3/2}u_\ell(\mathbf{k}, i)e^{i\mathbf{k}\cdot\mathbf{r}}$$

$$i = 1, 2 \qquad E \geq 0$$
$$i = 3, 4 \qquad E \leq 0 \tag{20-49a}$$

The u_ℓ's are given in (18-6) and (18-7) and we are using box normalization. It follows from the general theory that the orthonormality relations are

$$\int \sum_j v_j^*(\mathbf{k},\mathbf{r};i)\, v_j(\mathbf{k}',\mathbf{r};i')\ d\tau = \delta_{\mathbf{k}\mathbf{k}'}\,\delta_{ii'} \tag{20-49b}$$

We expand the wave amplitude spinors:

$$\psi(\mathbf{r},t) = \sum_{\mathbf{k},i} a(\mathbf{k},t;i)\, v(\mathbf{k},\mathbf{r};i) \tag{20-50a}$$

$$\psi^\dagger(\mathbf{r},t) = \sum_{\mathbf{k},i} a^\dagger(\mathbf{k},t;i)\, \tilde{v}^*(\mathbf{k},\mathbf{r};i) \tag{20-50b}$$

where $\tilde{v}^*$ is the complex-conjugate transposed spinor. (We do not use the dagger since we reserve that symbol for operators, and v is a function.) The anticommutation relations (20-47) and the orthonormality condition (20-49b) give

$$[a(\mathbf{k};i), a(\mathbf{k}';i')]_+ = [a^\dagger(\mathbf{k},i), a^\dagger(\mathbf{k}';i')]_+ = 0 \tag{20-51a}$$

$$[a(\mathbf{k};i), a^\dagger(\mathbf{k}';i')]_+ = \delta_{\mathbf{k}\mathbf{k}'}\,\delta_{ii'} \tag{20-51b}$$

where the suppression of t indicates that we are evaluating the commutators at the same time. The number operator becomes

$$\begin{aligned} N &= \sum_{\mathbf{k},i} N_{\mathbf{k}i} \\ N_{\mathbf{k}i} &= a^\dagger(\mathbf{k};i)\, a(\mathbf{k};i) \end{aligned} \tag{20-52}$$

From the general theory outlined above we know that the eigenvalues of $N_{\mathbf{k}i}$ are 0 and 1; thus the Dirac particles are, as we desired, fermions.

The total energy from (20-46b) becomes

$$E = c\int \sum_{\mathbf{k}i}\sum_{\mathbf{k}'i'} a^\dagger(\mathbf{k};i)\, a(\mathbf{k}';i')\, \tilde{v}^*(\mathbf{k},\mathbf{r};i) \times (-i\hbar\boldsymbol{\alpha}\cdot\boldsymbol{\nabla} + mc\beta)\, v(\mathbf{k}'\mathbf{r};i')\ d\tau \tag{20-53a}$$

The v's satisfy

$$E_{\mathbf{k}'i'}\, v(\mathbf{k}',\mathbf{r};i') = (-ic\hbar\boldsymbol{\alpha}\cdot\boldsymbol{\nabla} + mc^2\beta)\, v(\mathbf{k}',\mathbf{r};i') \tag{20-53b}$$

Thus

$$E = \int \sum_{\mathbf{k}i} \sum_{\mathbf{k}'i'} a^\dagger(\mathbf{k};i)\, a(\mathbf{k}';i')\, \tilde{v}^*(\mathbf{k},\mathbf{r};i)\, E_{\mathbf{k}'i'}\, v(\mathbf{k}',\mathbf{r};i')\; d\tau$$

$$= \sum_{\mathbf{k}i} \sum_{\mathbf{k}'i'} a^\dagger(\mathbf{k};i)\, a(\mathbf{k}';i')\, E_{\mathbf{k}'i'}\, \delta_{\mathbf{k}\mathbf{k}'}\, \delta_{ii'}$$

$$= \sum_{\mathbf{k}i} N_{\mathbf{k}i} E_{\mathbf{k}i} \tag{20-53c}$$

The momentum, according to (20-30a) (with the generalization that π and $\nabla\psi$ form row and column matrices, respectively) is given by

$$\mathbf{P} = -i\hbar \int \psi^\dagger \nabla \psi \; d\tau \tag{20-54a}$$

This becomes, with the same algebraic manipulations as above,

$$\mathbf{P} = \sum_{\mathbf{k},i} N_{\mathbf{k}i} \hbar\mathbf{k} \tag{20-54b}$$

POSITRONS

Examining (20-53c) we see that the field energy can become arbitrarily large and negative due to the negative energy solutions of the Dirac equation ($i = 3, 4$). This difficulty is overcome by Dirac's definition of the vacuum (see p. 220), which now takes the form

$$N_{\mathbf{k}1} = N_{\mathbf{k}2} = 0 \qquad N_{\mathbf{k}3} = N_{\mathbf{k}4} = 1 \tag{20-55}$$

Furthermore, since it is assumed that the filled negative energy states have no observable effects, we subtract their contribution to the energy and momentum. Hence if we redefine observable energy and momentum by

$$E_0 = E - E_{vac} \tag{20-56a}$$

$$\mathbf{P}_0 = \mathbf{P} - \mathbf{P}_{vac} \tag{20-56b}$$

we obtain from (20-53c) and (20-54b)

$$E_0 = \sum_{\mathbf{k}} \left(\sum_{i=1,2} N_{\mathbf{k}i} E_{\mathbf{k}i} + \sum_{i=3,4} (N_{\mathbf{k}i} - 1) E_{\mathbf{k}i} \right) \tag{20-57a}$$

$$\mathbf{P}_0 = \sum_{\mathbf{k}} \left(\sum_{i=1,2} N_{\mathbf{k}i} \hbar\mathbf{k} + \sum_{i=3,4} (N_{\mathbf{k}i} - 1) \hbar\mathbf{k} \right) \tag{20-57b}$$

Defining a new operator

$$M_{\mathbf{k}i} = 1 - N_{\mathbf{k}i} \tag{20-58}$$

which has the eigenvalue 1 when state $\mathbf{k}i$ is empty and 0 when it is full, (20-57) becomes

$$E_0 = \sum_{\mathbf{k}} \left(\sum_{i=1,2} N_{\mathbf{k}i} E_{\mathbf{k}i} + \sum_{i=3,4} M_{\mathbf{k}i} |E_{\mathbf{k}i}| \right) \tag{20-59a}$$

$$\mathbf{P}_0 = \sum_{\mathbf{k}} \left(\sum_{i=1,2} N_{\mathbf{k}i} \hbar\mathbf{k} - \sum_{i=3,4} M_{\mathbf{k}i} \hbar\mathbf{k} \right) \tag{20-59b}$$

This device allows the energy to be always positive definite. Furthermore, it indicates that a negative energy electron that is missing contributes a positive term to the energy. It is plausible to expect that this "hole" manifests itself as a physical particle. As was mentioned earlier in the discussion of the Dirac equation, these "holes" are taken to be positrons.

From (20-59b) it is seen that the momentum of a positron is $-\hbar\mathbf{k}$ (an electron of momentum $\hbar\mathbf{k}$ is absent). The velocity of the positron is

$$\mathbf{v} = \frac{c^2 \mathbf{p}}{|E|} = \frac{-\hbar\mathbf{k}c^2}{|E|} = c^2 \frac{\hbar\mathbf{k}}{-|E|} \tag{20-60}$$

which is the same as the velocity of the state that is empty.

Chapter 21

QUANTIZATION OF THE ELECTROMAGNETIC FIELD; QUANTUM ELECTRODYNAMICS

We shall develop first the classical canonical theory of electromagnetic fields and their interaction with charged particles. We follow essentially the formulation of Fermi (1932), also used in Heitler's book.

It is useful to expand the potential in a complete set of orthonormal plane waves. For the vector potential we let

$$\mathbf{A}(\mathbf{r},t) = \sum_{k\lambda}{}' \{q_{k\lambda}(t)\,\mathbf{u}_{k\lambda}(\mathbf{r}) + q_{k\lambda}^{\dagger}(t)\,\mathbf{u}_{k\lambda}^{*}(\mathbf{r})\}^{\ddagger} \tag{21-1}$$

The prime in the summation indicates that only one hemisphere of the **k** space is included, so that $u_{k\lambda}^{*}$ does not duplicate $u_{k\lambda}$. The index λ takes on values 1, 2, and 3, corresponding to the three perpendicular polarization directions. The $q_{k\lambda}^{\dagger}$'s are (Hermitian) conjugates of the $q_{k\lambda}$'s, so that $\mathbf{A}(\mathbf{r},t)$ is real (Hermitian). The $\mathbf{u}_{k\lambda}$ are plane waves,

$$\mathbf{u}_{k\lambda} = \frac{\sqrt{4\pi}\,c}{L^{3/2}}\,\mathbf{e}_{k\lambda}\,e^{i\mathbf{k}\cdot\mathbf{r}} \tag{21-2}$$

The plane wave is normalized in a box of side L, with the factor $\sqrt{4\pi}\,c$ being introduced for future usefulness. The three quantities $\mathbf{e}_{k\lambda}$ are unit vectors forming an orthonormal set with

$$\mathbf{e}_{k3} = \frac{i\mathbf{k}}{|k|} \tag{21-3}$$

The factor $i = \sqrt{-1}$ again is inserted for future usefulness. The scalar potential φ could be expanded in a similar fashion and we shall

‡The index k in the summations and in the subscripts occurring in this chapter is to be understood as a vector.

do this later. It is clear that the following orthogonality relations are satisfied.

$$\int \mathbf{u}_{k\lambda} \cdot \mathbf{u}_{k'\lambda'} \, d\tau = 0 \tag{21-4a}$$

$$\int \mathbf{u}^*_{k\lambda} \cdot \mathbf{u}^*_{k'\lambda'} \, d\tau = 0 \tag{21-4b}$$

$$\int \mathbf{u}^*_{k\lambda} \cdot \mathbf{u}_{k'\lambda'} \, d\tau = 4\pi c^2 \, \delta_{kk'} \, \delta_{\lambda\lambda'} \tag{21-4c}$$

The magnetic field, which is $\nabla \times \mathbf{A}$, is

$$\mathcal{H} = i \sum_{\substack{k \\ \lambda=1,2}}' \{q_{k\lambda}(\mathbf{k} \times \mathbf{u}_{k\lambda}) - q^\dagger_{k\lambda}(\mathbf{k} \times \mathbf{u}^*_{k\lambda})\} \tag{21-5}$$

Note that the longitudinally polarized plane waves ($\lambda = 3$) in the expansion of $\mathbf{A}$ do not contribute to $\mathcal{H}$. Conversely, the equation also shows that the plane-wave expansion of $\mathcal{H}$ contains no longitudinally polarized components. For the electric field we have the usual expression

$$\boldsymbol{\mathcal{E}} = -\frac{1}{c}\frac{\partial \mathbf{A}}{\partial t} - \nabla\varphi \tag{21-6}$$

We split $\boldsymbol{\mathcal{E}}$ into solenoidal and irrotational components, which are also the transverse and longitudinal components, respectively. When the fields are free there are no longitudinal components.

$$\boldsymbol{\mathcal{E}}_{tr} = -\frac{1}{c}\frac{\partial \mathbf{A}_{tr}}{\partial t} \tag{21-7a}$$

$$\boldsymbol{\mathcal{E}}_{lg} = -\frac{1}{c}\frac{\partial \mathbf{A}_{lg}}{\partial t} - \nabla\varphi \tag{21-7b}$$

From (21-1)

$$\boldsymbol{\mathcal{E}}_{tr} = -\frac{1}{c} \sum_{\substack{k \\ \lambda=1,2}}' \{\dot{q}_{k\lambda}\mathbf{u}_{k\lambda} + \dot{q}^\dagger_{k\lambda}\mathbf{u}^*_{k\lambda}\} \tag{21-8}$$

The total energy of the transverse part of the field (the energy of the free field) is

$$W_{tr} = \frac{1}{8\pi}\int (\mathcal{H}^2 + \mathcal{E}^2_{tr}) \, d\tau \tag{21-9}$$

To evaluate the first term in the integral, use is made of (21-5). To get $\mathcal{H}^2$, it is simplest to note that $\mathbf{k} \times \mathbf{e}_{k1} = k\mathbf{e}_{k2}$ and $\mathbf{k} \times \mathbf{e}_{k2} = -k\mathbf{e}_{k1}$, and then to use the orthogonality relations (21-4). The final result is

$$\frac{1}{8\pi} \int \mathcal{H}^2 \, d\tau = \sum_{\substack{k \\ \lambda=1,2}}' k^2 c^2 q_{k\lambda}^{\dagger} q_{k\lambda}$$

$$= \sum_{\substack{k \\ \lambda=1,2}}' \omega^2 q_{k\lambda}^{\dagger} q_{k\lambda} \tag{21-10a}$$

Similarly, the second term is easily evaluated with the help of (21-8) and (21-4) and gives

$$\frac{1}{8\pi} \int \mathcal{E}_{tr}^2 \, d\tau = \sum_{\substack{k \\ \lambda=1,2}}' \dot{q}_{k\lambda}^{\dagger} \dot{q}_{k\lambda} \tag{21-10b}$$

Thus

$$W_{tr} = \sum_{\substack{k \\ \lambda=1,2}}' \{\dot{q}_{k\lambda}^{\dagger} \dot{q}_{k\lambda} + \omega^2 q_{k\lambda}^{\dagger} q_{k\lambda}\} \tag{21-10c}$$

Guided by the above expression we can form the transverse Hamiltonian,

$$H_{tr} = \sum_{\substack{k \\ \lambda=1,2}}' \{p_{k\lambda}^{\dagger} p_{k\lambda} + \omega^2 q_{k\lambda}^{\dagger} q_{k\lambda}\} \tag{21-11}$$

with

$$\begin{aligned} \dot{q}_{k\lambda} &= \frac{\partial H}{\partial p_{k\lambda}} = p_{k\lambda}^{\dagger} \\ \dot{q}_{k\lambda}^{\dagger} &= \frac{\partial H}{\partial p_{k\lambda}^{\dagger}} = p_{k\lambda} \end{aligned} \tag{21-12}$$

The other canonical equation of motion gives

$$\begin{aligned} \dot{p}_{k\lambda} &= -\frac{\partial H}{\partial q_{k\lambda}} = -\omega^2 q_{k\lambda}^{\dagger} \\ \dot{p}_{k\lambda}^{\dagger} &= -\frac{\partial H}{\partial q_{k\lambda}^{\dagger}} = -\omega^2 q_{k\lambda} \end{aligned} \tag{21-13a}$$

Comparing (21-13a) with (21-12) we see that

$$\ddot{q}_{k\lambda} = -\omega^2 q_{k\lambda}$$

and (21-13b)

$$\ddot{q}^{\dagger}_{k\lambda} = -\omega^2 q^{\dagger}_{k\lambda}$$

Thus we see that the transverse field is described by an infinite number of oscillators. Equations (21-13) are equivalent to the classical wave equation, which follows from Maxwell's equations.

INTERACTION WITH A PARTICLE

Next we consider the relativistic Hamiltonian for point particles, each with charge e_j, in a given electromagnetic field. This is well known to be

$$H_j = e_j \varphi(\mathbf{r}_j) + \sqrt{\mu_j^2 + [c\mathbf{p}_j - e_j \mathbf{A}(\mathbf{r}_j)]^2}$$
$$\mu_j = m_j c^2 \tag{21-14}$$

The index j is the particle index and $\varphi(\mathbf{r}_j)$, $\mathbf{A}(\mathbf{r}_j)$ are the potentials at the position of the jth particle. The nonrelativistic limit is seen to be

$$H_j = e_j \varphi + \mu_j \sqrt{1 + \frac{[c\mathbf{p}_j - e_j \mathbf{A}]^2}{\mu_j^2}}$$

$$\approx e_j \varphi + \mu_j + \frac{[c\mathbf{p}_j - e_j \mathbf{A}]^2}{2\mu_j} \tag{21-15}$$

which is the ordinary nonrelativistic Hamiltonian of a particle. The canonical equations of motion following from (21-14) can be verified to be the correct relativistic Lorentz force equation. The Hamiltonian for all the particles is of course

$$H_p = \sum_j H_j \tag{21-16}$$

where no interaction between the particles is yet included.

The potentials that are to be inserted in (21-14) are the potentials experienced by the jth particle due to external sources, as well as the potentials produced by the particles themselves. For the time being we shall ignore any external fields. The potentials satisfy the usual wave equations:

$$\nabla^2 \mathbf{A} - \frac{1}{c^2}\ddot{\mathbf{A}} = -\frac{4\pi}{c}\rho \mathbf{v} \tag{21-17a}$$

$$\nabla^2 \varphi - \frac{1}{c^2}\ddot{\varphi} = -4\pi\rho \tag{21-17b}$$

$$\nabla \cdot \mathbf{A} + \frac{1}{c}\dot{\varphi} = 0 \tag{21-17c}$$

where ρ is the charge density and $\mathbf{v}$ the charge velocity. Since these fields are no longer free, there will be longitudinal components.

If we use (21-1), (21-17a) becomes

$$-\sum_{k\lambda}{}' k^2\left(q_{k\lambda}\mathbf{u}_{k\lambda} + q_{k\lambda}^{\dagger}\mathbf{u}_{k\lambda}^*\right) - \frac{1}{c^2}\sum_{k\lambda}\left(\ddot{q}_{k\lambda}\mathbf{u}_{k\lambda} + \ddot{q}_{k\lambda}^{\dagger}\mathbf{u}_{k\lambda}^*\right)$$

$$= -\frac{4\pi}{c}\rho\mathbf{v} \tag{21-18a}$$

Multiplying by $\mathbf{u}_{k'\lambda'}^*$ and integrating gives

$$4\pi c^2 k^2 q_{k\lambda} + 4\pi \ddot{q}_{k\lambda} = \frac{4\pi}{c}\int \rho\mathbf{v}\cdot\mathbf{u}_{k\lambda}^*\, d\tau \tag{21-18b}$$

Since ρ is actually a sum of delta functions specifying the positions of the charges, we write (21-18b) as

$$\ddot{q}_{k\lambda} + \omega^2 q_{k\lambda} = \frac{1}{c}\sum_j e_j\,\mathbf{u}_{k\lambda}^*(\mathbf{r}_j)\cdot\mathbf{v}_j \tag{21-18c}$$

So we obtain forced oscillators with natural frequency ω, the forcing term being due to the presence of charged particles.

Similarly we can expand the scalar potential,

$$\varphi = \sum_k{}'\{a_k(t)\,f_k(\mathbf{r}) + a_k^{\dagger}(t)\,f_k^*(\mathbf{r})\}$$

$$f_k(\mathbf{r}) = \frac{\sqrt{4\pi}\,c}{L^{3/2}}\,e^{i\mathbf{k}\cdot\mathbf{r}} \tag{21-19}$$

Then

$$\ddot{a}_k + \omega^2 a_k = \sum_j e_j\,f_k^*(\mathbf{r}_j) \tag{21-20}$$

Furthermore from (21-19), (21-3), and (21-2) it follows that

$$\mathbf{u}_{k3} = \frac{i\mathbf{k}}{|\mathbf{k}|} f_k \tag{21-21a}$$

or, what is the same,

$$\mathbf{u}_{k3} = \frac{1}{k} \nabla f_k \tag{21-21b}$$

since $f_k \propto e^{i\mathbf{k}\cdot\mathbf{r}}$.

The Lorentz condition (21-17c) is

$$\sum_k{}' \left\{ q_{k3} \nabla \cdot \mathbf{u}_{k3} + q_{k3}^\dagger \nabla \cdot \mathbf{u}_{k3}^* \right\}$$

$$+ \frac{1}{c} \sum_k{}' \left\{ \dot{a}_k f_k + \dot{a}_k^\dagger f_k \right\} = 0 \tag{21-22a}$$

In view of (21-21b) this is

$$\sum_k{}' \left\{ \left(-kq_{k3} + \frac{1}{c} \dot{a}_k \right) f_k + \left(-kq_{k3}^\dagger + \frac{1}{c} \dot{a}_k \right) f_k^* \right\} = 0 \tag{21-22b}$$

or

$$\dot{a}_k = \omega q_{k3} \tag{21-22c}$$

Hence our equations of motion for the fields (21-17) are equivalent to (21-18c), (21-20), and (21-22c).

The last equation can be expressed as an initial condition by the following device. Differentiating (21-20) with respect to time,

$$\dddot{a}_k + \omega^2 \dot{a}_k = \sum_j e_j \dot{f}_k^*(\mathbf{r}_j) = \sum_j e_j \nabla_j f_k^*(\mathbf{r}_j) \cdot \mathbf{v}_j$$

$$= \sum_j e_j k \mathbf{u}_{k3}^* \cdot \mathbf{v}_j$$

$$= \omega \left(\ddot{q}_{k3} + \omega^2 q_{k3} \right) \tag{21-23a}$$

or

$$\left(\frac{d^2}{dt^2} + \omega^2 \right) \left(\dot{a}_k - \omega q_{k3} \right) = 0 \tag{21-23b}$$

Therefore, if at time $t = 0$,

$$\begin{aligned} \dot{a}_k &= \omega q_{k3} \\ \ddot{a}_k &= \omega \dot{q}_{k3} \end{aligned} \tag{21-24}$$

(21-22c) will always hold. Thus we replace the Lorentz condition, which must hold at all times, by two conditions which must hold at $t = 0$. We therefore restrict ourselves to solutions satisfying (21-24) and then we can consider the oscillators q_{k3} and a_k as independent.

We are now ready to write the differential equations of motion in canonical form. It is claimed that the Hamiltonian for the entire system is

$$H = \sum_j H_j + H_{tr} + H_{lg} \tag{21-25}$$

where $\Sigma_j H_j$ is the particle Hamiltonian (21-14); $H_{tr} + H_{lg}$ are the field Hamiltonians with H_{tr} given by (21-11); and

$$\begin{aligned} H_{lg} &= \sum_k{}' \left\{ p_{k3}^\dagger p_{k3} + \omega^2 q_{k3}^\dagger q_{k3} \right\} \\ &\quad - \sum_k \left\{ \alpha_k^\dagger \alpha_k + \omega^2 a_k^\dagger a_k \right\} \end{aligned} \tag{21-26}$$

The α_k's represent the momenta canonically conjugate to the a_k's. The canonical equations are entirely equivalent to (21-18c) and (21-20). For example, (21-20) can be obtained from them.

$$\begin{aligned} \frac{\partial H}{\partial a_k} &= \sum_j e_j f_k(\mathbf{r}_j) - \omega^2 a_k^\dagger & \qquad \frac{\partial H}{\partial a_k^\dagger} &= \sum_j e_j f_k^*(\mathbf{r}_j) - \omega^2 a_k \\ \frac{\partial H}{\partial \alpha_k} &= -\alpha_k^\dagger & \qquad \frac{\partial H}{\partial \alpha_k^\dagger} &= -\alpha_k \end{aligned} \tag{21-27}$$

Then

$$\begin{aligned} \dot{a}_k &= -\alpha_k^\dagger & \qquad \dot{a}_k^\dagger &= -\alpha_k \\ -\dot{\alpha}_k &= \sum_j e_j f_k(\mathbf{r}_j) - \omega^2 a_k^\dagger & \qquad -\dot{\alpha}_k^\dagger &= \sum_j e_j f_k^*(\mathbf{r}_j) - \omega^2 a_k \\ \ddot{a}_k^\dagger &= \sum_j e_j f_k(\mathbf{r}_j) - \omega^2 a_k & \qquad \ddot{a}_k &= \sum_j e_j f_k^*(\mathbf{r}_j) - \omega^2 a_k \end{aligned} \tag{21-28}$$

$$\ddot{a}_k + \omega^2 a_k = \sum_j e_j f_k^*(\mathbf{r}_j) \tag{21-20}$$

COULOMB INTERACTION

We consider that part of the Hamiltonian (21-25) which is a function of $q_{k3}^\dagger$, q_{k3}, $a_k^\dagger$, and a_k (i.e., that part which depends on longitudinal waves). This dependence occurs in H_j, the jth particle Hamiltonian, and in H_{lg}. We write

$$H_c = H_{lg} + \sum_j e_j \varphi(\mathbf{r}_j)$$

$$= \sum_k{}' \left(p_{k3}^\dagger p_{k3} + \omega^2 q_{k3}^\dagger q_{k3}\right) - \sum_k{}' \left(\alpha_k^\dagger \alpha_k + \omega^2 a_k^\dagger a_k\right)$$

$$+ \sum_j \sum_k{}' e_j \left(a_k f_k(\mathbf{r}_j) + a_k f_k^*(\mathbf{r}_j)\right) \qquad (21\text{-}29)$$

From (21-22c) and (21-29)

$$\alpha_k^\dagger \alpha_k = \omega^2 q_{k3}^\dagger q_{k3} \qquad (21\text{-}30)$$

From (21-20) and (21-22c) and the canonical equations

$$\dot{q}_{k3} = p_{k3}^\dagger = \frac{1}{\omega} \ddot{a}_k = -\omega a_k + \frac{1}{\omega} \sum_j e_j f_k^*(\mathbf{r}_j) \qquad (21\text{-}31)$$

Substituting (21-30) and (21-31) into (21-29), most terms cancel and there remains

$$H_c = \sum_k{}' \sum_{i,j} \frac{1}{\omega^2} e_i e_j f_k(\mathbf{r}_i) f_k^*(\mathbf{r}_j) \qquad (21\text{-}32)$$

Since the summation is over i and j independently, H_c can be rewritten in a way which explicitly shows it to be real.

$$H_c = \frac{1}{2} \sum_{i,j} \sum_k{}' \frac{1}{\omega^2} e_i e_j$$

$$\times \left[f_k(\mathbf{r}_i) f_k^*(\mathbf{r}_j) + f_k^*(\mathbf{r}_i) f_k(\mathbf{r}_j)\right] \qquad (21\text{-}33)$$

The k sum can be evaluated easily:

$$H_c = \tfrac{1}{2}\sum_{i,j} e_i e_j H_{ij}$$

$$H_{ij} = \sum_k{}' \frac{1}{\omega^2}\,[f_k(\mathbf{r}_i)\,f_k^*(\mathbf{r}_j) + f_k^*(\mathbf{r}_i)\,f_k(\mathbf{r}_j)] \tag{21-34}$$

$$f_k(\mathbf{r}) = \frac{\sqrt{4\pi}\;c}{L^{3/2}}\;e^{i\mathbf{k}\cdot\mathbf{r}}$$

Then

$$H_{ij} = \frac{4\pi}{L^3}\sum_k{}' \frac{1}{k^2}\left[e^{i\mathbf{k}\cdot\mathbf{r}_{ij}} + e^{i\mathbf{k}\cdot\mathbf{r}_{ji}}\right]$$

$$\mathbf{r}_{ij} = \mathbf{r}_i - \mathbf{r}_j \tag{21-35}$$

$$H_{ij} = \frac{4\pi}{L^3}\sum_k \frac{1}{k^2}\,e^{i\mathbf{k}\cdot\mathbf{r}_{ij}}$$

Observe that the prime is no longer present in the last summation, i.e., the sum is now over all k. Taking the Laplacian with respect to $\mathbf{r}_i$,

$$\nabla_i^2 H_{ij} = \frac{-4\pi}{L^3}\sum_k e^{i\mathbf{k}\cdot\mathbf{r}_{ij}} = -4\pi\,\delta(\mathbf{r}_{ij}) \tag{21-36}$$

The last equality is the closure relation for any complete orthonormal set of functions.

Integrating (21-36), bearing in mind that H_{ij} must satisfy the usual boundary condition at infinity, we obtain

$$H_{ij} = \frac{1}{r_{ij}}$$

$$H_c = \frac{1}{2}\sum_{i,j}\frac{e_i e_j}{r_{ij}} \tag{21-37}$$

We see therefore that the part of the total Hamiltonian (21-25) which depends on the longitudinal components of the fields corresponds to the static Coulomb interaction between the particles and can be expressed in terms of the coordinates of the particles alone. It might be objected that we have not accounted for the entire dependence of (21-25) on the longitudinal components since we have not discussed the longitudinal components of $\mathbf{A}(\mathbf{r}_j)$ which occur in the radical (21-14). We now show that all solutions satisfying the initial conditions (21-24) can be obtained from a new Hamiltonian, which is obtained from (21-25) by inserting (21-37) for H_c and omitting the longitudinal components of $\mathbf{A}$ in the remaining terms.

To obtain this result we make use of the Hamilton-Jacobi differential equation for the action S:

$$\frac{\partial S}{\partial t} + H\left(q, \frac{\partial S}{\partial q}\right) = 0 \tag{21-38}$$

S is a function of all the canonical coordinates: q_j (position of particles), $q_{k\lambda}$ (expansion of $\mathbf{A}$), a_k (expansion of φ); and of their complex conjugates. The usual relation for conjugate momentum holds:

$$p = \frac{\partial S}{\partial q} \tag{21-39}$$

and has been used in (21-38). We try a solution of the form

$$S = S_1\left(q_j, q_{k1}, q_{k2}, q_{k1}^\dagger, q_{k2}^\dagger\right) + S_2\left(q_j, q_{k3}, a_k, q_{k3}^\dagger, a_k^\dagger\right) \tag{21-40}$$

$$\begin{aligned}\frac{\partial S}{\partial q_{k3}} &= \frac{\partial S_2}{\partial q_{k3}} = p_{k3} = \frac{1}{\omega}\ddot{a}_k^\dagger = -\omega a_k^\dagger + \frac{1}{\omega}\sum_j e_j f_k(\mathbf{r}_j)\\ \frac{\partial S}{\partial q_{k3}^\dagger} &= \frac{\partial S_2}{\partial q_{k3}^\dagger} = p_{k3}^\dagger = -\omega a_k + \frac{1}{\omega}\sum_j e_j f_k^*(\mathbf{r}_j)\end{aligned} \tag{21-41}$$

In (21-41), (21-31) has been used. We therefore assume the following form for S_2:

$$S_2 = \sum_k{}' \left\{ q_{k3}\left[-\omega a_k^\dagger + \frac{1}{\omega}\sum_j e_j f_k(\mathbf{r}_j)\right] + q_{k3}^\dagger\left[-\omega a_k + \frac{1}{\omega}\sum_j e_j f_k^*(\mathbf{r}_j)\right]\right\} \tag{21-42}$$

Then, taking $q_j = \mathbf{r}_j$ and remembering (21-21b),

$$\frac{\partial S_2}{\partial \mathbf{q}_j} = \sum_k{}' \frac{1}{\omega} e_j \left(q_{k3} \boldsymbol{\nabla}_j f_k(\mathbf{r}_j) + q_{k3}^\dagger \boldsymbol{\nabla}_j f_k^*(\mathbf{r}_j)\right)$$

$$= \frac{e_j}{c} \sum_k{}' \left(q_{k3} \mathbf{u}_{k3}(\mathbf{r}_j) + q_{k3}^\dagger \mathbf{u}_{k3}^*(\mathbf{r}_j)\right)$$

$$= \frac{e_j}{c} \mathbf{A}_3(\mathbf{r}_j) \tag{21-43}$$

Therefore the term $c\mathbf{p}_j - e_j \mathbf{A}(\mathbf{r}_j)$, occurring in H_j, becomes

$$c \frac{\partial S_1}{\partial \mathbf{q}_j} + c \frac{\partial S_2}{\partial \mathbf{q}_j} - e_j \mathbf{A}(\mathbf{r}_j)$$

$$= c \frac{\partial S_1}{\partial \mathbf{q}_j} - e_j \sum_{\substack{k \\ \lambda=1,2}}{}' \left(q_{k\lambda} \mathbf{u}_{k\lambda} + q_{k\lambda}^\dagger u_{k\lambda}^*\right) \tag{21-44}$$

The right-hand side of (21-44) has no longitudinal components. Hence if we set $\partial S_1/\partial q_j = p_j$ the Hamiltonian (21-25) can be rewritten as

$$H = \sum_j \sqrt{\mu_j^2 + (c\mathbf{p}_j - e_j \mathbf{A}_{tr}(\mathbf{r}_j))^2} + \frac{1}{2} \sum_{i,j} \frac{e_i e_j}{r_{ij}}$$

$$+ \sum_{\substack{k \\ \lambda=1,2}}{}' \left(p_{k\lambda}^\dagger p_{k\lambda} + \omega^2 q_{k\lambda}^\dagger q_{k\lambda}\right) \tag{21-45}$$

To understand (21-45), it should be remembered that the part H_c of (21-25), as defined in (21-29), was transformed in (21-37); H_{tr} was directly taken over from (21-11) into (21-45), and this leaves only the "kinetic energy" of the particles, $\sqrt{\mu_j^2 + (c\mathbf{p}_j - e_j \mathbf{A}_j(\mathbf{r}_j))^2}$. This term seemingly depends on the longitudinal components of $\mathbf{A}$, but (21-44) shows that in fact it does not. The definition $\mathbf{p}_j = \partial S_1/\partial \mathbf{q}_j$ ensures that this quantity also does not involve the longitudinal components of $\mathbf{A}$.

The second term in (21-45) is seen to contain terms e_i^2/r_{ii}, which of course are infinite. This is a simple example of the famous divergences in field theory and corresponds to the infinite electrostatic self-energy of a point charge. We must omit these terms or assume that they are contained in the rest energy μ_j of the particle. The procedure of eliminating divergences in a relativistically covariant way is called *renormalization*; this problem goes beyond the scope of this book.

Equation (21-45) is a complete Hamiltonian. However, just as in classical electrodynamics, it is sometimes convenient not to include all charges in the system we consider, but to represent the effect of some of them by an external field. This means effectively that the motion of these charges, and hence the external field, are considered to be known as functions of time. We describe the external field by potentials φ^e, $\mathbf{A}^e$, which should satisfy the Lorentz condition. These fields are given functions of the time; hence they should not be quantized. Examples are an external magnetic field to study the Zeeman effect, the field due to the nucleus of an atom if only the electrons are considered as part of the quantum mechanical system, etc. For the external field, the longitudinal components are of course not eliminated. Therefore, the general Hamiltonian for a system of interacting point charges in an external field is

$$H = \sum_j \left[\sqrt{\mu_j^2 + (c\mathbf{p}_j - e_j \mathbf{A}_{tr}(\mathbf{r}_j) - e_j \mathbf{A}^e(\mathbf{r}_j))^2} + e_j \varphi^e(\mathbf{r}_j) \right] + \sum_{i<j} \frac{e_i e_j}{r_{ij}} + \sum_{\substack{k \\ \lambda = 1,2}}{}' \left(p_{k\lambda}^\dagger p_{k\lambda} + \omega^2 q_{k\lambda}^\dagger q_{k\lambda} \right) \qquad (21\text{-}46)$$

The physical interpretation of the above terms is as follows. The first term includes the rest energy and kinetic energy of the particles and the interaction energy with the external magnetic and with the radiation field. The second term is the interaction with the external electric field, and the third is the static interaction of the point particles. The last term is the energy of the free radiation field.

This approach to quantum electrodynamics is due to Heisenberg and Pauli (1929) and to Fermi (1932). It was preceded by a theory of the transverse radiation field by Dirac (1928). Heisenberg and Pauli used the field as a function of spatial coordinates and time, which is important for questions of principle, such as the problem of the simultaneous measurability of various field components at the same or different space-time points, a problem investigated in great detail by Bohr and Rosenfeld. However, the use of space coordinates introduces additional technical complications which were avoided by Fermi by using the Fourier components of the field. Heitler's book (1936) and our presentation follow Fermi.

All these formulations, which were a great achievement at the time, suffer from the fact that the separation of the fields into longitudinal and transverse components is not Lorentz-invariant. Nevertheless this is the most basic approach and is fundamental to the more elegant methods of Schwinger and Feynman (1947-1953).

QUANTIZATION OF THE TRANSVERSE FIELD

The quantization of the transverse field is achieved by the usual commutator relations,

$$\left[q_{k\lambda}, p_{k'\lambda'}\right] = \left[q^{\dagger}_{k\lambda}, p^{\dagger}_{k'\lambda'}\right] = i\hbar\, \delta_{kk'}\, \delta_{\lambda\lambda'} \tag{21-47}$$

The commutation relations between the Fourier components of the fields can be changed by Fourier synthesis into commutation relations between the fields themselves. Thus with much algebra we obtain

$$[A_s(\mathbf{r},t), \mathcal{E}_{s'}(\mathbf{r}',t)] = -4\pi c\, \delta_{ss'}\, \delta(\mathbf{r} - \mathbf{r}')\, i\hbar$$

$$+ i\hbar c \frac{\partial}{\partial r_s} \frac{\partial}{\partial r'_{s'}} \left(\frac{1}{|\mathbf{r} - \mathbf{r}'|}\right) \tag{21-48}$$

The subscripts s, s′ indicate Cartesian components of the respective vectors. Equation (21-48) does not vanish for $\mathbf{r}' \neq \mathbf{r}$, which is not a contradiction of the principle that there can be no interference between measurements separated by a space-like interval, since **A** is not an observable. From (21-48) it follows that

$$\begin{aligned} [\mathcal{E}_s(\mathbf{r},t), \mathcal{H}_s(\mathbf{r}',t)] &= 0 \\ [\mathcal{E}_x(\mathbf{r},t), \mathcal{H}_y(\mathbf{r}',t)] &= 4\pi c i\hbar \frac{\partial}{\partial z'} \delta(\mathbf{r} - \mathbf{r}') \end{aligned} \tag{21-49}$$

and cyclic permutations of x, y, z.

The time dependence of the $q_{k\lambda}$ and $p_{k\lambda}$ can be readily found:

$$i\hbar\dot{q}_{k\lambda} = \left[q_{k\lambda}, H\right] = i\hbar p^{\dagger}_{k\lambda} \tag{21-50a}$$

$$i\hbar\dot{p}_{k\lambda} = \left[p_{k\lambda}, H\right] = -i\hbar\omega^2 q^{\dagger}_{k\lambda} \tag{21-50b}$$

where H is the free-field Hamiltonian (21-11). [It is to be noted that (21-50a) is true even when H is the complete Hamiltonian (21-46); however, (21-50b) is only true for the free-field case.] These equations are of course consistent with the classical equations (21-12) and (21-13). Eliminating $p_{k\lambda}$ from the above gives

$$\ddot{q}_{k\lambda} = -\omega^2 q_{k\lambda} \tag{21-51a}$$

which integrates to

$$q_{k\lambda} = \sqrt{\frac{\hbar}{2\omega}} \left[b_{k\lambda} e^{-i\omega t} + b'^{\dagger}_{k\lambda} e^{i\omega t} \right] \tag{21-51b}$$

The factor $\sqrt{\hbar/2\omega}$ is inserted for later convenience, and (21-51b) defines the operators $b_{k\lambda}$ and $b'_{k\lambda}$. From (21-50a)

$$p^{\dagger}_{k\lambda} = \sqrt{\frac{\hbar}{2\omega}} \; [-i\omega] \left[b_{k\lambda} e^{-i\omega t} - b'^{\dagger}_{k\lambda} e^{i\omega t} \right] \tag{21-51c}$$

Then, using (21-1) and (21-2),

$$\mathbf{A}_{tr} = \frac{1}{L^{3/2}} \sum_{\substack{k \\ \lambda=1,2}}{}' \sqrt{\frac{2\pi\hbar c}{k}} \; \mathbf{e}_{k\lambda} \Big[b_{k\lambda} e^{i(\mathbf{k}\cdot\mathbf{r}-\omega t)}$$

$$+ b'^{\dagger}_{k\lambda} e^{i(\mathbf{k}\cdot\mathbf{r}+\omega t)} + b^{\dagger}_{k\lambda} e^{-i(\mathbf{k}\cdot\mathbf{r}-\omega t)}$$

$$+ b'_{k\lambda} e^{-i(\mathbf{k}\cdot\mathbf{r}+\omega t)} \Big] \tag{21-52}$$

Thus $\mathbf{A}_{tr}$ is a superposition of running waves traveling in the $+\mathbf{k}$ and $-\mathbf{k}$ directions.

Solving for the $b_{k\lambda}$, from (21-51) we have

$$\begin{aligned} b_{k\lambda} &= \frac{1}{2} \sqrt{\frac{2\omega}{\hbar}} \; e^{i\omega t} \left(q_{k\lambda} + \frac{i}{\omega} p^{\dagger}_{k\lambda} \right) \\ b'^{\dagger}_{k\lambda} &= \frac{1}{2} \sqrt{\frac{2\omega}{\hbar}} \; e^{-i\omega t} \left(q_{k\lambda} - \frac{i}{\omega} p^{\dagger}_{k\lambda} \right) \end{aligned} \tag{21-53}$$

The commutation relations which follow from (21-47) now become

$$\begin{aligned} \left[b_{k\lambda}, b^{\dagger}_{k'\lambda'} \right] &= \left[b'_{k\lambda}, b'^{\dagger}_{k'\lambda'} \right] = \delta_{kk'}\,\delta_{\lambda\lambda'} \\ \left[b_{k\lambda}, b'^{\dagger}_{k'\lambda'} \right] &= \left[b_{k\lambda}, b_{k'\lambda'} \right] = 0 \end{aligned} \tag{21-54}$$

All other commutators are zero. The Hamiltonian (21-11) becomes

$$H = \sum_{\substack{k \\ \lambda=1,2}} \hbar\omega \left(b^{\dagger}_{k\lambda} b_{k\lambda} + \tfrac{1}{2} \right) \tag{21-55}$$

where we have identified $b_{-k\lambda}$ with $b'_{k\lambda}$ and removed the restriction on the k summation. Since all this arises from an oscillator Hamiltonian, we can immediately define a number operator

$$N_{k\lambda} = b^{\dagger}_{k\lambda} b_{k\lambda} \tag{21-56}$$

which is a constant of the motion and has eigenvalues 0, 1, 2, ... From the general theory of Chapter 20 we also know that

$$\begin{aligned} \langle N'_{k\lambda} + 1 \mid b^{\dagger}_{k\lambda} \mid N'_{k\lambda} \rangle &= \sqrt{N'_{k\lambda} + 1} \\ \langle N'_{k\lambda} - 1 \mid b_{k\lambda} \mid N'_{k\lambda} \rangle &= \sqrt{N'_{k\lambda}} \end{aligned} \tag{21-57a}$$

or, what is the same,

$$\begin{aligned} b_{k\lambda} \mid N'_{k\lambda} \rangle &= \sqrt{N'_{k\lambda}} \mid N'_{k\lambda} - 1 \rangle \\ b^{\dagger}_{k\lambda} \mid N'_{k\lambda} \rangle &= \sqrt{N'_{k\lambda} + 1} \mid N'_{k\lambda} + 1 \rangle \end{aligned} \tag{21-57b}$$

If we renormalize the free-field Hamiltonian (21-55) by omitting the constant $\frac{1}{2}\hbar\omega$, it becomes, in terms of the number operator,

$$H_{free} = \sum_{\substack{k \\ \lambda=1,2}} \hbar\omega N_{k\lambda} \tag{21-58}$$

The field momentum **P** can be obtained by recalling that it is equal to $1/c^2$ times the space integral of the Poynting vector. In the quantum theory this result becomes

$$\mathbf{P} = \sum_{\substack{k \\ \lambda=1,2}} \hbar \mathbf{k} N_{k\lambda} \tag{21-59}$$

INTERACTION WITH CHARGED PARTICLES

We write the Hamiltonian for the entire system as

$$H = H^0 + H^1 \tag{21-60}$$

H^0 consists of two parts: H_p, the energy of the particles including their static interaction, and H_r the energy of the free radiation field.

$$H_p = \sum_j \left(\alpha_j \cdot c\mathbf{p}_j + \beta_j \mu_j \right) + \sum_{i<j} \frac{e_i e_j}{r_{ij}} \tag{21-61a}$$

$$H_p = \sum_j \frac{p_j^2}{2m_j} + \sum_{i<j} \frac{e_i e_j}{r_{ij}} \tag{21-61b}$$

The first equation is the Dirac Hamiltonian, the second the nonrelativistic Schrödinger Hamiltonian. The field Hamiltonian is always

$$H_r = \sum_k \hbar\omega N_k \tag{21-62}$$

where the index k stands for both k and λ. H^1 is the interaction Hamiltonian:

$$H^1 = -\sum_j e_j\left(\boldsymbol{\alpha}_j \cdot \mathbf{A}_{tr}(\mathbf{r}_j)\right) \tag{21-63a}$$

$$H^1 = -\sum_j \frac{e_j}{m_j c}\, \mathbf{p}_j \cdot \mathbf{A}_{tr}(\mathbf{r}_j) + \sum_j \frac{e_j^2}{2m_j c^2}\, A_{tr}^2(\mathbf{r}_j) \tag{21-63b}$$

The second equation corresponds to the nonrelativistic Schrödinger equation and follows from (21-45) by expansion of the square root. The first equation corresponds to the Dirac equation; it gives the correct Dirac equation for a particle in an electromagnetic field, and also the correct equation (21-18c) for the Fourier components of the field if we remember that $c\boldsymbol{\alpha}_j$ is the velocity of particle j. We assume no unquantized external fields.

In either case we consider H^1 as a time-dependent perturbation. The eigenstate Ψ of H is expanded in solutions of H_p and H_r:

$$\Psi = \sum_{n,N'_k} c(n, \ldots, N'_k, \ldots, t)\, \psi_n(\mathbf{r}_j, t)\, \Phi(\ldots, N'_k, \ldots) \tag{21-64}$$

Assuming initially a state $n = a$, $N'_k = N'_k$ we have for a final state, b, $N'_k + 1$ (emission):

$$\begin{aligned} i\hbar \frac{d}{dt} c(b, \ldots, N'_k + 1, \ldots, t) &= \int \psi_b^*(\mathbf{r},t)\, \Phi^*(\ldots, N'_k + 1, \ldots)\, H^1 \psi_a(\mathbf{r},t) \\ &\quad \times \Phi(\ldots, N'_k, \ldots)\; d\tau \\ &= -\frac{e}{L^{3/2}} \sqrt{\frac{2\pi\hbar c}{k}} \int \psi_b^*(\mathbf{r})\boldsymbol{\alpha} \cdot \mathbf{e}_{k\lambda}\, \psi_a(\mathbf{r})\, e^{-i\mathbf{k}\cdot\mathbf{r}}\; d\tau \\ &\quad \times \sqrt{N'_k + 1}\; e^{i\omega t}\; e^{(i/\hbar)(E_b - E_a)t} \end{aligned} \tag{21-65}$$

where we have taken the Dirac Hamiltonian. The first integral is over space and number variables, the second, only over space variables. The time dependence gives energy conservation

$$E_b = E_a - \hbar\omega \tag{21-66}$$

and it is seen that the transition probability for emission is proportional to $N'_k + 1$. This shows that even if there are no fields present ($N'_k = 0$), there exists a nonzero transition probability for emission. Thus we see that spontaneous and induced emission are combined into one phenomenon. It can further be shown that the ratio of induced to spontaneous emission is N'_k, which gives the correct Einstein probabilities (see Chapter 12).

The absorption process is calculated in the same fashion except that the final state is taken to be b, $N'_k - 1$. The analysis proceeds as above except that $\sqrt{N'_k + 1}$ is replaced by $\sqrt{N'_k}$. Hence the absorption probability is proportional to N'_k and is nonzero only in the presence of a field.

REFERENCES

The arabic numerals standing in brackets at the end of each entry indicate the chapter in this book in which the reference is made.

Anderson, C. D., *Phys. Rev.,* **41**, 405 (1932). [18]

Bethe, H. A., "Quantenmechanik der Ein- und Zwei-Electronenprobleme," *Handbuch der Physik,* Bd 24/1, Springer, Berlin, 1933. [11]

——— and R. F. Bacher, *Rev. Mod. Phys.,* **8**, 193 (1936). [3]

——— and J. Ashkin, "Passage of Radiation through Matter" in *Experimental Nuclear Physics,* E. Segrè (ed.), Wiley, New York, 1953. [15]

——— and E. E. Salpeter, *Quantum Mechanics of One- and Two-Electron Atoms,* Academic Press, New York, 1957. [1,4,5,13,14]

Bohr, N., and L. Rosenfeld, *Kgl. Danske Vid. Sels., Mat.-Fys. Medd.,* **12**, No. 8 (1933). [19,21]

Born, M., and J. R. Oppenheimer, *Ann. Physik,* **84**, 457 (1927). [11]

Bowen, I. S., *Astrophys. J.,* **67**, 1 (1928). [12]

Condon, E. U., and G. H. Shortley, *The Theory of Atomic Spectra,* Cambridge University Press, Cambridge, 1959. [9,10,13]

Dirac, P. A. M., *Proc. Roy. Soc. (London),* **A117**, 610 (1928). [17]

———, *Proc. Cambridge Phil. Soc.,* **26**, 376 (1930). [7]

———, *The Principles of Quantum Mechanics,* 4th ed., Clarendon Press, Oxford, 1958. [8]

Einstein, A., *Phys. Z.,* **18**, 121 (1917). [12]

Fermi, E., *Z. Physik,* **48**, 73 (1928). [7]

———, *Rev. Mod. Phys.,* **4**, 87 (1932). [21]

Feynman, R. P., N. Metropolis, and E. Teller, *Phys. Rev.,* **75**, 1561 (1949). [7]

Foldy, L. L., and S. A. Wouthuysen, *Phys. Rev.,* **78**, 29 (1950). [17]

Frenkel, J., *Z. Physik,* **37**, 243 (1926). [10]

Heisenberg, W., *Z. Physik,* **39**, 499 (1927). [4]
———, *Ann. Physik,* **120**, 888 (1931). [9]
———, *Z. Physik,* **90**, 209 (1934). [18]
——— and W. Pauli, *Z. Physik,* **56**, 1 (1929). [21]
——— and W. Pauli, *Z. Physik,* **59**, 168 (1929). [21]
Heitler, W., *The Quantum Theory of Radiation,* 1st ed., Clarendon Press, Oxford, 1936. [21]
Hylleraas, E. A., *Z. Physik,* **54**, 347 (1929). [5]
Jordan, P., and E. P. Wigner, *Z. Physik,* **47**, 631 (1928). [19,20]
Kramers, H. A., *Proc. Kgl. Ned. Acad. Wet.,* **40**, 814 (1937). [18]
Kuhn, W., *Z. Physik,* **33**, 408 (1925). [13]
Lenz, W., *Z. Physik,* **77**, 713 (1932). [7]
Morse, P. M., *Phys. Rev.,* **34**, 57 (1929). [11]
Newton, R. G., and E. P. Wigner, *Rev. Mod. Phys.,* **21**, 400 (1949). [16]
Panofsky, W. K. H., and M. Phillips, *Classical Electricity and Magnetism,* 2nd ed., Addison-Wesley, Reading, Mass., 1962. [12,13]
Pauli, W., *Phys. Rev.,* **58**, 716 (1940). [3,20]
———, and V. Weisskopf, *Helv. Phys. Acta,* **7**, 709 (1934). [16,18]
Pekeris, C. L., *Phys. Rev.,* **112**, 1649 (1958). [5]
Rasetti, F., *Z. Physik,* **61**, 598 (1930). [30]
Reiche, F., and W. Thomas, *Z. Physik,* **34**, 510 (1925). [13]
Salpeter, E. E., and M. H. Zaidi, *Phys. Rev.,* **125**, 248 (1962). [5]
Schiff, L. I., *Quantum Mechanics,* 2nd ed., McGraw-Hill, New York, 1955. [1,2,5,6,10,11,12,20]
Schrödinger, E., *Sitzungsb. d. Berlin Akad.,* p. 418 (1930). [18]
Schweber, S. S., *An Introduction to Relativistic Quantum Field Theory,* Harper & Row, New York, 1961. [17]
Slater, J. C., *Phys. Rev.,* **34**, 1293 (1929). [9]
———, *Phys. Rev.,* **36**, 57 (1930). [6,8,9]
———, *Quantum Theory of Atomic Structure,* McGraw-Hill, New York, 1960. [5,6,10]
Thomas, L. H., *Nature,* **117**, 514 (1926). [10]
———, *Proc. Cambridge Phil. Soc.,* **23**, 542 (1927). [7]
Thomas, W., *Naturwiss.,* **13**, 627 (1925). [13]
Weisskopf, V. F., and E. P. Wigner, *Z. Physik,* **63**, 54 (1930). [12]
———, *Z. Physik,* **65**, 18 (1930). [12]
Weyl, H., *Z. Physik,* **56**, 330 (1929). [17]
Wigner, E. P., *Group Theory and Its Application to the Quantum Mechanics of Atomic Spectra,* translated by J. J. Griffin, Academic Press, New York, 1959. [3]

INDEX

A 70 49?

sueente